Glencoe Science The Nature of Matter
Contents in Brief

S0-AYX-090

SAFETY SYMBOLS

SAFETY SYMBOLS	HAZARD	EXAMPLES	PRECAUTION	REMEDY
DISPOSAL	Special disposal procedures need to be followed.	certain chemicals, living organisms	Do not dispose of these materials in the sink or trash can.	Dispose of wastes as directed by your teacher.
BIOLOGICAL	Organisms or other biological materials that might be harmful to humans	bacteria, fungi, blood, unpreserved tissues, plant materials	Avoid skin contact with these materials. Wear mask or gloves.	Notify your teacher if you suspect contact with material. Wash hands thoroughly.
EXTREME TEMPERATURE	Objects that can burn skin by being too cold or too hot	boiling liquids, hot plates, dry ice, liquid nitrogen	Use proper protection when handling.	Go to your teacher for first aid.
SHARP OBJECT	Use of tools or glassware that can easily puncture or slice skin	razor blades, pins, scalpels, pointed tools, dissecting probes, broken glass	Practice common-sense behavior and follow guidelines for use of the tool.	Go to your teacher for first aid.
FUME	Possible danger to respiratory tract from fumes	ammonia, acetone, nail polish remover, heated sulfur, moth balls	Make sure there is good ventilation. Never smell fumes directly. Wear a mask.	Leave foul area and notify your teacher immediately.
ELECTRICAL	Possible danger from electrical shock or burn	improper grounding, liquid spills, short circuits, exposed wires	Double-check setup with teacher. Check condition of wires and apparatus.	Do not attempt to fix electrical problems. Notify your teacher immediately.
IRRITANT	Substances that can irritate the skin or mucous membranes of the respiratory tract	pollen, moth balls, steel wool, fiberglass, potassium permanganate	Wear dust mask and gloves. Practice extra care when handling these materials.	Go to your teacher for first aid.
CHEMICAL	Chemicals that can react with and destroy tissue and other materials	bleaches such as hydrogen peroxide; acids such as sulfuric acid, hydrochloric acid; bases such as ammonia, sodium hydroxide	Wear goggles, gloves, and an apron.	Immediately flush the affected area with water and notify your teacher.
TOXIC	Substance may be poisonous if touched, inhaled, or swallowed	mercury, many metal compounds, iodine, poinsettia plant parts	Follow your teacher's instructions.	Always wash hands thoroughly after use. Go to your teacher for first aid.
OPEN FLAME	Open flame may ignite flammable chemicals, loose clothing, or hair	alcohol, kerosene, potassium permanganate, hair, clothing	Tie back hair. Avoid wearing loose clothing. Avoid open flames when using flammable chemicals. Be aware of locations of fire safety equipment.	Notify your teacher immediately. Use fire safety equipment if applicable.

Eye Safety
Proper eye protection should be worn at all times by anyone performing or observing science activities.

Clothing Protection
This symbol appears when substances could stain or burn clothing.

Animal Safety
This symbol appears when safety of animals and students must be ensured.

Radioactivity
This symbol appears when radioactive materials are used.

Teacher Wraparound Edition

Glencoe Science

The Nature of Matter

NATIONAL GEOGRAPHIC SOCIETY

science.glencoe.com

Glencoe
McGraw-Hill

New York, New York   Columbus, Ohio   Woodland Hills, California   Peoria, Illinois

GLENCOE SCIENCE
The Nature of Matter

Student Edition
Teacher Wraparound Edition
Interactive Teacher Edition CD-ROM
Interactive Lesson Planner CD-ROM
Lesson Plans
Content Outline for Teaching
Directed Reading for Content Mastery
Foldables: Reading and Study Skills
Assessment
    Chapter Review
    Chapter Tests
    ExamView® Pro Test Bank CD-ROM
    Assessment Transparencies
    Performance Assessment in the Science Classroom
    The Princeton Review Test Practice Booklet
Directed Reading for Content Mastery in Spanish
Spanish Resources
English/Spanish Guided Reading Audio Program
Reinforcement
Enrichment

Activity Worksheets
Section Focus Transparencies
Teaching Transparencies
Laboratory Activities
Science Inquiry Labs
Critical Thinking/Problem Solving
Reading and Writing Skill Activities
Mathematics Skill Activities
Cultural Diversity
Laboratory Management and Safety in the Science
    Classroom
MindJogger Videoquizzes and Teacher Guide
Interactive CD-ROM with Presentation
    Builder
Vocabulary PuzzleMaker Software
Cooperative Learning
Environmental Issues in the Science Classroom
Home and Community Involvement
Using the Internet in the Science Classroom
Dinah Zike's Teaching Science with Foldables

"Test-Taking Tip," "Study Tip," and "Test Practice" features in this book were written by The Princeton Review, the nation's leader in test preparation. Through its association with McGraw-Hill, The Princeton Review offers the best way to help students excel on standardized assessments.

The Princeton Review is not affiliated with Princeton University or Educational Testing Service.

Glencoe/McGraw-Hill

A Division of The McGraw-Hill Companies

Copyright © 2002 by Glencoe/McGraw-Hill. All rights reserved. Except as permitted under the United States Copyright Act, no part of this publication may be reproduced or distributed in any form or by any means, or stored in a database or retrieval system, without prior written permission of the publisher.

The "Visualizing" features in each chapter of this textbook were designed and developed by the National Geographic Society's Education Division, copyright © 2002 National Geographic Society. The name "National Geographic Society" and the yellow border rectangle are trademarks of the Society, and their use without prior written permission is strictly prohibited. All rights reserved.

The "Science and Society" and the "Science and History" features that appear in this book were designed and developed by TIME School Publishing, a division of TIME Magazine. TIME and the red border are trademarks of Time, Inc. All rights reserved.

Send all inquiries to:

Glencoe/McGraw-Hill
8787 Orion Place
Columbus, OH 43240

ISBN 0-07-825525-2

Printed in the United States of America

2 3 4 5 6 7 8 9 10 111/043 10 09 08 07 06 05 04 03 02

Authors, Reviewers, and Consultants

for the *15-Book Series*

Authors

National Geographic Society
Education Division
Washington, D.C.

Alton Biggs
Biology Teacher
Allen High School
Allen, Texas

Lucy Daniel, EdD
Teacher/Consultant
Rutherford County Schools
Rutherfordton, North Carolina

Cathy Ezrailson
Science Department Head
Academy for Science and Health
Professions
Conroe, Texas

Ralph M. Feather Jr., PhD
Science Department Chair
Derry Area School District
Derry, Pennsylvania

Nicholas Hainen
Chemistry/Physics Teacher
Worthington City Schools
Worthington, Ohio

Patricia Horton
Mathematics/Science Teacher
Summit Intermediate School
Etiwanda, California

Norman G. Lederman, PhD
Professor of Science and Math
Education
Oregon State University
Corvallis, Oregon

Deborah Lillie
Math and Science Writer
Sudbury, Massachusetts

Thomas McCarthy, PhD
Science Department Chair
St. Edwards School
Vero Beach, Florida

Edward Ortleb
Science Consultant
St. Louis Public Schools
St. Louis, Missouri

Susan Leach Snyder
Earth Science Teacher,
Consultant
Jones Middle School
Upper Arlington, Ohio

Peter Rillero, PhD
Professor of Science Education
Arizona State University West
Phoenix, Arizona

Eric Werwa, PhD
Department of Physics and
Astronomy
Otterbein College
Westerville, Ohio

Dinah Zike
Educational Consultant
Dinah-Might Activities, Inc.
San Antonio, Texas

Margaret K. Zorn
Science Writer
Yorktown, Virginia

Reviewers

Sandra K. Enger, PhD
Coordinator
UAH Institute for Science Education
Huntsville, Alabama

Lee Meadows, PhD
Associate Professor of Science Education
University of Alabama
Birmingham, Alabama

Gilbert Naizer, PhD
Assistant Professor of Elementary Education
Texas A&M University
Commerce, Texas

Kimberly S. Roempler, PhD
Associate Director
Eisenhower National Clearinghouse
for Math and Science
The Ohio State University
Columbus, Ohio

Cultural Diversity Consultants

Nedaro Bellamy
Associate Director,
Rice Model Science Laboratory
Lanier Middle School, Houston ISD
Houston, Texas

Joyce Hilliard-Clark, PhD
Director, Imhotep Academy
North Carolina State University
Raleigh, North Carolina

Inclusion Strategies Consultant

Barry Barto
Special Education Teacher
John F. Kennedy Elementary School
Manistee, Michigan

Introducing the
Glencoe Science 15-Book Series

Teach science your way!

With the 15 Life, Earth, and Physical Science titles in our modular series, you can select the science topics you want to cover and customize your science curriculum in any way you choose.

The *Glencoe 15-Book Series* provides:

- Flexibility—you can easily meet your curriculum requirements.
- Convenience—the books are easy for students to carry and ideal for whenever locker space isn't available.
- A sense of accomplishment—as students complete each book, they can see the progress they're making.

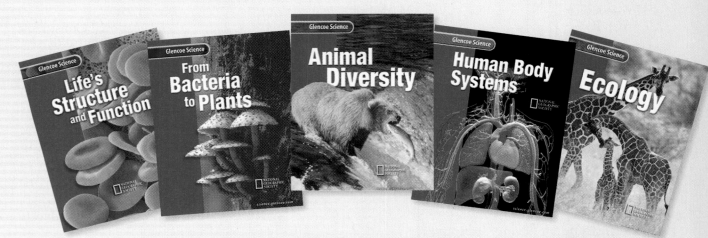

A Life's Structure and Function
1 Exploring and Classifying Life
2 Cells
3 Cell Processes
4 Cell Reproduction
5 Heredity
6 Adaptations Over Time

B From Bacteria to Plants
1 Bacteria
2 Protists and Fungi
3 Plants
4 Plant Reproduction
5 Plant Processes

C Animal Diversity
1 Introduction to Animals
2 Mollusks, Worms, Arthropods, Echinoderms
3 Fish, Amphibians, and Reptiles
4 Birds and Mammals
5 Animal Behavior

D Human Body Systems
1 Structure and Support
2 Nutrients and Digestion
3 Circulation
4 Respiration and Excretion
5 Control and Coordination
6 Regulation and Reproduction
7 Immunity and Disease

E Ecology
1 Interactions of Life
2 The Nonliving Environment
3 Ecosystems
4 Conserving Resources
5 Conserving Life

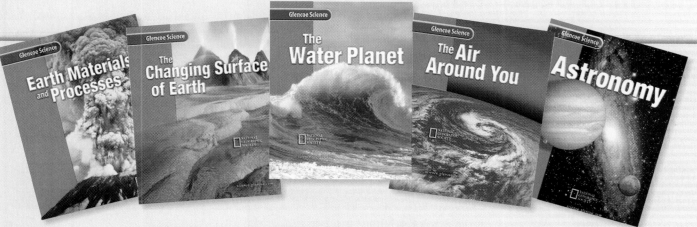

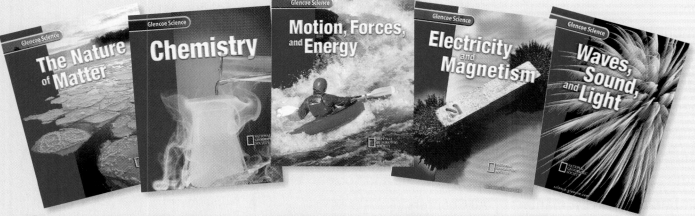

Correlation to **Benchmarks**

The five **Physical Science** books in the *Glencoe 15-Book Series* address many of the benchmarks for science literacy. These benchmarks are presented in *Benchmarks for Science Literacy*, a publication of the American Association for the Advancement of Science.

K	The Nature of Matter
L	Chemistry
M	Motion, Forces, and Energy
N	Electricity and Magnetism
O	Waves, Sound, and Light

Benchmark	Book and Chapter
4 **The Physical Setting**	
4D. Structure of Matter	K1, K2, K3, K4, L1, L2, L3, L4
4E. Energy Transformation	K2, K3, L1, L2, L3, L4, M4, M5, M6, N1, N2, N3, O1, O2, O3, O4
4F. Motion	M1, M2, M3, M4, N1, O1, O2
4G. Forces of Nature	K1, K3, L1, M1, M2, M3, M4, M5, M6, N1, N2, O3
8 **The Designed World**	
8B. Materials and Manufacturing	K3, L1, M4, M5, N3, O4
8C. Energy Sources and Use	M4, M6, N1, N2, N3, O1, O2, O3
8D. Communication	N3, O1, O2, O3, O4
9 **The Mathematical World**	
9A. Numbers	Chapter 2; All Math Skills and Problem-Solving Activities
9B. Symbolic Relationships	Chapter 2; All Math Skills and Problem-Solving Activities
9E. Reasoning	All Math Skills and Problem-Solving Activities
10 **Historical Perspectives**	
10B. Uniting the Heavens and Earth	K1, K4, O3
10G. Harnessing Power	M3, M4, M5, N1, N2, N3, O1
12 **Habits of Mind**	
12A. Values and Attitudes	K1, All Science and Society Fetures
12B. Computation and Estimation	All Chapters
12D. Communication Skills	All Activities and Skill Builders

Correlation to National Science Education Standards

The following chart illustrates how the five **Physical Science** books in the *Glencoe 15-Book Series* address the National Science Education Standards.

Content Standard	Book, Chapter, and Section
(UCP) Unifying Concepts and Processes	
1. Systems, order, and organization	K2-1, K4-1, M4-1, M4-2, M4-3
2. Evidence, models, and explanation	K1-1, K1-2, K1-3, K4-2, L1-1, L1-2, L3-1, L3-2, L3-3, N1-1, N1-2, N1-3, N2-1, N2-2, O1-3, O2-1, O2-2, O3-1, O3-2, O3-3
3. Change, constancy, and measurement	K2-2, K2-3, K3-1, K3-2, K4-3, L2-1, L2-2, L3-1, L3-2, L3-3, L4-1, L4-2, L4-3, M1-1, M1-2, M1-3, M2-1, M2-2, M2-3, M3-1, M3-2, M3-3, M4-1, M4-2, M4-3, M5-1, M5-2, M6-1, M6-2, M6-3, O1-2
4. Evolution and equilibrium	L3-1, L3-2, L3-3, M4-1, M4-2, M4-3
5. Form and function	M5-3, N3-1, N3-2, O1-1
(A) Science as Inquiry	
1. Abilities necessary to do scientific inquiry	K1-1, K1-2, K1-3, K2-2, K2-3, K3-1, K3-2, K4-1, K4-3, L1-1, L1-2, L2-1, L2-2, L4-1, L4-2, L4-3, M1-1, M1-2, M1-3, M2-1, M2-3, M3-1, M3-2, M3-3, M4-1, M4-3, M5-2, M5-3, M6-2, M6-3, N1-2, N1-3, N2-1, N2-2, N3-1, N3-2, O1-1, O1-2, O1-3, O2-1, O2-2, O3-1, O3-2, O3-3
2. Understandings about scientific inquiry	K4-1, M2-1, M2-2, M2-3, N3-1, N3-2
(B) Physical Science	
1. Properties and changes of properties in matter	K1-1, K1-2, K1-3, K2-1, K2-2, K2-3, K3-1, K3-2, K4-1, K4-2, K4-3, L1-1, L1-2, L2-1, L3-1, L3-2, L3-3, L4-1, L4-2, L4-3, M5-1, M5-2, M5-3, M6-1, M6-2, M6-3, N2-1, N2-2, O1-1, O1-2, O1-3
2. Motion and forces	M1-1, M1-2, M1-3, M2-1, M2-2, M2-3, M3-1, M3-2, M3-3, M4-1, M4-2, M4-3, N2-1, N2-2, O1-1, O1-2, O1-3, O2-1
3. Transfer of energy	K2-2, L2-1, L2-2, M4-1, M4-2, M4-3, M6-1, M6-2, M6-3, N1-1, N1-2, N1-3, N2-2, N3-1, N3-2, O1-1, O1-2, O1-3, O2-1, O2-2, O3-1, O3-2, O3-3
(C) Life Science	
1. Structure and function in living systems	L4-1, L4-2, L4-3, N1-1, O2-2
(D) Earth and Space Science	
1. Structure of the Earth system	K1-3, K2-3, L3-2, M3-2, M3-3, N1-1, N3-1, N3-2
2. Earth's history	N2-2
3. Earth in the solar system	O2-1, O3-2
(E) Science and Technology	
1. Abilities of technological design	K1-1, M1-3, M2-1, M2-2, M2-3, M4-2, M4-3, M6-3
2. Understandings about science and technology	L4-1, L4-2, L4-3, M2-3, M3-2, M3-3, M4-2, M4-3, M6-2, M6-3, N1-2, N1-3, N2-1
(F) Science in Personal and Social Perspectives	
1. Personal health	L3-2, L4-1, L4-2, L4-3, M4-3, N1-3, O1-2, O2-2
2. Populations, resources, and environments	M5-3
3. Natural hazards	M3-3, N1-1, O1-2, O2-2
4. Risks and benefits	L3-3, L4-3, M1-3, M2-3, M5-3, M6-3
5. Science and technology in society	K1-1, K3-2, K4-2, L2-2, L3-2, L3-3, L4-1, L4-2, L4-3, M2-3, M3-3, M5-2, M6-3, N1-3, N2-2, N3-1, N3-2, O2-1, O2-2, O3-2, O3-3
(G) History and Nature of Science	
1. Science as a human endeavor	K1-1, K1-2, K1-3, K4-1, K4-3, L1-2, L3-3, L4-3, M1-3, M3-3, N1-3, N2-2, N3-1, N3-2
2. Nature of science	K1-1, K1-3, K2-3, K3-2, K4-1, L1-2, L4-3, M1-3, M3-3, N3-1, N3-2, O1-3
3. History of science	K1-1, K1-3, L2-2, L4-3, M1-3, M3-2, M3-3, N1-3, N3-1, N3-2, O3-3

Technology Resources

Online Science

The Glencoe Science Web site **science.glencoe.com** is an invaluable resource for all teachers and students. You will find current information, Web links, chapter content, and Internet activities that allow students to connect to other students worldwide.

Teaching TODAY

Access *Teaching Today* at **teachingtoday.glencoe.com** for teaching tips, annotated Web resources, educational news, and more. New material is added each week to meet the diverse needs of secondary classroom teachers.

Interactive CD-ROM with Presentation Builder

This program provides students the opportunity to develop hypotheses, manipulate variables, build presentations, review content, and think critically.

ExamView Pro® Test Bank CD-ROM

Use this software to design and create your own test instruments in minutes. This versatile program allows you to create paper tests, tests for your school LAN system, or tests posted to a class Web site.

Interactive Lesson Planner

Here's the perfect solution for help in planning your lessons and organizing your resources. Every page of your Teacher Classroom Resources is available in this product at the click of a mouse.

MindJogger Videoquizzes

The interactive quiz-show format of this program, with three levels of difficulty, provides excitement for your students in reviewing key concepts for every chapter. It's a fun way to help you assess students' understanding of science content.

Guided Reading Audio Program
English/Spanish

Students can listen to complete chapter texts read in English or listen to chapter summaries in Spanish. They're perfect for students who are auditory learners or for English Language Learners.

Vocabulary PuzzleMaker Software

This software program allows you to create crossword puzzles, jumble puzzles, or word searches in minutes to review chapter vocabulary. The puzzles can be printed or played on the computer screen.

Interactive **Student** and **Teacher Editions**

With the Interactive Teacher Edition, you can view your entire *Teacher Wraparound Edition* and Teacher Classroom Resources on your computer screen. Export all worksheet masters to your own word processor for editing, if you choose. With the Interactive Student Edition, students can carry home a CD-ROM instead of a book! With interactive assessments and many more exciting tools, these CD-ROMs become powerful learning resources.

Teacher Classroom Resources

Chapter Resources Booklets

We've organized all of the materials you need for each chapter into convenient chapter-based booklets! The Fast File system provides an easy way to stay organized.

Each **Chapter Resources** booklet contains:

Reproducible Student Pages

Assessment
- Chapter Review
- Chapter Test

Hands-On Activities
- Activity Worksheets for each activity in the *Student Edition*
- Two additional laboratory activities
- Foldables: Reading and Study Skills

Meeting Individual Needs (Extension and Intervention)
- Directed Reading for Content Mastery

- Directed Reading for Content Mastery *in Spanish*
- Reinforcement
- Enrichment
- Note-taking Worksheets

Transparency Activities
- Section Focus Activity
- Teaching Transparency Activity
- Assessment Transparency Activity

Teacher Support and Planning
- Content Outline for Teaching
- Spanish Resources
- Teacher Guide and Answers

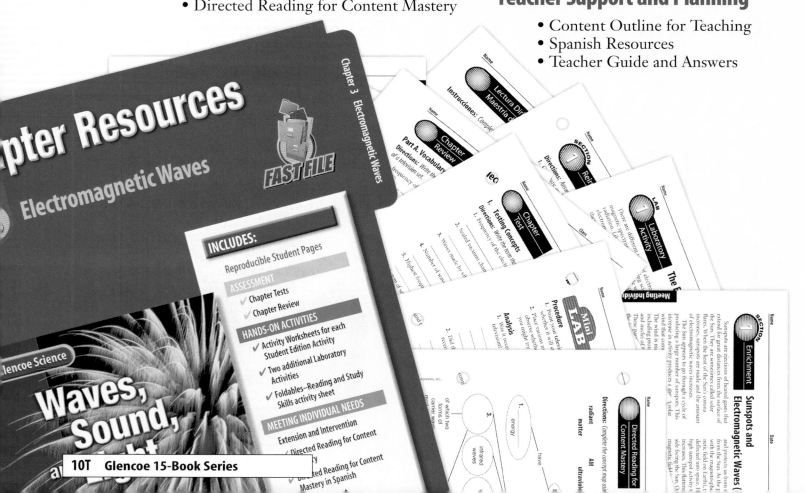

Additional Resources

Glencoe Professional Series

Foldables: Improving Reading and Study Skills

Students love Foldables because they're fun. Teachers love them because they're effective.

What is a Foldable?

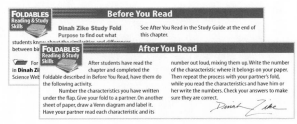

Foldables are three-dimensional, interactive graphic organizers. As students fold paper, cut tabs, write, and manipulate what they have made, they are kinesthetically involved in learning. These unique, hands-on tools for studying and reviewing were created exclusively for Glencoe Science by teaching specialist Dinah Zike.

Foldables are Useful!

Reading in the Content Area

Foldables help students develop ways of organizing information that are fun and creative. These useful activities help students practice basic writing skills, find and report main ideas, organize information, review key vocabulary terms, and much more!

Every chapter begins with a Foldable activity. Students make the physical structure of a Foldable that incorporates one of many prereading strategies. Then, as students read through the chapter and do the activities, students record information as they learn it in the appropriate part of the foldable. In the Chapter Study Guide, the After You Read feature gives students a strategy for using the fold they made to help them review the chapter concepts.

Review One advantage of Foldables is that they result in an organized study guide. The Foldables then can be used not only while preparing for the chapter test, but they can also be used for reviewing for unit tests, end of course exams, and even standardized tests.

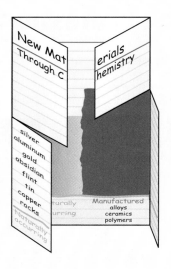

Assessment Foldables present an ideal opportunity for you to probe the depth of your students' knowledge. You'll get detailed feedback on exactly what they know and what misconceptions they may have.

Foldables are Easy!

Anyone who has paper, scissors, and maybe a stapler or some glue can implement Foldables in the classroom. Glencoe's Foldables have been tested with teachers and middle school students to make sure the directions are easy for both students and teachers. After doing a couple of them, your class will quickly become seasoned experts. Don't be surprised if you find them inventing their own for use in projects and reports in all of their classes!

A message from **the creator of Foldables**, Dinah Zike

You might not know my name or me, but I bet you have seen at least one of my graphic organizers or folds used in supplemental programs or teacher workshops. Today, my graphic organizers and manipulatives are used internationally. I present workshops and keynote presentations to over 50,000 teachers a year, sharing the manipulatives I began inventing, designing, and adapting over thirty years ago. Around the world, students of all ages are using them as daily work, note-taking activities, student-directed projects, forms of alternative assessment, science lab journals, quantitative and qualitative observation books, graphs, tables, and more. But through all my years of teaching, designing, and publishing, my materials had never been featured in a middle school textbook. When Glencoe/McGraw-Hill approached me to share some of my three-dimensional, manipulative graphic organizers with you in this new and innovative science series, I was thrilled.

Working with Glencoe, we all had the vision that Foldables should be an integral part of the curriculum, not simply tacked on. What we ended up with was a strategy that will help students read and learn science concepts. One of the advantages of using the same manipulative repeatedly is that students are immersed in what they are learning. It is not out of sight and out of mind. How long is your average student actively involved with a duplicated activity sheet? Ten minutes? Fifteen? Students will use the Foldable at the beginning of each chapter, before reading the chapter, during reading, and after reading. That's a lot of immersion!

Dinah Zike

Students often make personal, educational, and career choices on their own that can influence the rest of their lives. Throughout their school years, they acquire skills that help them make these decisions. The development of keen mathematical skills can ensure that students have a wide variety of life options.

Principles and Standards for School Mathematics of the National Council of Teachers of Mathematics describes the foundation of mathematical concepts and applications that can provide students with the necessary mathematical skills to help achieve their life goals.

The ten categories of mathematical concepts and applications, as shown in the table below, allow students to increase their abilities to visualize, describe, and analyze situations in mathematical terms.

In the *Glencoe 15-Book Series*, each Math Skill Activity and Problem-Solving Activity provides students with the opportunity to practice and apply some of the mathematical concepts and applications described in the Standards. These activities serve to reinforce mathematical skills in real-life situations, thus preparing students to meet their needs in an ever-changing world.

K The Nature of Matter	M Motion, Forces, and Energy	O Waves, Sound, and Light
L Chemistry	N Electricity and Magnetism	

Correlation of Math Skills Activities and Problem Solving Activities in the **Physical Science** books, *Glencoe 15-Book Series,* to **NCTM Standards Grades 6–8**

Standard	Book and Page
1. Number and Operations	M-10, L-13, M-16, M-20, N-21, N-24, L-42, M-45, M-67, N-73, O-75, L-75, M-78, K-84, L-112, M-160
2. Algebra	M-10, O-13, L-13, M-16, M-20, N-21, N-24, N-41, L-42, M-45, M-67, N-73, O-75, L-75, M-78, K-84, M-100, M-101, M-105, M-107, M-160
3. Geometry	N-41
4. Measurement	M-10, M-16, M-20, M-45, M-67, M-78, K-84, M-100, M-101, M-105, M-107, M-160
5. Data Analysis and Probability	O-13, K-27, K-103, O-112, M-142
6. Problem Solving	M-10, O-13, M-16, M-20, N-21, N-24, N-41, O-42, K-49, K-59, M-67, N-73, L-75, M-78, K-84, K-103, O-112, L-112, M-142, M-160
7. Reasoning and Proof	O-112, M-142
8. Communication	M-10, O-13, M-16, M-20, N-21, N-24, O-42, K-49, K-59, M-67, O-75, L-75, M-78, M-100, M-101, K-103, M-105, M-107, O-112, L-112, M-142
9. Connections	M-10, O-13, L-13, M-16, M-20, N-21, N-24, K-27, N-41, O-42, L-42, M-45, K-49, K-59, M-67, N-73, O-75, L-75, M-78, K-84, M-100, M-101, K-103, M-105, M-107, O-112, L-112, M-142, M-160
10. Representation	O-13, K-27, N-41, M-67, M-78, K-103, M-142, M-160

Materials List

All laboratory activities have been thoroughly reviewed by a safety expert.

All full-length labs were bench tested by Science Kit to ensure quality and safety.

BENCH TESTED

It is assumed that goggles, laboratory aprons, tap water, textbooks, paper, calculators, pencils, and pens are available for all activities.

Materials support is provided by Science Kit® & Boreal® Laboratories. Call Science Kit at 1-800-828-7777 to get your activity materials folder. This folder makes it easy for you to order materials and equipment for the program.

Consumables

Item	EXPLORE ACTIVITY Page	Mini LAB Page	Activity Chapter and 1-page or 2-page
Clay	7		
Food-apple			3-1
Food-apple juice			3-2
Food-baking soda			1-2
Food-bread slice			3-1
Food-cereal, dry			3-1
Food-corn starch			1-2
Food-egg(s)			3-1, 3-2
Food-lemon juice, concentrated			3-2
Food-salad oil		26	
Food-sugar		26	1-2
Food-vegetable			3-1
Food-white vinegar			1-2
Glue		15	
Ice			2-1
Index cards		57	1-1
Markers, colored			1-1
Matches			1-2
Paper plate		81	
Plastic cups		57	2-2
Rubbing alcohol		26, 50	
Toothpaste, 2 or 3 different brands			3-2
Toothpick	7		
Water		26, 81	1-2, 3-1, 4-1

Non-Consumables

Item	EXPLORE ACTIVITY Page	Mini LAB Page	Activity Chapter and 1-page or 2-page
Balance			2-2
Basin			2-2
Beakers		26	1-2, 2-1, 4-1
Bowl			3-2
Carpet			3-1
Clock with second hand			2-1
Drawing compass		15	
Dropper		50	
Dropper bottles			1-2
Evaporating dishes			4-1
Faucet		57	
Feather			3-1
Glass, drinking			3-1, 3-2
Graduated cylinder			2-2
Hot plate			1-2, 2-1, 4-1
Magnet			3-1
Marbles			2-2
Metal bar			3-1
Metal nuts	7		
Metal ruler			3-1
Metal screws	7		
Metal washers	7		
Paint brush			3-2
Paper clip(s)	7		

Non-Consumables *continued*

Item	**EXPLORE ACTIVITY** Page	**Mini LAB** Page	**Activity** Chapter and 1-page or 2-page
Penny, copper			4-1
Pie pan, small			1-2
Plastic bin			3-1
Reference-Merck Index			1-1
Rock/Mineral-obsidian	71		
Rock/Mineral-pumice	71		
Rock/Mineral-rock			3-1
Rubber ball			3-1
Sand			3-1
Scoops, small (3)			1-2
Soil			3-1
Spoons (3)		26	
Spring scale			3-1
Steel wool, fine		81	
Stirring rod			2-1
Teaspoon			4-1
Test tubes	39		1-2
Test-tube holder	39		1-2
Thermometer	39		2-1
Thumbtacks			1-1
Tongs			4-1
Wood block			3-1
Zinc, 30-mesh			4-1

Chemical Supplies

Iodine solution			1-2
Nitric acid, dilute			4-1
Sodium hydroxide, dilute			4-1

Live Organisms

Flower			3-1
Plant			3-1

Lab Safety

The activities in the *Glencoe 15-Book Series* have been tested in the laboratory and have been reviewed by safety consultants. Even so, there are no guarantees against accidents. For additional help, refer to the *Laboratory Management and Safety* booklet, which contains safety guidelines and masters to test students' lab and safety skills. Understand and make note of the Safety Symbols used in each activity.

Handling Chemicals

Treat all chemicals as potentially dangerous. Always wear safety goggles, gloves, and an apron when handling them. Never ingest chemicals. Use a fume hood when handling chemicals that are poisonous, corrosive, or give off a vapor. *Always add acids to water, never the reverse.* Prepare solutions by adding the solid to a small amount of distilled water and then diluting with water to the volume listed.

Disclaimer

Glencoe/McGraw-Hill makes no claims to the completeness of this discussion of laboratory safety. The material presented is not all-inclusive, nor does it address all of the hazards associated with handling, storage, and disposal of chemicals, or with laboratory management.

Glencoe Science

The Nature of Matter

NATIONAL GEOGRAPHIC SOCIETY

science.glencoe.com

Glencoe McGraw-Hill

New York, New York   Columbus, Ohio   Woodland Hills, California   Peoria, Illinois

Glencoe Science

The Nature of Matter

Student Edition
Teacher Wraparound Edition
Interactive Teacher Edition CD-ROM
Interactive Lesson Planner CD-ROM
Lesson Plans
Content Outline for Teaching
Dinah Zike's Teaching Science with Foldables
Directed Reading for Content Mastery
Foldables: Reading and Study Skills
Assessment
    Chapter Review
    Chapter Tests
    ExamView Pro Test Bank Software
    Assessment Transparencies
    Performance Assessment in the Science Classroom
    The Princeton Review Standardized Test Practice Booklet
Directed Reading for Content Mastery in Spanish
Spanish Resources
English/Spanish Guided Reading Audio Program

Reinforcement
Enrichment
Activity Worksheets
Section Focus Transparencies
Teaching Transparencies
Laboratory Activities
Science Inquiry Labs
Critical Thinking/Problem Solving
Reading and Writing Skill Activities
Mathematics Skill Activities
Cultural Diversity
Laboratory Management and Safety in the Science Classroom
MindJogger Videoquizzes and Teacher Guide
Interactive CD-ROM with Presentation Builder
Vocabulary PuzzleMaker Software
Cooperative Learning in the Science Classroom
Environmental Issues in the Science Classroom
Home and Community Involvement
Using the Internet in the Science Classroom

THE PRINCETON REVIEW

"Study Tip," "Test-Taking Tip," and "Test Practice" features in this book were written by The Princeton Review, the nation's leader in test preparation. Through its association with McGraw-Hill, The Princeton Review offers the best way to help students excel on standardized assessments.

The Princeton Review is not affiliated with Princeton University or Educational Testing Service.

Glencoe/McGraw-Hill

A Division of The McGraw-Hill Companies

Copyright ©2002 by the McGraw-Hill Companies, Inc. All rights reserved. Except as permitted under the United States Copyright Act, no part of this publication may be reproduced or distributed in any form or by any means, or stored in a database or retrieval system, without the prior written permission of the publisher.

The "Visualizing" features found in each chapter of this textbook were designed and developed by the National Geographic Society's Education Division, copyright ©2002 National Geographic Society. The name "National Geographic Society" and the yellow border rectangle are trademarks of the Society, and their use, without prior written permission, is strictly prohibited. All rights reserved.

The "Science and Society" and the "Science and History" features that appear in this book were designed and developed by TIME School Publishing, a division of TIME Magazine. TIME and the red border are tradmarks of Time Inc. All rights reserved.

Cover Images: Pancake ice forms on a river in Sweden. Pancake ice results when the top of a patch of surface slush freezes.

Send all inquiries to:
Glencoe/McGraw-Hill
8787 Orion Place
Columbus, OH 43240

ISBN 0-07-825524-4
Printed in the United States of America.
3 4 5 6 7 8 9 10 027/111 06 05 04 03 02

Authors

National Geographic Society
Education Division
Washington, D.C.

Patricia Horton
Mathematics/Science Teacher
Summit Intermediate School
Etiwanda, California

Eric Werwa, PhD
Department of
Physics/Astronomy
Otterbein College
Westerville, Ohio

Dinah Zike
Educational Consultant
Dinah-Might Activities, Inc.
San Antonio, Texas

Consultants

Content

Jack Cooper
Adjunct Faculty Math and Science
Navarro College
Corsicana, Texas

Lisa McGaw
Science Teacher
Hereford High School
Hereford, Texas

Reading

Barry Barto
Special Education Teacher
John F. Kennedy Elementary
Manistee, Michigan

Math

Michael Hopper, DEng
Manager of Aircraft Certification
Raytheon Company
Greenville, Texas

Safety

Aileen Duc, PhD
Science II Teacher
Hendrick Middle School
Plano, Texas

Sandra West, PhD
Associate Professor of Biology
Southwest Texas State University
San Marcos, Texas

Reviewers

Sharla Adams
McKinney High School North
McKinney, Texas

Patricia Croft
Westside High School
Martinez, Georgia

Anthony DiSipio
Octorana Middle School
Atglen, Pennsylvania

Sandra Everhart
Honeysuckle Middle School
Dothan, Alabama

George Gabb
Great Bridge Middle School
Chesapeake, Virginia

Eddie K. Lindsay
Vansant Middle School
Buchanan County, Virginia

Pam Starnes
North Richland Middle School
Fort Worth, Texas

Series Activity Testers

José Luis Alvarez, PhD
Math/Science Mentor Teacher
Ysleta ISD
El Paso, Texas

Nerma Coats Henderson
Teacher
Pickerington Jr. High School
Pickerington, Ohio

Mary Helen Mariscal-Cholka
Science Teacher
William D. Slider Middle School
El Paso, Texas

José Alberto Marquez
TEKS for Leaders Trainer
Ysleta ISD
El Paso, Texas

Science Kit and Boreal Laboratories
Tonawanda, New York

CONTENTS

Interdisciplinary Connections/Activities

Activities/Science Connections

Problem-Solving Activities

Math Skills Activities

Skill Builder Activities

Science

Math

Technology

Science INTEGRATION

SCIENCE *Online*

THE PRINCETON REVIEW

Pencils into Diamonds

Introduction

This feature introduces students to the history of the manufacture synthetic of diamonds. It first describes the structure of natural diamonds and graphite and how the first synthetic diamonds were made from graphite. It then explains the subtle differences between natural and synthetic diamonds that can be used to tell them apart. Finally it discusses uses of synthetic diamonds and the places where research is carried on to find better ways to make synthetic diamonds and new uses for these synthetic gems.

1 Motivate

Use a glass cutter to score and cut a piece of glass. Then use a diamond-tipped engraving tool to write a series of numbers on a piece of metal or glass. Hold up both tools for the class to see. **Why is it possible to cut glass with this tool and to write on glass or metal with this tool?** Possible answers: Both tools have sharp edges; both tools have hard edges or points.

What do both of the tools have in common? Some students may know that both have diamond edges or points. Explain that diamond is the hardest substance known, which is why it is used in cutting tools.

Pencils into Diamonds

Diamond, the hardest mineral, is both beautiful and strong. Diamonds can cut steel, conduct heat, and withstand boiling acid. Unfortunately, to find a one carat gem-quality diamond, an average of 250 tons of rock must be mined!

But what if there were another way to get gems? In 1902, Auguste Verneuil, a French scientist, created the world's first synthetic ruby by carefully heating aluminum oxide powder. When other elements were added to this mixture, other colored gemstones were created.

Figure 1
Uncut diamonds are ground and shaped into highly prized gems.

Natural Diamonds

During World War II (1939–1945), there was a sudden need for hard gems used in the manufacturing of precision instruments. Around this time, scientists made the first diamond from carbon, or graphite—the same substance that is in #2 pencils. Graphite is made up of sheets of well-bonded carbon atoms. However, the sheets are only loosely bonded together. This gives graphite its flaky, slippery quality. Diamond, however, is made up of carbon atoms bonded strongly in three dimensions.

Figure 2
 Graphite has a layered structure of carbon atoms. Strong bonds exist within the layers and weak bonds exist between the layers.
B **All bonds between carbon atoms in diamond are strong.**

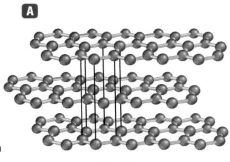

Graphite

Diamond

Inclusion Strategies

Visually Impaired Allow these students to feel the texture of graphite that is used as a lubricant. Ask them to describe how it feels and why its physical properties make it a good lubricant. Have students wash their hands when finished. Then, if possible, allow students to feel a diamond in a piece of jewelry and compare it to the graphite.

Making Synthetic Diamond

To change graphite to diamond, scientists expose it to extreme pressures and to temperatures as high as 3,000°C. The first experiments were unsuccessful. Scientists then reasoned that since diamond is a crystal, it might grow out of a super-concentrated solution as other crystals do. To dissolve carbon, they added melted troilite, a metal found surrounding tiny diamonds at meteorite impact sites, to their experiments. Finally, they had success. The first synthetics were yellowish, but they could be used in industry.

Diamond is a valuable material for industry. It is used to make machine tool coatings, contact lenses, and electrodes. Computer engineers expect that diamond will soon be used to make high-speed computer chips.

Telling Them Apart

Of course, no one has forgotten the diamond's first use: decoration. The first synthetic diamonds were flawed by tiny pieces of metal from the diamond-making process and yellowed by the nitrogen in our atmosphere. Today, diamond makers have eliminated these problems. In just five days, labs now produce colorless, jewelry-grade synthetic diamonds that are much less expensive than natural diamonds. One natural diamond company now determines which stones are synthetic by using phosphorescence. Synthetic, unlike natural, diamonds will glow in the dark for a few seconds after being exposed to ultraviolet light. The synthetic diamond makers are already working to eliminate this difference, too.

Some people are excited about affordable diamonds. Others are concerned that synthetic gem quality diamonds will be sold as natural diamonds. Some people also wonder if a diamond that was made in a laboratory in days has the same symbolic significance as a diamond formed naturally over millions of years.

Figure 4
A machine like this one can produce the temperature and pressure required to create a diamond.

Figure 3
Diamond is sought after for its beauty and for its useful properties.

Fun Fact

Diamonds were once thought to hold magical and medicinal powers. The phosphorescence of certain natural diamonds was considered proof of a stone's extraordinary powers. A house touched at each corner with a diamond was thought to be protected from lightning and storms.

② Teach

Content Background

Fewer than 20% of the diamonds mined each year are suitable for use as gems. The rest go to industrial uses such as diamond-studded rotary bits used to drill oil wells or bore tunnels. Much low-grade diamond is crushed and used as abrasive powder. The powder is used in grinding wheels, glass cutters, and glass-etching pencils. Today synthetic diamonds are made throughout the world. In many industrial uses, synthetic diamonds are preferred over natural diamonds because they can be manufactured to the specific size and shape requirements of an application. The estimated world market for synthetic diamonds is about one billion dollars and could grow as new applications are developed.

Discussion

Explain that during the Middle Ages, alchemists unsuccessfully tried to find ways to turn common metals, such as lead, into gold, which is very valuable. Ask students to think about scientists' attempts to make synthetic diamonds. **How is the work of these scientists similar to that of the alchemists? How is it different?** Like the alchemists who tried to turn lead into gold, the scientists were trying to turn graphite, a common substance, into diamond, a valuable substance. Unlike the alchemists, the scientists succeeded in making diamonds from graphite.

Use Science Words

Word Origin Have students use a dictionary to find the origin of the word *diamond*. Ask them to explain why they think the substance was given that name. The word *diamond* comes from the Greek work *adamas* meaning "indestructible." Diamond is the hardest substance known, so it seems indestructible.

Activity

Have small groups of students research the characteristics of diamonds that are used to describe and judge gem-quality diamonds. Have students make a poster titled *The Five Cs of Diamonds* that illustrates what they learned. Students should find that diamonds are judged by carat, cost, clarity, color, and cut.

Teacher FYI

In 1999 a method was developed for making poor-quality, brownish diamonds into much whiter (E-color) stones that are indistinguishable from natural white stones. These stones are labeled, but the labels can be ground off with diamond-powder sanders.

Extension

Interested students can work together to research the technology used to tell the difference between natural and synthetic diamonds. Have them make an oral presentation on how the technology was developed and how it works. COOP LEARN
Interpersonal

Figure 5
The need for diamond-coated drill bits and cutting blades sparked research into the creation of gem-quality diamonds.

Science

The path to tomorrow's high-speed diamond computer chips will have begun with people trying to make jewelry! Such pathways are reminders of how science touches many aspects of human life. Like the pieces in a puzzle, each scientific breakthrough reveals more about how the world works.

Physical science includes the chemistry that produces synthetic diamonds. In this book, you'll learn how the elements on the periodic table combine to make up everything you see around you. You'll also learn how chemistry can change many aspects of the world around you.

Science Today

Scientists work to find solutions and to answer questions. As people's needs change, scientists who are developing new technologies change the direction of their work. For example, the need for diamonds during World War II triggered research into making synthetic diamonds.

Where Do Today's Scientists Work?

Scientists today work in a variety of places for a variety of reasons. Both scientists who study natural diamonds and people who make synthetic diamonds might work in controlled laboratory environments. They may also study diamonds where they are found in nature.

Public and Private Research

The United States government supports a great deal of scientific research. Publicly funded research usually deals with topics that affect the health and welfare of the country's citizens.

In the private sector, many companies, large and small, have their own laboratories. Their scientists research new technologies, use the technologies in the products that they sell, and test the new products. The world's first synthetic diamond was created by a private company that needed diamond for its products. Another private company, a diamond company, has created many of the world's synthetics in its laboratory! Why? The diamond company wants to understand how synthetics are made so that they can see the differences between their naturally formed diamonds and their competitors' manufactured diamonds. Research has helped them to develop a machine that identifies synthetic diamonds.

Curriculum Connection

Mathematics Explain to students that diamonds are measured in carats and that 5 carats equals 1 gram. Have students calculate the masses in grams of the following diamonds: 44.5-carat Hope Diamond 9.1 g, 127-carat Portuguese Diamond 25.4 g, 2.9-carat DeYoung Pink Diamond 0.58 g, 31-carat Eugenie Blue Diamond 6.2 g

Natural Versus Synthetic Ask students to describe in their Science Journals how large quantities of synthetic industrial and gem-quality diamonds might affect the value of natural diamonds. Ask if they would be willing to pay more for jewelry made with natural diamonds than they would pay for jewelry made with synthetic diamonds. **Linguistic**

Research at Universities

Major universities also have laboratories. Their work with the government or corporations allows academic and industrial scientists to learn from one another. Industry and the government also provide grants and funding for university laboratories.

Dr. Rajiv K. Singh is a professor at the University of Florida, Gainesville. He and his colleague James Adair created the world's largest synthetic diamond using a process called chemical vapor deposition (CVD). Dr. Singh researches many different materials for the University. His work with synthetic diamonds also involves research in flat-panel displays, thin film batteries, electronics, and superconductors.

Figure 6
Researchers at the University of Florida created the world's largest synthetic diamond.

You probably have many devices at home that new discoveries in science have made possible. For example, DVD and MP3 players are technologies that didn't exist just a few years ago. Research the science behind your favorite "gadget" and explain to the class how it works.

Make a Model

Using **Figure 2** as a guide, have students use clay balls or gumdrops and toothpick halves to model the structure of carbon atoms in graphite and in diamonds. Then have them research the third form of carbon, the buckeyball or buckminsterfullerence, and make a model of that structure. **LS Visual-Spatial and Kinesthetic**

Use An Analogy

Ask students if they have ever seen a movie or TV show in which Superman squeezes a lump of coal in his powerful fist, then opened his hand to reveal a diamond. Point out to students that, like Superman, scientists at the University of Florida make synthetic diamonds using extremely high pressures and temperatures.

3 Assess

Use the presentations in You Do It to assess understanding. Presentations should relate to the science behind each student's favorite "gadget" and be as specific as possible.

Have each student name several of his or her favorite gadgets as you list them on the board. You may want to have students who share an interest in the same gadget work together on their research and presentation. Encourage students to use Internet as well as library resources to find out how the gadgets work. Students could make multimedia presentations, including an actual gadget, a labeled diagram explaining how it works, and an oral account of the research behind its development. COOP LEARN **LS Linguistic and Interpersonal**

Section/Objectives	Standards		Activities/Features
	National	State/Local	
Chapter Opener	See p. 7T for a Key to Standards.		**Explore Activity:** Model the unseen, p. 7 **Before You Read,** p. 7
Section 1 Models of the Atom ⏱ 2 sessions 📦 1 block 1. **Explain** how scientists discovered subatomic particles. 2. **Explain** how today's model of the atom developed. 3. **Describe** the structure of the nuclear atom.	National Content Standards: UCP2, A1, B1, E1, F5, G1, G2, G3		**Try at Home MiniLAB:** Modeling the Nuclear Atom, p. 15 **Physics Integration,** p. 16
Section 2 The Simplest Matter ⏱ 3 sessions 📦 1.5 blocks 1. **Describe** the relationship between elements and the periodic table. 2. **Explain** the meaning of atomic mass and atomic number. 3. **Identify** what makes an isotope. 4. **Contrast** metals, metalloids, and nonmetals.	National Content Standards: UCP2, A1, B1, G1		**Science Online,** p. 19 **Visualizing the Periodic Table,** p. 20 **Activity:** Elements and the Periodic Table, p. 24
Section 3 Compounds and Mixtures ⏱ 4 sessions 📦 2 blocks 1. **Identify** the characteristics of a compound. 2. **Compare and contrast** different types of mixtures.	National Content Standards: UCP2, A1, B1, D1, G1, G2, G3		**MiniLAB:** Comparing Compounds, p. 26 **Problem-Solving Activity:** What's the best way to desalt ocean water?, p. 27 **Science Online,** p. 28 **Earth Science Integration,** p. 29 **Activity:** Mystery Mixture, pp. 30–31 **Science and History:** Ancient Views of Matter, pp. 32–33

Activity Materials	Reproducible Resources	Section Assessment	Technology
Explore Activity: ball of clay, metal objects (paper clips, screws, nuts, washers), toothpick	**Chapter Resources Booklet** Foldables Worksheet, p. 13 Directed Reading Overview, p. 15 Note-taking Worksheets, pp. 29–31	GLENCOE'S **ASSESSMENT** ADVANTAGE	
MiniLAB: sheet of paper, drawing compass, colored paper dots, glue	**Chapter Resources Booklet** Transparency Activity, p. 40 MiniLAB, p. 3 Lab Activity, pp. 9–10 Enrichment, p. 26 Reinforcement, p. 23 Directed Reading, p. 16 **Cultural Diversity,** pp. 55, 59	**Portfolio** Use Science Words, p. 14 Science Journal, p. 14 **Performance** MiniLAB, p. 15 Skill Builder Activities, p. 17 **Content** Section Assessment, p. 17	Section Focus Transparency Interactive CD-ROM Guided Reading Audio Program
Activity: colored markers, large index cards, Merck Index, encyclopedia, large bulletin board, 8 1/2 × 14-inch paper, thumbtacks *Need materials?* Contact Science Kit at 1-800-828-7777 or www.sciencekit.com on the Internet.	**Chapter Resources Booklet** Transparency Activity, p. 41 Enrichment, p. 27 Reinforcement, p. 24 Directed Reading, p. 17 Transparency Activity, pp. 43–44 Activity Worksheet, pp. 5–6 **Science Inquiry Labs,** pp. 19, 47	**Portfolio** Extension, p. 21 **Performance** Skill Builder Activities, p. 23 **Content** Section Assessment, p. 23	Section Focus Transparency Teaching Transparency Interactive CD-ROM Guided Reading Audio Program
MiniLAB: granular sugar, rubbing alcohol, salad oil, 3 beakers, hot water, 3 spoons **Activity:** 4 test tubes, cornstarch, sugar, baking soda, 3 small scoops, iodine solution and white vinegar in dropper bottles, hot plate, 250-mL beaker, water, test-tube holder, small pie pan, matches	**Chapter Resources Booklet** Transparency Activity, p. 42 MiniLAB, p. 4 Lab Activity, pp. 11–12 Enrichment, p. 28 Reinforcement, p. 25 Directed Reading, pp. 17, 18 Activity Worksheet, pp. 7–8 **Lab Management and Safety,** p. 49	**Portfolio** Curriculum Connection, p. 28 **Performance** MiniLAB, p. 26 Problem-Solving Activity, p. 27 Skill Builder Activities, p. 29 **Content** Section Assessment, p. 29	Section Focus Transparency Interactive CD-ROM Guided Reading Audio Program

GLENCOE'S ASSESSMENT ADVANTAGE	**End of Chapter Assessment**	
Blackline Masters	**Technology**	**Professional Series**
Chapter Resources Booklet Chapter Review, pp. 33–34 Chapter Tests, pp. 35–38 **Standardized Test Practice by The Princeton Review,** pp. 11–14	MindJogger Videoquiz Interactive CD-ROM Vocabulary PuzzleMakers ExamView Pro Test Bank Interactive Lesson Planner Interactive Teacher Edition	Performance Assessment in the Science Classroom (PASC)

Transparencies

Section Focus

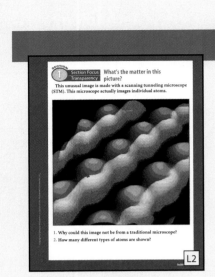

Section Focus Transparency 1 — What's the matter in this picture?

This unusual image is made with a scanning tunneling microscope (STM). This microscope actually images individual atoms.

1. Why could this image not be from a traditional microscope?
2. How many different types of atoms are shown?

L2

Section Focus Transparency 2 — Some Call It Quicksilver

This element is a liquid at room temperature. It is probably best known as the liquid in traditional thermometers; however, it is so toxic that people often choose digital or alcohol thermometers that do not contain this element.

1. Describe what you see in the picture. What characteristics does this element have?
2. Which element do you think this is? Do you know of any other uses for it?

L2

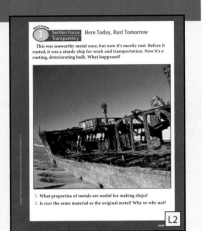

Section Focus Transparency 3 — Here Today, Rust Tomorrow

This was seaworthy metal once, but now it's mostly rust. Before it rusted, it was a sturdy ship for work and transportation. Now it's a rusting, deteriorating hulk. What happened?

1. What properties of metals are useful for making ships?
2. Is rust the same material as the original metal? Why or why not?

L2

This is a representation of key blackline masters available in the Teacher Classroom Resources. See Resource Manager boxes within the chapter for additional information.

Assessment

Assessment Transparency — Inside the Atom

Directions: *Carefully review the tables and answer the following questions.*

Table A
Gold
Water
Salt
Sugar

Table B
Vegetable soup
Pancake batter
Blood
Air

1. The substances in Table A are different from the substances in Table B because only the substances in Table B are ___.
   A mixtures
   B metals
   C compounds
   D pure elements
2. Which of the following belongs with the matter in Table A above?
   F chocolate-chip ice cream
   G chicken noodle soup
   H iron nail
   J milk shake
3. Heterogeneous mixtures are mixtures that have different parts that are large enough to be visibly identified. According to this information, which of the substances in Table B is a heterogeneous mixture?
   A vegetable soup
   B pancake batter
   C blood
   D air

L2

Teaching

Teaching Transparency 2 — Nonmetals in Humans

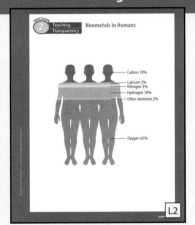

Carbon 18%
Calcium 2%
Nitrogen 3%
Hydrogen 10%
Other elements 2%

Oxygen 65%

L2

Key to Teaching Strategies

The following designations will help you decide which activities are appropriate for your students.

L1 Level 1 activities should be appropriate for students with learning difficulties.

L2 Level 2 activities should be within the ability range of all students.

L3 Level 3 activities are designed for above-average students.

ELL ELL activities should be within the ability range of English Language Learners.

COOP LEARN Cooperative Learning activities are designed for small group work.

LS Multiple Learning Styles logos are used throughout to indicate strategies that address different learning styles.

P These strategies represent student products that can be placed into a best-work portfolio.

Hands-on Activities

Activity Worksheets

Activity — Elements and the Periodic Table

Lab Preview

Directions: *Answer these questions before you begin the Activity.*

1. What safety practice is indicated by the safety symbol with the hand that is included in this activity?

2. List at least two research sources that might be useful in this activity.

The periodic table organizes the elements, but what do they look like? What are they used for? In this activity, you'll examine some elements and share your findings with your classmates.

What You'll Investigate
What are some of the characteristics and properties of the chemical elements?

Goals
• **Classify** the chemical elements.
• **Design** your own periodic table that shows the classification of the elements.

Materials
colored markers
large index cards
Merck Index
encyclopedia
*other reference materials
large bulletin board
8 ½, 14-inch paper
thumbtacks
*pushpins
*Alternate materials

Safety Precaution
Use care when handling sharp objects.

Procedure
1. Select the assigned number of elements from the list provided by your teacher.
2. **Design** an index card for each of your selected elements. On each card, mark the element's atomic number in the upper left-hand corner and write its symbol and name in the upper right-hand corner.
3. **Research** each of the elements and write several sentences on the card about its appearance, its other properties, and its uses.
4. **Classify** each of your elements as a metal, a metalloid, or a nonmetal based upon its properties.
5. **Write** the appropriate classification on each of your cards using the colored marker chosen by your teacher.
6. Work with your classmates to make a large periodic table. Use thumbtacks to attach your cards to a bulletin board in their proper positions on the periodic table.
7. **Draw** your own periodic table. Place the elements' symbols and atomic numbers in the proper locations on your table.

Inside the Atom L2

Laboratory Activities

Laboratory Activity 1 — Atoms—Smaller Than You Think!

Have you ever seen an atom? Unless you've been lucky enough to look through a very powerful microscope, you haven't seen anything close in size to an atom. Matter is composed of atoms, and atoms are everywhere. You can't see atoms or even molecules. They are too small. But even though you can't see an atom with your own eyes, you can use other senses to detect the presence of some of the small molecules made from atoms. In this experiment, you will study the small size of vanilla molecules.

Strategy
You will predict what happens when drops of a liquid that is made up of small molecules are placed in a balloon.
You will observe some aspects of small molecules.

Materials
rubber balloon
closet or locker
dropper
vanilla extract (2 mL)

Figure 1

Procedure
1. Use a dropper to place 20 to 40 drops of vanilla extract into a rubber balloon. (See Figure 1)
2. Blow up the balloon, and tie it tightly.
3. Place the balloon in a small, enclosed area such as a closet or locker for at least 30 minutes.
4. What do you think will happen to the molecules of vanilla extract in the balloon? Record your predictions in the table in the Data and Observations section.
5. After 30 minutes, open the closet or locker. What did you observe? Record your observation in the Data and Observations section.

Data and Observations

Predictions	Observations

Inside the Atom L2

Meeting Different Ability Levels

Content Outline

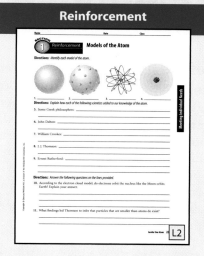

L2

Reinforcement

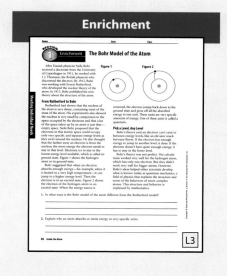

L2

Directed Reading

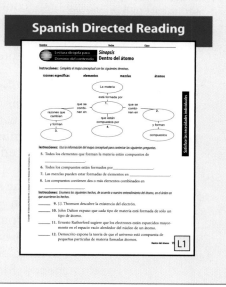

L1

Enrichment

L3

Spanish Directed Reading

L1

Assessment

Chapter Tests

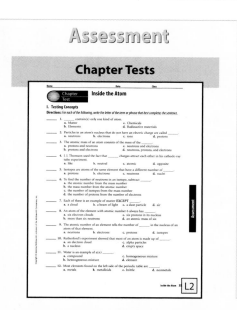

L2

Test Practice Workbook

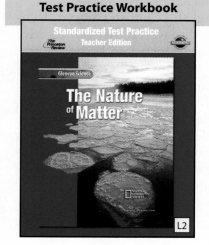

L2

Chapter Review

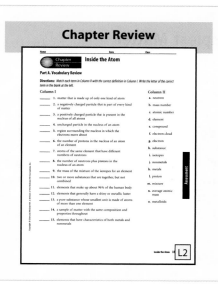

L2

Science Content Background

SECTION
1

Models of the Atom
Early Greek Philosophers

It is thought that the idea that matter can be divided into smaller particles called atoms was named and developed by the Greek philosopher Democritus around 430 B.C. Other early philosophers such as Aristotle, Titus Lucretius Carus, and Plato disagreed with Democritus' idea of atoms and proposed that matter was continuous and could not be divided. The idea of continuous matter, although incorrect, was widely accepted for the next 2,000 years.

Fun Fact

Democritus thought that atoms composed not only matter, but also qualities such as color and taste.

Evidence to Support Atomic Theory

Antione Lavoisier proposed the law of conservation of mass that states that although matter may undergo chemical reactions and change, it cannot be created or destroyed. Joseph Proust observed that specific substances always contain elements in the same ratio by mass. In the 1800s, John Dalton expanded upon the work of Lavoisier, Proust, and other chemists. Dalton proposed that matter is composed of atoms and now scientific evidence was available to support this theory. Since Dalton's time, the atomic model has undergone may changes as more scientific evidence became available.

SECTION
2

The Simplest Matter
Triads and Octaves

Dmitri Mendeleev arranged the 63 known elements into his first published periodic table in 1869. This was not the first attempt to organize the elements, nor was it the final version of the periodic table. In 1817 J.W. Döbereiner, a German chemist, showed that the atomic weight of strontium fell halfway between calcium and barium. He called this a triad. He showed that other triads also existed. John Newlands, an English chemist, proposed another method of organizing the elements in 1865. Newlands found that if the elements were organized in the order of increasing atomic weight, similarities occurred in intervals of seven. (The noble gases were not discovered until 1894.) Newlands' method of organizing the elements is called the law of octaves.

Mendeleev's Table

Mendeleev's periodic table was similar to Newlands' because he arranged the elements in order of increasing atomic mass and according to similar chemical and physical properties. But unlike Newlands' table, where the elements are in groups of seven, the first two rows of Mendeleev's table had seven elements, and the next two rows had seventeen. On the modern periodic table, periods 2–5 have this arrangement. Recall that the noble gases were not discovered until later.

Fun Fact

Initially, Dmitri Mendeleev was not accepted to a Russian university because the education that he received in Siberia was considered inferior. Mendeleev was eventually accepted, and later became a university professor and was nominated for the Nobel Prize in Chemistry.

Moseley's Contribution

In 1911, the English scientist Henry Gwyn-Jeffreys Moseley discovered that the positive charge in the nucleus increased by one as you went sequentially higher in Mendeleev's periodic table. When the table was organized by increasing positive charge or atomic number, the inconsistencies in Mendeleev's table were corrected. Moseley's work led to the modern statement of periodic law that states the properties of the elements are a periodic function of their atomic numbers.

Fine-Tuning the Table

As new elements were discovered and synthesized, they were added to the periodic table in order of increasing atomic number. Additional research in atomic structure revealed that the electron configuration of the elements was responsible for their chemical properties. Because electron configuration and chemical properties of the elements are considered when placing elements on the periodic table, the center of the table grew to a cumbersome width. For this reason, the lanthanide and actinide series of elements are placed below the periodic table. This gives the table a more manageable size.

SECTION 3 Compounds and Mixtures

Classifying Matter

Matter is organized and classified into groups based on its composition. The diagram below shows the hierarchy of matter classification. Notice that the broadest classification of matter is materials.

Materials are then broken down into homogeneous and heterogeneous materials.

Homogeneous and Heterogeneous Materials

Homogeneous materials have the same composition throughout; heterogeneous materials do not. For example, sodium chloride is a compound composed of sodium and chlorine. It has the same composition throughout the substance. A beaker of sand and iron filings is a mixture because it has distinct areas that have different properties. Substances (elements and compounds) and solution are homogenous materials. Mixtures are heterogeneous materials.

SCIENCE Online

For additional content background on this topic, go to the Glencoe Science Web site at science.glencoe.com.

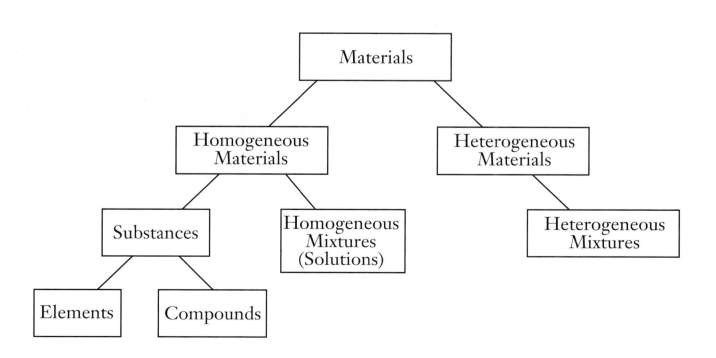

CHAPTER 1

Inside the Atom

Chapter Vocabulary

What do you think?

Science Journal This is a photo of a scanning tunneling microscope. It is used to make an image similar to a topographic map. From these images, scientists can visualize the interior of atoms.

CHAPTER 1

Inside the Atom

Everything in the world is made of atoms. But what are atoms and how were they discovered? Today, special microscopes help scientists see images created by atoms. This is an image of 48 iron atoms forming a "corral" around a single copper atom. It is amazing what scientists were able to discover about the makeup of matter before such microscopes were even thought of. In this chapter, you will learn about atoms and some of the people who discovered them.

What do you think?

Science Journal Look at the picture below with a classmate. Discuss what you think this might be. Here's a hint: *It is used to make images of atoms.* Write your description or best guess in your Science Journal.

Theme Connection

Stability and Change The nucleus of an atom can undergo changes that can be useful but dangerous. These changes occur in a predictable pattern.

Have you ever had a wrapped birthday present that you couldn't wait to open? What did you do to try to figure out what was in it? The atom is like that wrapped present. You want to investigate it, but you cannot see it easily.

Model the unseen

1. Your teacher will give you a piece of clay and some pieces of metal. Count the pieces of metal.

2. Bury these pieces in the modeling clay so they can't be seen.

3. Exchange clay balls with another group.

4. With a toothpick, probe the clay to find out how many pieces of metal are in the ball and what shape they are.

Observe

In your Science Journal, sketch the shapes of the metal pieces as you identify them. How does the number of pieces you found compare with the number that were in the clay ball? How do their shapes compare?

Before You Read

FOLDABLES
Reading & Study Skills

Making an Organizational Study Fold Make the following Foldable to help you organize your thoughts about parts of an atom.

1. Stack two sheets of paper in front of you so the short side of both sheets is at the top.

2. Slide the top sheet up so that about four centimeters of the bottom sheet show.

3. Fold both sheets top to bottom to form four tabs and staple along the top fold as shown.

4. Before you read the chapter, label the flaps *Atom, Electron, Proton,* and *Neutron* as shown.

5. As you read the chapter, describe how each part of the atom was discovered and record other facts under the flaps.

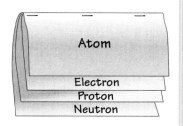

Purpose Use this Explore Activity to help students discover how scientists find out about things they can't see. L1 ELL COOP LEARN Ⓚ **Kinesthetic**

Materials small metal objects such as washers, nuts, and bolts; modeling clay; toothpick; paper towels

Teaching Strategy Demonstrate step 4 to show students how to use a probe to feel things that can't be seen.

Observe

Answers will vary. Some shapes will be easier to identify than others.

✓ *Assessment*

Oral Have students work in groups to share their results. Ask them to compare their evidence and to discuss how they discovered what each hidden item was. Use **Performance Assessment in the Science Classroom,** p. 169.

Before You Read

FOLDABLES
Reading & Study Skills

Dinah Zike Study Fold

Purpose Students make a Foldable on which to record information about atoms, protons, electrons, and neutrons.

📁 For additional help, see Foldables Worksheet, p. 13 in **Chapter Resources Booklet,** or go to the Glencoe Science Web site at **science.glencoe.com.** See After You Read in the Study Guide at the end of this chapter.

SECTION

Models of the Atom

1 Motivate

Bellringer Transparency

Display the Section Focus Transparency for Section 1. Use the accompanying Transparency Activity Master. L2

ELL

Tie to Prior Knowledge

Discuss with students what they already know about matter from having observed various substances and from having used matter and measured it. Tell them that now they will examine the things inside matter that make it behave the way it does.

As You Read

What You'll Learn

- **Explain** how scientists discovered subatomic particles.
- **Explain** how today's model of the atom developed.
- **Describe** the structure of the nuclear atom.

Vocabulary

element
electron
proton
neutron
electron cloud

Why It's Important

Atoms make up everything in your world.

First Thoughts

Do you like mysteries? Are you curious? Humans are curious. Someone always wants to know something that is not easy to detect or to see what can't be seen. For example, people began wondering about matter more than 2,500 years ago. Some of the Greek philosophers thought that matter was composed of tiny particles. They reasoned that you could take a piece of matter, cut it in half, cut the half piece in half again, and continue to cut again and again. Eventually, you wouldn't be able to cut any more. You would have only one particle left. They named these particles *atoms*, a term that means "cannot be divided." Another way to imagine this is to picture a string of beads like the one shown in **Figure 1.** If you keep dividing the string into pieces, you eventually come to one single bead.

Describing the Unseen The Greek philosophers didn't try to prove their theories by doing experiments as scientists now do. Their theories were the result of reasoning, debating, and discussion—not of evidence or proof. Today, scientists will not accept a theory that is not supported by experimental evidence. But even if the Greek philosophers had experimented, they could not have proven the existence of atoms. People had not yet discovered much about what is now called chemistry, the study of matter. The kind of equipment needed to study matter was a long way from being invented. Even as recently as 500 years ago, atoms were still a mystery.

Figure 1
You can divide this string of beads in half, and in half again until you have one, indivisible bead. Like this string of beads, all matter can be divided until you reach one basic particle, the atom.

Section ✓*Assessment* Planner

PORTFOLIO
Use Science Words, p. 14
Science Journal, p. 14
PERFORMANCE ASSESSMENT
Try At Home MiniLAB, p. 15
Skill Builder Activities, p. 17
See page 36 for more options.

CONTENT ASSESSMENT
Section, p. 17
Challenge, p. 17
Chapter, pp. 36–37

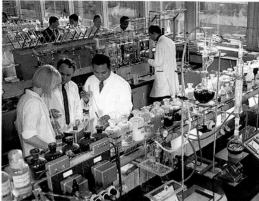

A Model of the Atom

A long period passed before the theories about the atom were developed further. Finally during the eighteenth century, scientists in laboratories, like the one on the left in **Figure 2**, began debating the existence of atoms once more. Chemists were learning about matter and how it changes. They were putting substances together to form new substances and taking substances apart to find out what they were made of. They found that certain substances couldn't be broken down into simpler substances. Scientists came to realize that all matter is made up of elements. An **element** is matter made of atoms of only one kind. For example, iron is an element made of iron atoms. Silver, another element, is made of silver atoms. Carbon, gold, and oxygen are other examples of elements.

Dalton's Concept John Dalton, an English schoolteacher in the early nineteenth century, combined the idea of elements with the Greek theory of the atom. He proposed the following ideas about matter: (1) Matter is made up of atoms, (2) atoms cannot be divided into smaller pieces, (3) all the atoms of an element are exactly alike, and (4) different elements are made of different kinds of atoms. Dalton pictured an atom as a hard sphere that was the same throughout, something like a tiny marble. A model like this is shown in **Figure 3.**

Scientific Evidence Dalton's theory of the atom was tested in the second half of the nineteenth century. In 1870, the English scientist William Crookes did experiments with a glass tube that had almost all the air removed from it. The glass tube had two pieces of metal called electrodes sealed inside. The electrodes were connected to a battery by wires.

Figure 2
Even though the laboratories of the time were simple compared to those of today, incredible discoveries were made during the eighteenth century.

Figure 3
Dalton pictured the atom as a hard sphere that was the same throughout.

SECTION 1 Models of the Atom **K ◆ 9**

Teacher **FYI**

Dalton based his theory of the atom on experiments with atomic weights. His results showed that the weight ratio of chemical elements in a given chemical compound was always the same. Although his measurements were poor and the values he assigned elements were incorrect, most of his conclusions were correct.

Resource Manager

Chapter Resources Booklet
   Transparency Activity, p. 40
   Directed Reading for Content Mastery, pp. 15, 16

2 Teach

First Thoughts

Make a Model

Have each student construct a three-dimensional model of the atom as it was first defined by Greek philosophers. Students can use materials such as clay, paper, aluminum foil, Velcro, toothpicks, and wire. As they progress through this section, have students modify their models to reflect each new scientific understanding of the structure of the atom. L2 ELL
Kinesthetic

Use an Analogy

To help students understand the concept that matter is made from atoms, have them observe a picture in a newspaper. Then have them take a closer look using a hand lens or microscope. Point out that from a distance we see a picture, but when we get close we can see the dots that make the picture. Atoms in matter are like the ink dots in a newspaper picture. L1 ELL
Visual-Spatial

A Model of the Atom

Activity

Have students locate the periodic table at the back of their book. Explain to students that the table includes all known elements. Have them read the names of the elements and discuss elements with which they are familiar. Explain that all things are made from these elements. L1 ELL **Linguistic**

A Model of the Atom, continued

Caption Answer
Figure 4 a stream of particles

Extension

Have students find out about other devices that have an anode and a cathode. Ask them to summarize what is similar in the devices they list. Students may list batteries, fuel cells, CRTs, and X-ray tubes. In all of these, electric current passes from one electrode to the other. L2
LS **Linguistic**

Discussion

Why was it necessary for the air to be removed from Crookes's tube during his experiments? so that the cathode rays could reach the glass without hitting air particles first L3
LS **Logical-Mathematical**

✔ Reading Check

Answer streams of particles produced at the cathode of a cathode ray tube

Figure 4
Crookes used a glass tube containing only a small amount of gas. When the glass tube was connected to a battery, something flowed from the negative electrode (cathode) to the positive electrode (anode). *Was this unknown thing light or a stream of particles?*

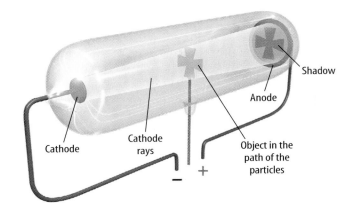

Shadow

Anode

Cathode

Cathode rays

Object in the path of the particles

A Strange Shadow An electrode is a piece of metal that can conduct electricity. One electrode, called the anode, has a positive charge. The other, called the cathode, has a negative charge. In the tube that Crookes used, the metal cathode was a disk at one end of the tube. In the center of the tube was an object shaped like a cross, as you can see in **Figure 4.** When the battery was connected, the glass tube suddenly lit up with a greenish-colored glow. A shadow of the object appeared at the opposite end of the tube—the anode. The shadow showed Crookes that something was traveling in a straight line from the cathode to the anode, similar to the beam of a flashlight. The cross-shaped object was getting in the way of the beam and blocking it, just like when a road crew uses a stencil to block paint from certain places on the road when they are marking lanes and arrows. You can see this in **Figure 5.**

Figure 5
Paint passing by a stencil is an example of what happened with Crookes' tube, the cathode ray, and the cross.

Cathode Rays Crookes hypothesized that the green glow in the tube was caused by rays, or streams of particles. These rays were called cathode rays because they were produced at the cathode. Crookes' tube is known as a cathode-ray tube, or CRT. **Figure 6** shows a CRT. They have been used for TV and computer display screens for many years now.

✔ Reading Check

What are cathode rays?

𝒮cience 𝔍ournal

Cathode-Ray Tube Ask students to pretend that they are coworkers with Crookes at the time of his experiments with a cathode-ray tube. Have students write letters in their Science Journals to a fellow scientist telling them about the exciting results they obtained and how they interpreted the results. L2 **LS** **Linguistic**

Cultural **Diversity**

Cathode Rays Much of the early work on cathode rays was done in Germany, made possible by a pump developed by Johann Heinrich Geissler that could make a much better vacuum than had been previously possible. In 1858 Julius Plücker used the pump in experiments that produced a greenish glow. A few years later Eugen Goldstein named the rays that caused the glow cathodenstrahlen, or cathode rays.

Discovering Charged Particles

The news of Crookes' experiments excited the scientific community of the time. But many scientists were not convinced that the cathode rays were streams of particles. Was the greenish glow light, or was it a stream of charged particles? In 1897, J.J. Thomson, an English physicist, tried to clear up the confusion. He placed a magnet beside the tube from Crookes' experiments. In **Figure 7,** you can see that the beam is bent in the direction of the magnet. Light cannot be bent by a magnet, so the beam couldn't be light. Therefore, Thomson concluded that the beam must be made up of charged particles of matter that came from the cathode.

The Electron Thomson then repeated the CRT experiment using different metals for the cathode and different gases in the tube. He found that the same charged particles were produced no matter what elements were used for the cathode or the gas in the tube. Thomson concluded that cathode rays are negatively charged particles of matter. How did Thomson know the particles were negatively charged? He knew that opposite charges attract each other. He observed that these particles were attracted to the positively charged anode, so he reasoned that the particles must be negatively charged.

These negatively charged particles are now called **electrons.** Thomson also inferred that electrons are a part of every kind of atom because they are produced by every kind of cathode material. Perhaps the biggest surprise that came from Thomson's experiments was the evidence that particles smaller than the atom do exist.

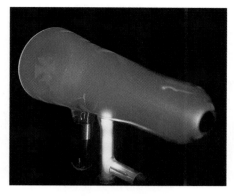

Figure 6
The cathode-ray tube got its name because the particles start at the cathode and travel to the anode. There used to be a cathode-ray tube, or CRT, in every TV and computer monitor.

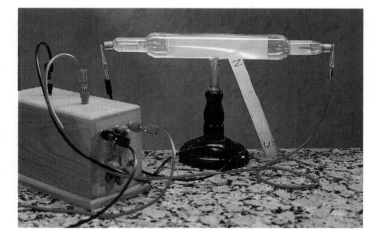

Figure 7
When a magnet was placed near a CRT, the cathode rays were bent. Since light is not bent by a magnet, Thompson determined that cathode rays were made up of charged particles.

IDENTIFYING Misconceptions

The green glow in Crookes's tube was caused by the excitation of electrons in the molecules of gas remaining in the tube. Only the molecules that were in the path of the high-energy electrons glowed, appearing like a stream of light. Students should be aware that the stream of light scientists saw was not the electrons, but evidence of their presence.

Quick Demo

Place a magnet and some iron filings on the overhead projector to demonstrate a magnet's ability to exert a force on an object at a distance. Students can see from this demo that the magnet used by J.J. Thomson could act on the cathode ray without touching it. L2 ELL
IS Visual-Spatial

Resource Manager

Chapter Resources Booklet
Note-taking Worksheets, pp. 29–31
Cultural Diversity, pp. 55, 59

✔ Active Reading

Think-Pair Share This strategy encourages students to think first before discussing their ideas or thoughts about a topic. Ask students to respond to a question by writing a response. After thinking for a few minutes, partners share responses to the question. Finally, ask the students to share responses with the class. Have students become involved in a Think-Pair Share about cathode rays.

12 ◆ K CHAPTER 1 Inside the Atom

Discovering Charged Particles, continued

Visual Learning

Figure 8 In the Thomson model of the atom, what do the ball bearings represent? electrons **Does the atom have a positive or negative charge, or is it neutral?** The atom is neutral because the positive charges of the protons are balanced by the negative charges of the electrons. L1 ELL
LS **Visual-Spatial**

✔ Reading Check

Answer Thomson's model had negative charges spread evenly among the positive charge.

Rutherford's Experiments

Teacher FYI

Rutherford began studying the scattering of alpha particles in 1906. He continued his experiments in 1907 and 1908 with the help of Hans Wilhelm Geiger. All of the experiments done during these three years looked for small scattering angles, and what they found confirmed Thomson's description of the atom. It wasn't until 1909 when a graduate student of Rutherford's detected alpha particles that had been deflected by large angles. This was the experiment that led to the new understanding of the atom.

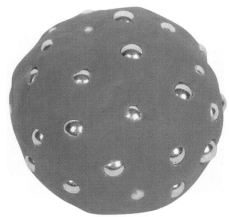

Figure 8
Modeling clay with ball bearings mixed through is another way to picture the J.J. Thomson atom. The clay contains all the positive charge of the atom. The ball bearings, which represent the negatively charged electrons, are mixed evenly in the clay.

Thomson's Atomic Model Some of the questions posed by scientists were answered in light of Thomson's experiments. However, the answers inspired new questions. If atoms contain one or more negatively charged particles, then all matter, which is made of atoms, should be negatively charged as well. But all matter isn't negatively charged. How can this be explained? Could it be that atoms also contain some positive charge? The negatively charged electrons and the unknown positive charge would then neutralize each other in the atom. Thomson came to this conclusion and included positive charge in his model of the atom.

Using his new findings, Thomson revised Dalton's model of the atom. Instead of a solid ball that was the same throughout, Thomson pictured a sphere of positive charge. The negatively charged electrons were spread evenly among the positive charge. This is modeled by the ball of clay shown in **Figure 8.** The positive charge of the clay is equal to the negative charge of the electrons. Therefore, the atom is neutral. It was later discovered that not all atoms are neutral. The number of electrons within an element can vary. If there is more positive charge than negative electrons, the atom has an overall positive charge. If there are more negative electrons than positive charge, the atom has an overall negative charge.

✔ Reading Check

What particle did Thomson's model have scattered through it?

Rutherford's Experiments

A model is not accepted in the scientific community until it has been tested and the tests support previous observations. In 1906, Ernest Rutherford and his coworkers began an experiment to find out if Thomson's model of the atom was correct. They wanted to see what would happen when they fired fast-moving, positively charged bits of matter, called alpha particles, at a thin film of a metal such as gold. Alpha particles come from unstable atoms. Alpha particles are positively charged, and so they are repelled by particles of matter which also have a positive charge.

Figure 9 shows how the experiment was set up. A source of alpha particles was aimed at a thin sheet of gold foil that was only 400nm thick. The foil was surrounded by a fluorescent (fluh RES unt) screen that gave a flash of light each time it was hit by a charged particle.

Inclusion Strategies

Learning Disabled Students will find it easier to deal with this abstract material if you use physical models of atoms or drawings as often as possible while you are discussing the parts of the atom. To help them organize the facts in this chapter, make flash cards for each section and help them add facts to their cards each day.
L1 LS **Linguistic**

Resource Manager

Chapter Resources Booklet
Enrichment, p. 26

Expected Results Rutherford was certain he knew what the results of this experiment would be. His prediction was that most of the speeding alpha particles would pass right through the foil and hit the screen on the other side, just like a bullet fired through a pane of glass. Rutherford reasoned that the thin, gold film did not contain enough matter to stop the speeding alpha particle or change its path. Also, there wasn't enough charge in any one place in Thomson's model to repel the alpha particle strongly. He thought that the positive charge in the gold atoms might cause a few minor changes in the path of the alpha particles. However, he assumed that this would only occur a few times.

That was a reasonable hypothesis because in Thomson's model, the positive charge is essentially neutralized by nearby electrons. Rutherford was so sure of what the results would be that he turned the work over to a graduate student.

The Model Fails Rutherford was shocked when his student rushed in to tell him that some alpha particles were veering off at large angles. You can see this in **Figure 9.** Rutherford expressed his amazement by saying, "It was about as believable as if you had fired a 15-inch shell at a piece of tissue paper, and it came back and hit you." How could such an event be explained? The positively charged alpha particles were moving with such high speed that it would take a large positive charge to cause them to bounce back. The uniform mix of mass and charges in Thomson's model of the atom did not allow for this kind of result.

Figure 9
In Rutherford's experiment, alpha particles bombarded the gold foil. Most particles passed right through the foil or veered slightly from a straight path, but some particles bounced right back. The path of a particle is shown by a flash of light when it hits the fluorescent screen.

Teacher FYI

When Rutherford published his new ideas about the structure of the atom in 1911, he had worked out a way to test his theory. He knew that by measuring the distribution of the scattering angles of the alpha particles, he could find the effective cross section of the atoms that scattered them. Between 1911 and 1913 his assistants did the necessary experiments. Their results confirmed Rutherford's theory.

Make a Model

Students can model how Rutherford did his experiment. Pound about twenty 2-inch nails into the center area of a 4´ × 4´ sheet of plywood. Simulate the thin gold foil by arranging the nails in three lines. Make sure the nails are several inches apart and not arranged one directly behind the other. Have students take turns shooting marbles at the nails from a spot perpendicular to the lines of nails. Have other students mark on the outer edges of the plywood where each marble rolls after going through the nails. Students can measure the scattering angle of each marble by measuring the angle between the straight line the marble would have traveled had it not hit a nail and the line it actually traveled. L3 |S **Kinesthetic**

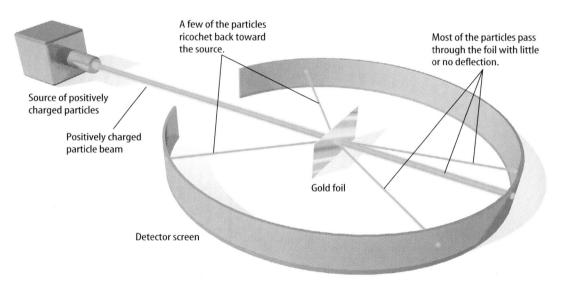

A few of the particles ricochet back toward the source.

Most of the particles pass through the foil with little or no deflection.

Source of positively charged particles

Positively charged particle beam

Gold foil

Detector screen

SECTION 1 Models of the Atom **K ◆ 13**

Science Journal

Rutherford's Graduate Student Have students find out more about the graduate student who performed Rutherford's historic experiment. Tell them to record in their Science Journals the name of the student and where he was born. His name was Ernest Marsden and he was from New Zealand. L2

|S **Linguistic**

Fun Fact

Alpha particles consist of two protons and two neutrons. They were first identified by Ernest Rutherford, who named them alpha particles for simplicity. Rutherford also named beta particles and the proton.

A Model with a Nucleus

Activity

Have students create a class time line of events that led to the modern model of the atom. Include the date or time period and contributions of John Dalton, William Crookes, J.J. Thomson, Ernest Rutherford, and the discovery of the neutron. L2 ELL COOP LEARN
IS **Visual-Spatial**

Use Science Words

Word Meanings The word *nucleus* means "central core." Have students find out how this term is used in other branches of science, and write paragraphs explaining the meaning of the term *central core* when describing the nucleus of an atom. The term nucleus is used in life science to describe structures in a cell, in astronomy to describe structures in a comet, and in physical science to describe structures in an atom. The central core is the dense center part of an atom containing protons and neutrons. L2 IS **Linguistic** P

Extension

Have students explore models of the atom in which charge is distributed differently from Rutherford's model. **Do the models agree with the results of Rutherford's experiment?** Answers will vary, but no other model will fit the experimental data as well as Rutherford's. L3 IS **Logical-Mathematical**

✔ **Reading Check**

Answer a massive positive center surrounded by empty space occupied by almost-massless electrons

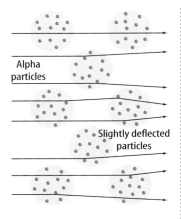

Alpha particles

Slightly deflected particles

Figure 10
Rutherford thought that if the atom could be described by Thomson's model, then only minor bends in the paths of the particles would have occurred.

Figure 11
The nuclear model was new and helped explain experimental results.

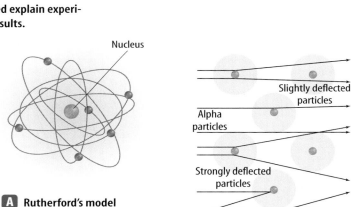

Nucleus

A Rutherford's model included the dense center of positive charge known as the nucleus.

Slightly deflected particles

Alpha particles

Strongly deflected particles

B This nucleus that contained most of the mass of the atom caused the deflections that were observed in his experiment.

A Model with a Nucleus

Now Rutherford and his team had to come up with an explanation for these unexpected results. They might have drawn diagrams like those in **Figure 10,** which uses Thomson's model and shows what Rutherford expected. Now and then, an alpha particle might be affected slightly by a positive charge in the atom and turn a bit off course. However, large changes in direction were not expected.

The Proton The actual results did not fit this model, so Rutherford proposed a new one, shown in **Figure 11A.** He hypothesized that almost all the mass of the atom and all of its positive charge are crammed into an incredibly small region of space at the center of the atom called the nucleus. Eventually, his prediction was proved true. In 1920 scientists identified the positive charges in the nucleus as protons. A **proton** is a positively charged particle present in the nucleus of all atoms. The rest of each atom is empty space occupied by the atom's almost-massless electrons.

✔ **Reading Check** *How did Rutherford describe his new model?*

Figure 11B shows how Rutherford's new model of the atom fits the experimental data. Most alpha particles could move through the foil with little or no interference because of the empty space that makes up most of the atom. However, if an alpha particle made a direct hit on the nucleus of a gold atom, which has 79 protons, the alpha particle would be strongly repelled and bounce back.

Science Journal

Atomic Models Have students draw diagrams of the Dalton, Thomson, and Rutherford models of the atom. Make sure they show Dalton's model as a featureless sphere, and Thomson's as a homogeneous spherical mass with electrons embedded in it at regular points. Rutherford's nuclear atom should have a tiny mass at the center of a large space occupied by electrons. L1 ELL IS **Visual-Spatial** P

Curriculum Connection

History Have students find out when and where Thomson and Rutherford lived and how they interacted. Thomson lived in England from 1856 to 1940. Rutherford was born in 1871 in New Zealand. In 1895 he earned a scholarship, which he used to go to Cambridge University in England, where Thomson invited him to help with his work on radiation and electricity. L3
IS **Linguistic**

The Neutron Rutherford's nuclear model was applauded as other scientists reviewed the results of the experiments. However, some data didn't fit. Once again, more questions arose and the scientific process continued. For instance, an atom's electrons have almost no mass. According to Rutherford's model, the only other particle in the atom was the proton. That meant that the mass of an atom should have been approximately equal to the mass of its protons. However, it wasn't. The mass of most atoms is at least twice as great as the mass of its protons. That left scientists with a dilemma and raised a new question. Where does the extra mass come from?

It was proposed that another particle must be in the nucleus to account for the extra mass. The particle, which was later called the **neutron** (NEW trahn), would have the same mass as a proton and be electrically neutral. Proving the existence of neutrons was difficult though, because a neutron has no charge. Therefore, the neutron doesn't respond to magnets or cause fluorescent screens to light up. It took another 20 years before scientists were able to show by more modern experiments that atoms contain neutrons.

✔ Reading Check *What particles are in the nucleus of the nuclear atom?*

The model of the atom was revised again to include the newly discovered neutrons in the nucleus. The nuclear atom, shown in **Figure 12,** has a tiny nucleus tightly packed with positively charged protons and neutral neutrons. Negatively charged electrons occupy the space surrounding the nucleus. The number of electrons in a neutral atom equals the number of protons in the atom.

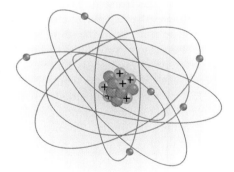

TRY AT HOME

Mini LAB

Modeling the Nuclear Atom

Procedure
1. On a sheet of **paper**, draw a circle with a diameter equal to the width of the paper.
2. Small dots of paper in two colors will represent protons and neutrons. Using a dab of **glue** on each paper dot, make a model of the nucleus of the oxygen atom in the center of your circle. Oxygen has eight protons and eight neutrons.

Analysis
1. What particle is missing from your model of the oxygen atom?
2. How many of that missing particle should there be, and where should they be placed?

Figure 12
This atom of carbon, atomic number 6, has six protons and six neutrons in its nucleus. *How many electrons are in the "empty" space surrounding the nucleus?*

TRY AT HOME

Mini LAB

Purpose Students will make a model of Rutherford's atom.
L2 IS **Visual-Spatial**

Materials unlined paper, dots of colored paper, glue

Teaching Strategy Demonstrate step 2 with an element other than oxygen. Emphasize the idea that these models do NOT represent the relative sizes of the nucleus and the atoms. In reality, the nucleus and the electrons are much smaller than the atom. The diameter of the atom is 100,000 times larger than the diameter of the nucleus.

Analysis
1. the electron
2. Eight electrons; they should be placed in the circle surrounding the nucleus.

✔ Assessment

Content Have each student make a model of a nucleus for a different element. Use the models to reinforce the concept of atomic number and its relationship to the number of protons and electrons in an atom. Use **PASC**, p. 123.

✔ Reading Check

Answer protons and neutrons

Caption Answer
Figure 12 six

Teacher FYI

In 1932, Iréne and Frédéric Joliot-Curie found that when they bombarded beryllium with alpha particles, neutral radiation was emitted. They thought it might be gamma radiation, but its energy was too high. James Chadwick proposed that the radiation was a stream of neutrons, particles having the same mass as the proton but no charge.

Resource Manager

Chapter Resources Booklet
    MiniLAB, p. 3
    Lab Activity, pp. 9–10

Further Developments

Activity

In 1927 the German physicist Werner Heisenberg developed his Uncertainty Principle. Have students find out about the Uncertainty Principle and how it affects scientists' understanding of the atom. The Heisenberg Uncertainty Principle states that it is impossible to know exactly both a subatomic particle's position and its momentum. This means that all information about the location and movement of these particles takes the form of statistical probabilities rather than statements of certainty. L3

 **Logical-Mathematical**

Extension

Have students find out more about how scientists today describe the locations of electrons in atoms. Electrons are distributed in energy levels around the nucleus. Each energy level is divided into atomic orbitals. The shapes of these orbitals are determined by probabilities derived from quantum mechanics. The *s* orbitals are spherical, each *p* orbital is shaped like a dumbbell, four *d* orbitals are shaped like pairs of crossed dumbbells, and one is shaped like a doughnut with a dumbbell through the middle. Each orbital can hold up to two electrons. L3 **Visual-Spatial**

Physics
INTEGRATION

In 1923, Louis de Broglie equated Einstein's matter and energy equation, $E = mc^2$, and Max Planck's frequency and energy equation, $E = h\Omega$. The basis for de Broglie's new equation became $mc^2 = h\Omega$. This enabled scientists to explain the constant, unpredictable motion of electrons.

Figure 13
If this ferris wheel in London, with a diameter of 132 m, were the outer edge of the atom, the nucleus would be about the size of a single letter *o* on this page.

Physics
INTEGRATION

Physicists in the 1920s began to think that electrons—like light—have a wave/particle nature. This is called quantum theory. Research which two scientists introduced this theory. In your Science Journal, infer how thoughts about atoms changed.

Size and Scale Drawings of the nuclear atom such as the one in **Figure 12** don't give an accurate representation of the extreme smallness of the nucleus compared to the rest of the atom. For example, if the nucleus were the size of a table-tennis ball, the atom would have a diameter of more than 2.4 km. Another way to compare the size of a nucleus with the size of the atom is shown in **Figure 13.** Perhaps now you can see better why in Rutherford's experiment, most of the alpha particles went directly through the gold foil without any interference from the gold atoms. Plenty of empty space allows the alpha particles an open pathway.

Further Developments

Even into the twentieth century, physicists were working on a theory to explain how electrons are arranged in an atom. It was natural to think that the negatively charged electrons are attracted to the positive nucleus in the same way the Moon is attracted to Earth. Then, electrons would travel in orbits around the nucleus. A physicist named Niels Bohr even calculated exactly what energy levels those orbits would represent for the hydrogen atom. His calculations explained experimental data found by other scientists. However, scientists soon learned that electrons are in constant, unpredictable motion and can't be described easily by an orbit. They determined that it was impossible to know the precise location of an electron at any particular moment. Their work inspired even more research and brainstorming among scientists around the world.

Inclusion Strategies

Gifted Physicists have identified particles called quarks that combine to form protons and neutrons. Have students find out about quarks and make oral reports of their findings to the class. It takes three quarks to make up a proton or a neutron. A proton is made up of two up quarks and one down quark. An up quark has a charge of $+2/3$, and a down quark has a charge of $-1/3$, so the total charge on a proton is $+2/3 + 2/3 - 1/3 = +1$. A neutron is made up of one up quark and two down quarks. Its charge is $+2/3 - 1/3 - 1/3 = 0$. L3

Logical-Mathematical

Electrons as Waves Physicists began to wrestle with explaining the unpredictable nature of electrons. Surely the experimental results they were seeing and the behavior of electrons could somehow be explained with new theories and models. The unconventional solution was to understand electrons not as particles, but as waves. This led to further mathematical models and equations that brought much of the experimental data together.

The Electron Cloud Model The new model of the atom allows for the somewhat unpredictable wave nature of electrons by defining a region where the electron is most likely to be found. Electrons travel in a region surrounding the nucleus, which is called the **electron cloud.** The current model for the electron cloud is shown in **Figure 14.** The electrons are more likely to be close to the nucleus rather than farther away because they are attracted to the positive charges of the protons. Notice the fuzzy outline of the cloud. Because the electrons could be anywhere, the cloud has no firm boundary. Interestingly, within the electron cloud, the electron in a hydrogen atom probably is found in the region Bohr calculated.

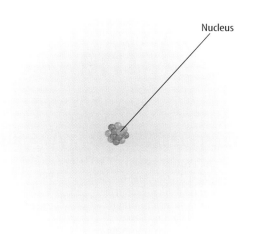
Nucleus

Figure 14
The electrons are more likely to be close to the nucleus rather than farther away, but they could be anywhere.

Section 1 Assessment

1. Name three scientists who contributed to current knowledge of the atom and explain their contributions.

2. How does the nuclear atom differ from the uniform sphere model of the atom?

3. If a neutral atom has 49 protons, how many electrons does it have?

4. Describe the three kinds of particles found in atoms. Where are they located in the atom and what are their charges?

5. **Think Critically** In Rutherford's experiment, why wouldn't the electrons in the atoms of the gold foil affect the paths of the alpha particles?

Skill Builder Activities

6. **Concept Mapping** Design and complete a concept map using all the words in the vocabulary list for this section. Add any other terms or words that will help create a complete diagram of the section and the concepts it contains. **For more help, refer to the** Science Skill Handbook.

7. **Solving One-Step Equations** The mass of an electron is 9.11×10^{-28} g. The mass of a proton is 1,836 times more than that of the electron. Calculate the mass of the proton in grams and convert that mass into kilograms. **For more help, refer to the** Math Skill Handbook.

Reteach
On the board, make diagrams of Dalton's, Thomson's, and Rutherford's models of the atom. Ask Students what evidence there was to support Dalton's model. What experiments led to the abandonment of Dalton's model and the adoption of Thomson's? Do the same for Thomson's and Rutherford's models. L2
LS Visual-Spatial

Challenge
Have students draw diagrams of Thomson's and Rutherford's experiments. Have them label all parts and write brief descriptions of how the experiments worked. L2 LS **Visual-Spatial**

✔Assessment

Content Have each student make a concept map using the terms *element, electron, proton, neutron,* and *electron cloud.* Use **Performance Assessment in the Science Classroom,** p. 161.

Answers to Section Assessment

1. Answers should include three of the following scientists: John Dalton, defined elements; William Crookes, made a vacuum tube for studying cathode rays; J.J. Thomson, discovered electron; Ernest Rutherford, modeled the nuclear atom; Neils Bohr, calculated electron energy levels.

2. In the nuclear atom, all the positive charge and almost all the mass are in a tiny nucleus with the electrons occupying the space around it. In the uniform sphere, the atom was the same throughout.

3. 49 electrons

4. protons: in the nucleus, positive charge; neutrons: in the nucleus, no charge; electrons: outside the nucleus, negative charge

5. Electrons are too small to affect the path of a fast-moving alpha particle.

6. Answers will vary. Students' maps should include all the parts of an atom.

7. $(9.11 \times 10^{-28}$ g$) \times 1,836 = 1.67 \times 10^{-24}$ g $= 1.67 \times 10^{-27}$ kg

Resource Manager

Chapter Resources Booklet
Reinforcement, p. 23

The Simplest Matter

SECTION

2

The Simplest Matter

1 Motivate

Bellringer Transparency

Display the Section Focus Transparency for Section 2. Use the accompanying Transparency Activity Master. L2 ELL

Tie to Prior Knowledge

Many students are familiar with the chemical formula for water, H_2O. Ask whether they know what the symbols *H* and *O* represent. H represents the element hydrogen; O represents the element oxygen. Have students list the names and symbols of any other elements they know.

As You Read

What You'll Learn

- **Describe** the relationship between elements and the periodic table.
- **Explain** the meaning of atomic mass and atomic number.
- **Identify** what makes an isotope.
- **Contrast** metals, metalloids, and nonmetals.

Vocabulary

atomic number	metals
isotope	nonmetals
mass number	metalloids
atomic mass	

Why It's Important

Everything on Earth is made of the elements that are listed on the periodic table.

The Elements

Have you watched television today? TV sets are common, yet each one is a complex system. The outer case is made mostly of plastic, and the screen is made of glass. Many of the parts that conduct electricity are metals or combinations of metals. Other parts in the interior of the set contain materials that barely conduct electricity. All of the different materials have one thing in common. They are made up of even simpler materials. In fact, if you had the proper equipment, you could separate the plastics, glass, and metals into these simpler materials.

One Kind of Atom Eventually, though, you would separate the materials into groups of atoms. At that point, you would have a collection of elements. Recall that an element is matter made of only one kind of atom. At this time, 115 elements are known and 90 of them occur naturally on Earth. These elements make up gases in the air, minerals in rocks, and liquids such as water. Examples of the 90 naturally occurring elements include the oxygen and nitrogen in the air you breathe and the metals gold, silver, aluminum, and iron. The other 25 elements are known as synthetic elements. These elements have been made by scientists with machines like the one shown in **Figure 15.** Some synthetic elements have important uses in medical testing and are found in smoke detectors and heart pacemaker batteries.

Figure 15

The Tevatron has a circumference of 6.3 km—a distance that allows particles to accelerate to high speeds. These high-speed collisions can create synthetic elements.

Section ✔*Assessment* Planner

PORTFOLIO
Extension, p. 21
PERFORMANCE ASSESSMENT
Skill Building Activities, p. 23
See page 36 for more options.

CONTENT ASSESSMENT
Section, p. 23
Challenge, p. 23
Chapter, pp. 36–37

Figure 16
When you look for information in the library, a system of organization called the Dewey Decimal Classification System helps you find a book quickly and efficiently.

Dewey Decimal Classification System	
000	Computers, information, and general reference
100	Philosophy and psychology
200	Religion
300	Social sciences
400	Language
500	Science
600	Technology
700	Arts and recreation
800	Literature
900	History and Geography

The Periodic Table

Suppose you go to a library, like the one shown in **Figure 16,** to look up information for a school assignment. How would you find the information? You could look randomly on shelves as you walk up and down rows of books, but the chances of finding your book would be slim. Not only that, you also would probably become frustrated in the process. To avoid such haphazard searching, some libraries use the Dewey Decimal Classification System to categorize and organize their volumes and to help you find books quickly and efficiently.

Charting the Elements When scientists need to look up information about an element or select one to use in the laboratory, they need to be quick and efficient, too. Chemists have created a chart called the periodic table of the elements to help them organize and display the elements. **Figure 17** shows how scientists changed their model of the periodic table over time.

On the inside back cover of this book, you will find a modern version of the periodic table. Each element is represented by a chemical symbol that contains one to three letters. The symbols are a form of chemical shorthand that chemists use to save time and space—on the periodic table as well as in written formulas. The symbols are an important part of an international system that is understood by scientists everywhere.

The elements represented by the symbols on the periodic table are placed purposely in their position on the table. There are rows and columns that represent relationships between the elements. The rows in the table are called periods. The elements in a row have the same number of energy levels. The columns are called groups. The elements in each group have similar properties related to their structure. They also tend to form similar bonds.

Data Update For an online update of the number of elements, visit the Glencoe Science Web site at **science.glencoe.com** and select the appropriate chapter.

Internet Addresses

_____

_____

_____

Explore the Glencoe Science Web site at **science.glencoe.com** to find out more about topics in this section.

Resource Manager

Chapter Resources Booklet
   Transparency Activity, p. 41
   Directed Reading for Content Mastery, p. 17
Home and Community Involvement, p. 43

---

2 Teach

The Elements

IDENTIFYING Misconceptions

Students may think that all aspects of the structure and building blocks of matter are completely known. Point out that much remains to be learned about atoms and elements.

The Periodic Table

Activity

Have students skim the periodic table for symbols and names of familiar elements. Have them share with the class the things that these elements are found in. Example: Ca—calcium is found in milk and other food products. L2 IS **Interpersonal**

Use an Analogy

Point out to students the ways in which a month's calendar is like the periodic table. The days are arranged from left to right, as periods of elements are arranged from left to right. Days with the same name are arranged in columns, as groups of elements are arranged in the table.

Teacher FYI

Elements such as gold, silver, tin, copper, lead, and mercury have been known since ancient times. As more elements were discovered, people began to recognize patterns in their properties. Later, scientists used the patterns to classify the elements.

Visualizing the Periodic Table

Have students examine the pictures and read the captions. Then ask the following questions.

Why do you think the periodic table is so useful to scientists? It helps them organize and understand the chemical properties of the elements.

One difference between Mendeleev's table and the one used today is that his table lacks the column containing the elements helium through radon. Why do you think this is? None of the elements in that column had been discovered in Mendeleev's time. This is because they are not common and they don't readily undergo chemical reactions.

Activity

Divide the class into eighteen groups. Assign each group a different group of elements from the periodic table. Have them research the similarities and differences among the elements in their respective groups and make posters illustrating the properties of these elements. L2
COOP LEARN **LS** Interpersonal

Extension

Ask students to find out how alchemists' ideas about matter were different from modern ideas and how modern chemistry developed from the methods of alchemy. Ask students to share their findings with the class. L3
LS Linguistic

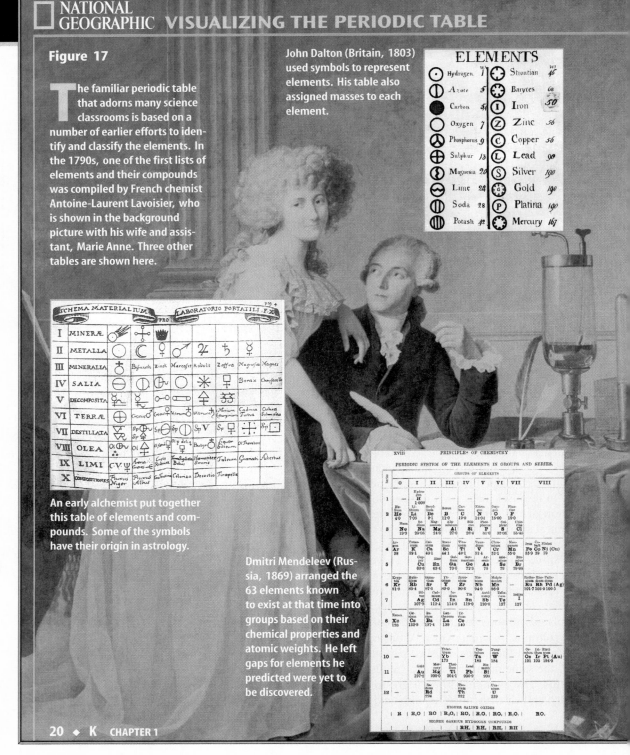

Figure 17

The familiar periodic table that adorns many science classrooms is based on a number of earlier efforts to identify and classify the elements. In the 1790s, one of the first lists of elements and their compounds was compiled by French chemist Antoine-Laurent Lavoisier, who is shown in the background picture with his wife and assistant, Marie Anne. Three other tables are shown here.

John Dalton (Britain, 1803) used symbols to represent elements. His table also assigned masses to each element.

An early alchemist put together this table of elements and compounds. Some of the symbols have their origin in astrology.

Dmitri Mendeleev (Russia, 1869) arranged the 63 elements known to exist at that time into groups based on their chemical properties and atomic weights. He left gaps for elements he predicted were yet to be discovered.

Teacher FYI

Dmitri Mendeleev published his periodic table in 1869. It was based on his recognition of patterns in the properties and atomic masses of certain elements. To understand the patterns, he made a card for each of the more than 60 known elements. Each card contained the element's symbol, atomic mass, and its characteristic chemical and physical properties. By arranging the cards on a table in order of increasing atomic mass, and by grouping elements of similar properties, he created a "periodic table" that showed vertical, horizontal, and diagonal relationships. Mendeleev left gaps in his table for future discovery of the then unknown elements, and was able to predict the properties of some of them in detail.

Identifying Characteristics

Each element is different and has unique properties. These differences can be described in part by looking at the relationships between the atomic particles in each element. The periodic table contains numbers that describe these relationships.

Number of Protons and Neutrons Look up the element chlorine on the periodic table found on the inside back cover of your book. Cl is the symbol for chlorine, as shown in **Figure 18,** but what are the two numbers? The top number is the element's **atomic number.** It tells you the number of protons in the nucleus of each atom of that element. Every atom of chlorine, for example, has 17 protons in its nucleus.

> ✔ **Reading Check** *What are the atomic numbers for Cs, Ne, Pb, and U?*

Isotopes Although the number of protons changes from element to element, every atom of the same element has the same number of protons. However, the number of neutrons can vary even for one element. For example, some chlorine atoms have 18 neutrons in their nucleus while others have 20. These two types of chlorine atoms are chlorine-35 and chlorine-37. They are called **isotopes** (I suh tohps), which are atoms of the same element that have different numbers of neutrons.

You can tell someone exactly which isotope you are referring to by using its mass number. An atom's **mass number** is the number of protons plus the number of neutrons it contains. The numbers 35 and 37, which were used to refer to chlorine, are mass numbers. Hydrogen has three isotopes with mass numbers of 1, 2, and 3. They are shown in **Figure 19.** Each hydrogen atom always has one proton, but in each isotope the number of neutrons is different.

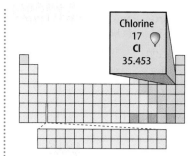

Figure 18
The periodic table block for chlorine shows its symbol, atomic number, and atomic mass. *Are chlorine atoms more or less massive than carbon atoms?*

Figure 19
Three isotopes of hydrogen are known to exist. They have zero, one, and two neutrons in addition to their one proton. Protium, with only the one proton, is the most abundant isotope.

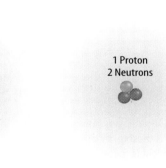

1 Proton	1 Proton 1 Neutron	1 Proton 2 Neutrons
Protium	Deuterium	Tritium

SECTION 2 The Simplest Matter **K ◆ 21**

Identifying Characteristics

Caption Answer
Figure 18 more massive

Extension
Have students read the labels on their favorite breakfast cereals and list the elements found in the cereals. Then have each student research and make a poster describing the use of these elements by the human body. L2 IS **Linguistic** P

✔ Reading Check

Answer Cs-55; Ne-10; Pb-82; U-92

Visual Learning

Figure 19 Have students identify the differences among the three isotopes of hydrogen. Then explain that almost all elements have some isotopes. As an extension, have students research the isotopes of some elements and draw the different nuclei. Carbon is an example; C-12: 6 p, 6 n; C-13: 6 p, 7 n; C-14: 6 p, 8 n. Remind students that all of the isotopes of one element have the same number of protons.

Resource Manager

Chapter Resources Booklet
Enrichment, p. 27
Transparency Activity, pp. 43–44

🔬 LAB DEMONSTRATION

Purpose To demonstrate the structures of isotopes of nitrogen

Materials gumdrops or small foam balls in various colors, toothpicks

Preparation Electrons, neutrons, and protons must be different colors.

Procedure Make a model of nitrogen-7 using 7 protons, 7 neutrons, and 7 electrons.

Place the neutrons and protons close together and the electrons away from the nucleus. Now make a model of nitrogen-8 using 7 protons, 8 neutrons, and 7 electrons.

Expected Outcome Students should observe differences in the models of the two nitrogen atoms.

✔ Assessment

What is used to determine the mass of an element? the total number of neutrons and protons **What is the mass number of the first nitrogen isotope?** 14 **What is the mass number of the second nitrogen isotope?** 15

Fun Fact

To get an idea of how small the mass of an atom is, consider that there are roughly 560 quintillion (560,000,000,000,000,000,000) atoms of hydrogen and oxygen combined in one drop of water.

Classification of Elements

Teacher FYI

The elements have an increasing nonmetallic characteristic as you read from left to right across the table. Along the stair-step line are metalloids, which have properties of both metals and nonmetals.

Quick Demo

To show how metal atoms slide over each other to produce the property of malleability, place a clear plastic lid from a container on the overhead projector. Next, layer in metal shot (BBs) to form a layer of rows. Now show how the rows can be moved from side to side with the movement of a ruler on one side of a layer. L2 IS **Visual-Spatial**

Extension

Polonium is in the area of the periodic table that might make it seem a metalloid, yet it is typically classed as a metal. Have students find out why. Like metals, polonium conducts electricity better when it is cooled. Metalloids conduct electricity better when they are heated. L3 IS **Logical-Mathematical**

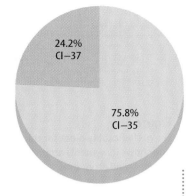

Circle Graph Showing Abundance of Chlorine Isotopes

Average atomic mass = 35.453 u

24.2%
Cl–37

75.8%
Cl–35

Figure 20
If you have 1,000 atoms of chlorine, about 758 will be chlorine-35 and have a mass of 34.97 u each. About 242 will be chlorine-37 and have a mass of 36.97 u each. The total mass of the 1,000 atoms is 35,454 u, so the average mass of one chlorine atom is about 35.45 u.

Figure 21
The artisan is chasing, or chiseling, the malleable metal into the desired form.

Atomic Mass The **atomic mass** is the weighted average mass of the isotopes of an element. The atomic mass is the number found below the element symbol in **Figure 18.** The unit that scientists use for atomic mass is called the atomic mass unit, which is given the symbol u. It is defined as 1/12 the mass of a carbon-12 atom.

The calculation of atomic mass takes into account the different isotopes of the element. Chlorine's atomic mass of 35.45 u could be confusing because there aren't any chlorine atoms that have that exact mass. About 76 percent of chlorine atoms are chlorine-35 and about 24 percent are chlorine-37, as shown in **Figure 20.** The weighted average mass of all chlorine atoms is 35.45 u.

Classification of Elements

Elements fall into three general categories—metals, metalloids (MET ul oydz), and nonmetals. The elements in each category have similar properties.

Metals generally have a shiny or metallic luster and are good conductors of heat and electricity. All metals, except mercury, are solids at room temperature. Metals are malleable (MAL yuh bul), which means they can be bent and pounded into various shapes. The beautiful form of the shell-shaped basin in **Figure 21** is a result of this characteristic. Metals are also ductile, which means they can be drawn into wires without breaking. If you look at the periodic table, you can see that most of the elements are metals.

Resource Manager

Chapter Resources Booklet
   Reinforcement, p. 24

Physical Science Critical Thinking/Problem Solving, p. 13

Cultural Diversity

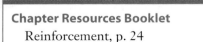

Forms of Money The use of metals for money began approximately 7000 B.C. In the Middle East, bronze likely was used first, with gold and silver also exchanged. There is evidence that standard weight and value coins were developed in the area of modern Turkey around 640 B.C. Have students discuss characteristics that make a material useful as money. value, portability, rarity, availability, sturdiness L2 IS **Linguistic**

Other Elements **Nonmetals** are elements that are usually dull in appearance. Most are poor conductors of heat and electricity. Many are gases at room temperature, and bromine is a liquid. The solid nonmetals are generally brittle, meaning they cannot change shape easily without breaking. The nonmetals are essential to the chemicals of life. More than 97 percent of your body is made up of various nonmetals, as shown in **Figure 22.** You can see that, except for hydrogen, the nonmetals are found on the right side of the periodic table.

Metalloids are elements that have characteristics of metals and nonmetals. On the periodic table, metalloids are found between the metals and nonmetals. All metalloids are solids at room temperature. Some metalloids are shiny and many are conductors, but they are not as good at conducting heat and electricity as metals are. Some metalloids, such as silicon, are used to make the electronic circuits in computers, televisions, and other electronic devices.

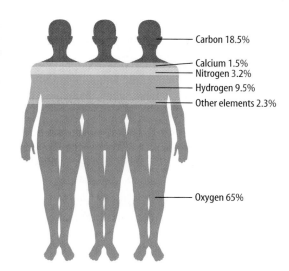

Carbon 18.5%
Calcium 1.5%
Nitrogen 3.2%
Hydrogen 9.5%
Other elements 2.3%
Oxygen 65%

Figure 22
You are made up of mostly nonmetals.

 **Reading Check** *What is a metalloid?*

Section 2 Assessment

1. What is an element?

2. Describe the difference between atomic number and atomic mass.

3. What are isotopes? What is different in each isotope?

4. Explain some of the uses of metals based on their properties.

5. **Think Critically** Hector is new to your class today. He missed the lesson on how to use the periodic table to find information about the elements. Describe how you would teach Hector to find the atomic number for the element oxygen. Explain what this information tells him about oxygen.

Skill Builder Activities

6. **Interpreting Data** Look up the atomic mass of the element boron in the periodic table inside the back cover of this book. The naturally occurring isotopes of boron are boron-10 and boron-11. Which of the two isotopes is more abundant? Explain your reasoning. **For more help, refer to the** Science Skill Handbook.

7. **Solving One-Step Equations** An atom of niobium has a mass number of 93. How many neutrons are in the nucleus of this atom? An atom of phosphorus has 15 protons and 15 neutrons in the nucleus. What is the mass number of this isotope? **For more help, refer to the** Math Skill Handbook.

Reading Check

Answer an element with characteristics of both metals and nonmetals

3 Assess

Reteach

Write all the information found on the periodic table for one element on the board. Have students tell what each symbol or number represents. L2
IS **Visual-Spatial**

Challenge

Have small groups of students classify classroom objects as being made mostly of metals or nonmetals and record their answers on chart. Then have students write a statement that can be used to determine if their chart is correct.

Possible Answers:

Metal	Nonmetal
File cabinet	Carpet
Chair legs	Plastic seat

Metal items are shiny, solid at room temperature, conduct heat and electricity, and can be pounded into different shapes without breaking. Nonmetals do not have these properties.

Assessment

Oral Name elements on the periodic table at random. Ask students to tell whether each selected element is a metal, a metalloid, or a nonmetal. Use **Performance Assessment in the Science Classroom,** p. 89.

Answers to Section Assessment

1. A type of matter that contains only one type of atom.

2. atomic number: the number of protons in the nucleus of each atom of an element; mass number: the sum of an atom's protons and neutrons

3. Isotopes are atoms of the same element that contain different numbers of neutrons.

4. good conductors of heat and eletricity (electrical circuits and cookware), malleable (formed into tools), ductile (drawn into wires)

5. Hector should locate oxygen on the periodic table. Oxygen's atomic number (8) is the whole number in the element's box (above the element symbol) and means that every atom

of oxygen contains eight protons in its nucleus.

6. Boron-11; boron's atomic mass is 10.811, which is closer to 11 than 10.

7. $93 - 41 = 52\,n$; $15\,p + 15\,n = 30$

Activity

Purpose Students classify elements and build a periodic table that shows their classifications.
L2 **IS** **Visual-Spatial**
Process Skills classifying, comparing and contrasting, making and using tables, interpreting data, predicting
Time Required 2–3 hours
Teaching Strategy Because a large amount of information is available for most elements, advise students to focus their efforts and collect only key information.

Answers to Questions

1. The table students make will look like the periodic table, but only certain elements will be present.
2. This element should be shiny in the solid state, have such metallic characteristics as high electrical and thermal conductivities, and be reactive with nonmetals to form compounds.

Assessment

Portfolio Take a photograph of the class periodic table and have a copy made for each student. Have students include the index cards for their elements and the photograph of the class periodic table in their portfolios. Use **PASC**, p. 177.

Activity

Elements and the Periodic Table

The periodic table organizes the elements, but what do they look like? What are they used for? In this activity, you'll examine some elements and share your findings with your classmates.

What You'll Investigate
What are some of the characteristics and purposes of the chemical elements?

Goals
- **Classify** the chemical elements.
- **Organize** the elements into the groups and periods of the periodic table.

Materials
colored markers
large index cards
Merck Index
encyclopedia
*other reference
    materials

large bulletin board
$8\frac{1}{2} \times 14$ inch paper
thumbtacks
*pushpins

*Alternate materials

Safety Precaution
Use care when handling sharp objects.

Procedure

1. Select the assigned number of elements from the list provided by your teacher.
2. **Design** an index card for each of your selected elements. On each card, mark the element's atomic number in the upper left-hand corner and write its symbol and name in the upper right-hand corner.
3. **Research** each of the elements and write several sentences on the card about its appearance, its other properties, and its uses.
4. **Classify** each of your elements as a metal, a metalloid, or a nonmetal based upon its properties.

5. **Write** the appropriate classification on each of your cards using the colored marker chosen by your teacher.
6. Work with your classmates to make a large periodic table. Use thumbtacks to attach your cards to a bulletin board in their proper positions on the periodic table.
7. **Draw** your own periodic table. Place the elements' symbols and atomic numbers in the proper locations on your table.

Conclude and Apply

1. **Interpret** the class data and classify the elements into the categories metal, metalloid, and nonmetal. Highlight each category in a different color on your periodic table.
2. **Predict** the properties of a yet-undiscovered element located directly under francium on the periodic table.

Communicating Your Data

Compare and contrast your table with that of a friend. Discuss the differences. **For more help, refer to the** Science Skill Handbook.

Communicating Your Data

Have students use a database program to display their results. The printed database can be shared with a small group or with the class.

Resource Manager

Chapter Resources Booklet
    Activity Worksheet, pp. 5–6
Science Inquiry Labs, pp. 19, 47

Compounds and Mixtures

Substances

Scientists classify matter in several ways that depend on what it is made of and how it behaves. For example, matter that has the same composition and properties throughout is called a **substance.** Elements, such as a bar of gold or a sheet of aluminum, are substances. When different elements combine, other substances are formed.

Compounds   What do you call the colorless liquid that flows from the kitchen faucet? You probably call it water, but maybe you've seen it written H_2O. The elements hydrogen and oxygen exist as separate, colorless gases. However, these two elements can combine, as shown in **Figure 23,** to form the compound water, which is different from the elements that make it up. A **compound** is a substance whose smallest unit is made up of atoms of more than one element bonded together.

Compounds often have properties that are different from the elements that make them up. Water is distinctly different from the elements that make it up. It is also different from another compound made from the same elements. Have you ever used hydrogen peroxide (H_2O_2) to disinfect a cut? This compound is a different combination of hydrogen and oxygen and has different properties.

Water is a nonirritating liquid that is used for bathing, drinking, cooking, and much more. In contrast, hydrogen peroxide carries warnings on its labels such as *Keep Hydrogen Peroxide Out of the Eyes.* Although it is useful in solutions for cleaning contact lenses, it is not safe for your eyes as it comes from the bottle.

As You Read

What You'll Learn
- **Identify** the characteristics of a compound.
- **Compare and contrast** different types of mixtures.

Vocabulary
substance
compound
mixture

Why It's Important
The food you eat, the materials you use, and all matter can be classified by these terms.

Figure 23
A space shuttle is powered by the reaction between liquid hydrogen and liquid oxygen. The reaction produces a large amount of energy and the compound water. *Why would a car that burns hydrogen rather than gasoline be friendly to the environment?*

Section ✓ *Assessment* Planner

PORTFOLIO
Curriculum Connection, p. 28
PERFORMANCE ASSESSMENT
MiniLAB, p. 26
Problem-Solving Activity, p. 27
Skill Building Activities, p. 29
See page 36 for more options.

CONTENT ASSESSMENT
Section, p. 29
Challenge, p. 29
Chapter, pp. 36–37

Compounds and Mixtures

① Motivate

Bellringer Transparency
Display the Section Focus Transparency for Section 3. Use the accompanying Transparency Activity Master. L2 ELL

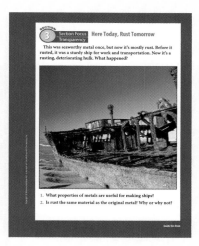

Tie to Prior Knowledge
Have students recall chemical formulas for substances such as water or salt. H_2O and NaCl Show a periodic table and point out that these substances are combinations of elements from the periodic table.

Caption Answer
Figure 23 It would produce water rather than pollution.

Substances

Visual Learning

Figure 24 Ask students to write the formula for hydrogen peroxide. H_2O_2 Point out how much easier it is to write the chemical formulas than it is to write out all of the words.

Mini LAB

Purpose Students observe and compare the properties of three compounds. **L2** **ELL**
LS **Visual-Spatial**
Materials sugar, rubbing alcohol, salad oil, 3 beakers, hot water, spoon
Teaching Strategy Warn students to use hot, not boiling, water.
Analysis
1. Rubbing alcohol is colorless; salad oil is golden, and sugar is white in color. Sugar is a solid; rubbing alcohol and the oil are liquids. Salad oil is more viscous than alcohol. Rubbing alcohol has a strong chemical smell; the other substances have little or no odor. Sugar and rubbing alcohol dissolve easily in water, but salad oil floats on the water.
2. The number of atoms of each element and their arrangement account for the different properties.

✔ Assessment

Content Have students draw pictures showing how the substances mixed with water in the MiniLAB. Use **PASC**, p. 127.

✔ Reading Check

Answer C_3H_8

Figure 24
The elements hydrogen and oxygen can form two compounds—water and hydrogen peroxide. Note the differences in their structure.

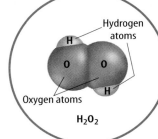
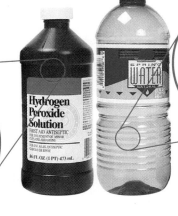
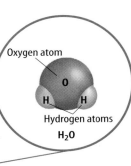

Hydrogen atoms

Oxygen atoms

H_2O_2

Oxygen atom

Hydrogen atoms

H_2O

Mini LAB

Comparing Compounds

Procedure
1. Collect the following substances—granular **sugar, rubbing alcohol,** and **salad oil.**
2. Observe the color, appearance, and state of each substance. Note the thickness or texture of each substance.
3. Stir a spoonful of each substance into separate **beakers** of **hot water** and observe.

Analysis
1. Compare the different properties of the substances.
2. The formulas of the three substances are made of only carbon, hydrogen, and oxygen. Infer how they can have different properties.

Compounds Have Formulas What's the difference between water and hydrogen peroxide? H_2O is the chemical formula for water, and H_2O_2 is the formula for hydrogen peroxide. The formula tells you which elements make up a compound as well as how many atoms of each element are present. Look at **Figure 24.** The subscript number written below and to the right of each element's symbol tells you how many atoms of that element exist in one unit of that compound. For example, hydrogen peroxide has two atoms of hydrogen and two atoms of oxygen. Water is made up of two atoms of hydrogen and one atom of oxygen.

Carbon dioxide, CO_2, is another common compound. Carbon dioxide is made up of one atom of carbon and two atoms of oxygen. Carbon and oxygen also can form the compound carbon monoxide, CO, which is a gas that is poisonous to all warm-blooded animals. As you can see, no subscript is used when only one atom of an element is present. A given compound always is made of the same elements in the same proportion. For example, water always has two hydrogen atoms for every oxygen atom, no matter what the source of the water is. No matter what quantity of the compound you have, the formula of the compound always remains the same. If you have 12 atoms of hydrogen and six atoms of oxygen, the compound is still written H_2O, but you have six molecules of H_2O (6 H_2O), not $H_{12}O_6$. The formula of a compound communicates its identity and makeup to any scientist in the world.

✔ Reading Check *Propane has three atoms of carbon and eight atoms of hydrogen. What is propane's chemical formula?*

Cultural Diversity

Ocher Ocher is an iron oxide (Fe_2O_3) that occurs naturally. It is formed by the weathering of rocks. It was used historically to produce rock paintings and continues to be used for artwork today. It comes in a variety of colors, depending on the percentage of iron oxide present. Hematite ore is one source of ocher that can be ground to produce a bright red color. Ocher has also been found in burial plots of several different cultures. Have students find out the other colors produced by iron oxide ores. Other colors produced include black (magnetite), brown to dark yellow (limonite), and brown (siderite and pyrite).

Mixtures

When two or more substances (elements or compounds) come together but don't combine to make a new substance, a **mixture** results. Unlike compounds, the proportions of the substances in a mixture can be changed without changing the identity of the mixture. For example, if you put some sand into a bucket of water, you have a mixture of sand and water. If you add more sand or more water, it's still a mixture of sand and water. Its identity has not changed. Air is another mixture. Air is a mixture of nitrogen, oxygen, and other gases, which can vary at different times and places. Whatever the proportion of gases, it is still air. Even your blood is a mixture that can be separated, as shown in **Figure 25** by a machine called a centrifuge.

 **Reading Check** *How do the proportions of a mixture relate to its identity?*

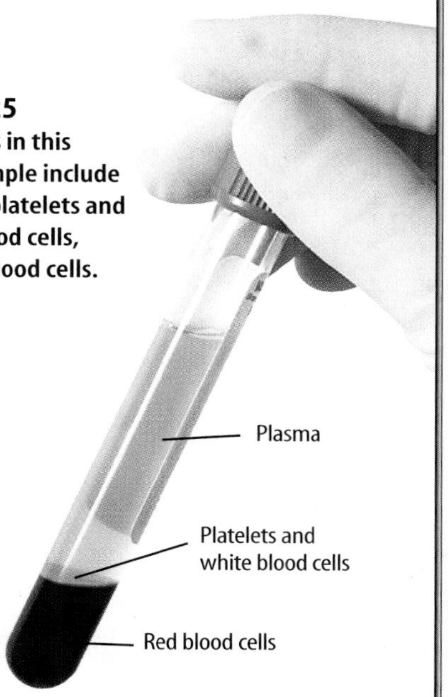

Figure 25
The layers in this blood sample include plasma, platelets and white blood cells, and red blood cells.

Plasma

Platelets and white blood cells

Red blood cells

Mixtures

Discussion

Remind students that a compound is a pure substance whose smallest unit is made up of atoms of more than one element. **What compounds do you use in your daily activities?** Examples include table salt, water, and sugar.

Extension

Use labels from popular food items and work with students to determine whether each of the ingredients is an element, a compound, or a mixture. [L3] ELL COOP LEARN

Reading Check

Answer They can change without changing the identity of a mixture.

Problem-Solving Activity

What's the best way to desalt ocean water?

You can't drink ocean water because it contains salt and other suspended materials. Or can you? In many areas of the world where drinking water is in short supply, methods for getting the salt out of salt water are being used to meet the demand for fresh water. Use your problem solving skills to find the best method to use in a particular area.

Methods for Desalting Ocean Water			
Process	**Amount of Water a Unit Can Desalt in a Day (m³)**	**Special Needs**	**Number of People Needed to Operate**
Distillation	1,000 to 200,000	lots of energy to boil the water	many
Electrodialysis	10 to 4,000	stable source of electricity	1 to 2 persons

Identifying the Problem

The table above compares desalting methods. In distillation, the ocean water is heated. Pure water boils off and is collected, and the salt is left behind. Electrodialysis uses electric current to pull salt particles out of water.

Solving the Problem

1. What method(s) might you use to desalt the water for a large population where energy is plentiful? What method(s) would you chose to use in a single home?

Problem-Solving Activity

National Math Standards

Correlation to Mathematics Objectives
5, 9, 10

Answer

1. Distillation would be best to use for a large population. Although the unit needs many operators and lots of energy, it produces the largest amount of fresh water. Electrodialysis works in a home or small resort hotel. This method produces smaller amounts of fresh water and does not require many skilled operators.

SECTION 3 Compounds and Mixtures   **K ◆ 27**

 Resource Manager

Chapter Resources Booklet
Transparency Activity, p. 42
MiniLAB, p. 4
Directed Reading for Content Mastery, pp. 17, 18
Mathematics Skill Activities, p. 19

Mixtures, continued

Life Science
INTEGRATION

Whole blood is often separated into plasma and packed cells. The plasma component contains substances that dissolve in water.

SCIENCE
Online
Internet Addresses

_____
_____
_____
_____

Explore the Glencoe Science Web site at **science.glencoe.com** to find out more about topics in this section.

Use Science Words

Word Usage Ask students to classify the following mixtures as heterogeneous or homogeneous: clear apple juice homogeneous; oil and vinegar heterogeneous. L2
Linguistic

Teacher FYI

Homogeneous mixtures are defined by the sizes of the particles that make them up. A solution has particles less than 10^{-7} cm in size. A homogenous mixture with particles between 10^{-7} and 10^{-4} cm in size is called a colloid. An emulsion is a colloid consisting of two liquids. An aerosol is a colloid in which either a solid is dispersed in a gas (smoke) or a liquid is dispersed in a gas (fog).

Figure 26
Mixtures are part of your everyday life.

SCIENCE
Online

Research Visit the Glencoe Science Web site at **science.glencoe.com** for more information about separating mixtures.

Life Science
INTEGRATION

Your blood is a mixture made up of elements and compounds. It contains white blood cells, red blood cells, water, and a number of dissolved substances. The different parts of blood can be separated and used by doctors in different ways. The proportions of the substances in your blood change daily, but the mixture does not change its identity.

Separating Mixtures Sometimes you can use a liquid to separate a mixture of solids. For example, if you add water to a mixture of sugar and sand, only the sugar dissolves in the water. The sand then can be separated from the sugar and water by pouring the mixture through a filter. Heating the remaining solution will separate the water from the sugar.

At other times, separating a mixture of solids of different sizes might be as easy as pouring them through successively smaller sieves or filters. A mixture of marbles, pebbles, and sand could be separated in this way.

Curriculum Connection

Art Have students make collages that demonstrate the difference between a homogeneous mixture and a heterogeneous mixture. Have them search through magazines to collect illustrations for their collages. Images could include: homogeneous—any type of solution; heterogeneous: strawberry ice cream, salad, chocolate chip cookie. L1
Visual-Spatial

Resource Manager

Chapter Resources Booklet
Enrichment, p. 28
Reinforcement, p. 25
Activity Worksheet, pp. 7–8
Cultural Diversity, p. 65

Homogeneous or Heterogeneous Mixtures, such as the ones shown in **Figure 26,** can be classified as homogeneous or heterogeneous. *Homogeneous* means "the same throughout." You can't see the different parts in this type of mixture. In fact, you might not always know that homogeneous mixtures are mixtures because you can't tell by looking. Which mixtures in **Figure 26** are homogeneous? No matter how closely you look, you can't see the individual parts that make up air or the parts of the mixture called brass in the lamp shown. Homogeneous mixtures can be solids, liquids, or gases.

A heterogeneous mixture has larger parts that are different from each other. You can see the different parts of a heterogeneous mixture, such as sand and water. How many heterogeneous mixtures are in the figure? A pepperoni and mushroom pizza is a tasty kind of heterogeneous mixture. Other examples of this kind of mixture include tacos, vegetable soup, a toy box full of toys, or a tool box full of nuts and bolts.

Earth Science INTEGRATION

Scientists called geologists study rocks and minerals. A mineral is composed of a pure substance. Rocks are mixtures and can be described as being homogeneous or heterogeneous. Research to learn more about rocks and minerals and note some examples of homogeneous and heterogeneous rocks in your Science Journal.

Earth Science INTEGRATION

Strictly speaking, the term *rocks* applies to the solid materials that make up Earth's crust. These materials are not homogeneous and have no definite chemical composition. Minerals, on the other hand, have more or less definite chemical compositions, crystal structures, and properties. Heterogeneous rocks include granite, gneiss, and conglomerate. Homogeneous rocks include obsidian, some limestones, and basalt.

③ Assess

Reteach

Ask a medical technologist to make a class presentation explaining the different parts of the mixture known as human blood and describing how these parts can be separated by physical means. L1 IS **Auditory-Musical**

Challenge

The compound hydrochloric acid can be written HCl. What elements does it contain? hydrogen and chlorine **How many atoms of each element are in a molecule of hydrochloric acid?** one atom of hydrogen and one atom of chlorine Hydrochloric acid reacts with sodium hydroxide to form table salt and water. The reaction can be written HCl + NaOH = NaCl + H_2O. **What is the chemical formula for table salt?** NaCl

---

Section ③ Assessment

1. List three examples of compounds and three examples of mixtures. Explain your choices.

2. How can you tell that a substance is a compound by looking at its formula?

3. Which kind of mixture is sometimes difficult to distinguish from a compound? Why?

4. What is the difference between homogeneous and heterogeneous mixtures?

5. **Think Critically** Was your breakfast a compound, a homogeneous mixture, or a heterogeneous mixture? Explain.

Skill Builder Activities

6. **Comparing and Contrasting** Compare and contrast compounds and mixtures based on what you have learned from this section. **For more help, refer to the** Science Skill Handbook.

7. **Using a Database** Use a computerized card catalog or database to find out about one element from the periodic table. Include information about the properties and uses of the mixtures and/or compounds the element is found in. **For more help, refer to the** Technology Skill Handbook.

✓ Assessment

Process Have students design an experimental procedure that they could use to separate a mixture of white sand and sugar. Use **PASC**, p. 95.

Answers to Section Assessment

1. Possible answers: Compounds—water, carbon dioxide, table salt; mixtures—air, ocean water, brass; mixtures can be separated by physical means; compounds can't.

2. The formula of a compound includes more than one element.

3. Homogeneous mixtures; the mixture is the same throughout.

4. Homogeneous: cannot see individual parts; heterogeneous: can see different parts.

5. Answers will vary, but most breakfasts, such as orange juice and cold cereal with milk, are heterogeneous mixtures.

6. Possible answer: Compounds are pure substances whose properties

vary from the original elements that they are made from. Mixtures are made from different parts and can be separated by physical means.

7. Have students document the sources of their information.

Activity

What You'll Investigate

Purpose

Students test for certain compounds and decide which are present in a mystery mixture. L2

ELL IS **Kinesthetic**

Process Skills

forming a hypothesis, communicating, observing and inferring, recognizing cause and effect, separating and controlling variables, interpreting data

Time Required

45 minutes

Materials

Compounds used are a cornstarch, powdered sugar, and baking soda. Combine any two of these compounds to make the mystery mixture. Prepare iodine test solution by adding 7 g of iodine and 5 g of potassium iodide to 5 mL of water, then diluting to 100 mL with denatured alcohol.

Safety Precautions

Students must wear goggles and aprons. Remind students that when heating a test tube, the opening of the tube should never be pointed at themselves or others.

Iodine is poisonous and will stain clothing.

Remind students that test tubes should not be touched while they are hot.

Activity

Mystery Mixture

You will encounter many compounds that look alike. For example, a laboratory stockroom is filled with white powders. It is important to know what each is. In a kitchen, cornstarch, baking powder, and powdered sugar are compounds that look alike. To avoid mistaking one for another, you can learn how to identify them. Different compounds can be identified by using chemical tests. For example, some compounds react with certain liquids to produce gases. Other combinations produce distinctive colors. Some compounds have high melting points. Others have low melting points.

What You'll Investigate

How can the compounds in an unknown mixture be identified by experimentation?

Goals

- **Test** for the presence of certain compounds.
- **Decide** which of these compounds are present in an unknown mixture.

Materials

test tubes (4)
cornstarch
powdered sugar
baking soda
mystery mixture
small scoops (3)
dropper bottles (2)
iodine solution
white vinegar
hot plate
250-mL beaker
water (125 mL)
test-tube holder
small pie pan

Safety Precautions

WARNING: *Use caution when handling hot objects. Substances could stain or burn clothing. Be sure to point the test tube away from your face and your classmates while heating.*

Inclusion Strategies

Learning Disabled Assist these students in completing the activity using a skill sequence—model one skill at a time and have students perform the skill immediately after it is observed. Copy the data table for students and distribute. Model Step 2, and then, have students perform Step 2. Continue to model each step and write students' responses to questions on the board.

✓ Active Reading

Reflective Journal Have students write reflective journals about their experiences in this activity. Have students divide sheets of paper into several columns and record their thoughts under headings such as "What I Did," "What I Learned," "Questions I Have," "Surprises I Experienced," and "Overall Response." Ask volunteers to share their reflections with the class.

Procedure

1. Copy the data table into your Science Journal. Record your results for each of the following steps.

2. Place a small scoopful of cornstarch on the pie pan. Do the same for the sugar and baking soda. Add a drop of vinegar to each. Wash and dry the pan after you record your observations.

3. Place a small scoopful of cornstarch, sugar, and baking soda on the pie pan. Add a drop of iodine solution to each one.

4. Place a small scoopful of each compound in a separate test tube. Hold the test tube with the test-tube holder and with an

Identifying Presence of Compounds			
Substance to Be Tested	Fizzes with Vinegar	Turns Blue with Iodine	Melts When Heated
Cornstarch	No	Yes	No
Sugar	No	No	Yes
Baking soda	Yes	No	No
Mystery mix	Answers will vary		

oven mitt. Gently heat the test tube in a beaker of boiling water on a hot plate.

5. Follow steps 2 through 4 to test your mystery mixture for each compound.

Conclude and Apply

1. Use your observations to form a hypothesis about compounds in your mystery mixture. Describe how you arrived at your conclusion.

2. How would you be able to tell if all three compounds were not in your mystery mixture sample?

3. What would you conclude if you tested baking powder from your kitchen and found that it fizzed with vinegar, turned blue with iodine, and did not melt when heated?

𝒞ommunicating
Your Data

Make a different data table to display your results in a new way. **For more help, refer to the** Science Skill Handbook.

✓𝒜ssessment

Performance After students have determined the two compounds that were present in the mystery mixture, have them determine other possible two-material combinations and explain how the combinations would react when tested. Use **Performance Assessment in the Science Classroom,** p. 93.

𝒞ommunicating
Your Data

Students could add illustrations, chemical symbols, or color to their data tables.

Procedure
Teaching Strategies

- In Steps 2 and 3, have students use only sufficient amounts of solids to produce satisfactory test results. Test your scoops to determine how much to use.

- In Step 4, have students use only enough solid to fill the bottom rounded portion of the test tubes.

Expected Outcome

Cornstarch will react with iodine to make a blue color. Sugar will melt when heated. Baking soda will fizz in the presence of vinegar.

Conclude and Apply

1. Answers will vary depending on the two compounds used for the mystery mixture. In describing their conclusions, students should include the data they gathered.

2. If the mixture did not turn blue in the presence of iodine, did not melt when heated, and did not fizz with vinegar, you would know that all three compounds were absent from the mystery mixture.

3. It had properties similar to baking soda and cornstarch.

Error Analysis

If students let their experiments run together or do not clean their equipment, they may get erroneous results. Have students compare their results with the results of other groups. If results differ, discuss errors that could have caused the difference.

Content Background

Because of his interest in minuscule objects, Kashyapa was given the name Kanada, from the Indian word *kana*, which means "a grain." He lived during the 6th century B.C., and was the first to use the word parmanu, which can also be written *paramanu*. Kanada derived this word from the two Sanskrit words *param*, meaning "beyond" and *anu* meaning "atom." Among other things, he proposed that two different classes of parmanu could combine to form what he called *dwinuka*, or binary molecules, of new substances.

The Chinese term for the five material agents of matter, as they called the five elements, is *wu hsing*. They believed that these material agents took part in cyclical patterns of change that resulted in the opposites, yin and yang. The Chinese applied these patterns of change not only to matter, but also to other phenomena, including politics, ethics, medicine, music, time, the seasons, and history.

Historians believe that the idea of yin and yang developed separately from the concept of wu hsing, and that Tsou Yen (305 B.C. to 204 B.C. ?) was the first to put the two together.

TIME SCIENCE AND HISTORY

SCIENCE CAN CHANGE THE COURSE OF HISTORY!

Ancient Views

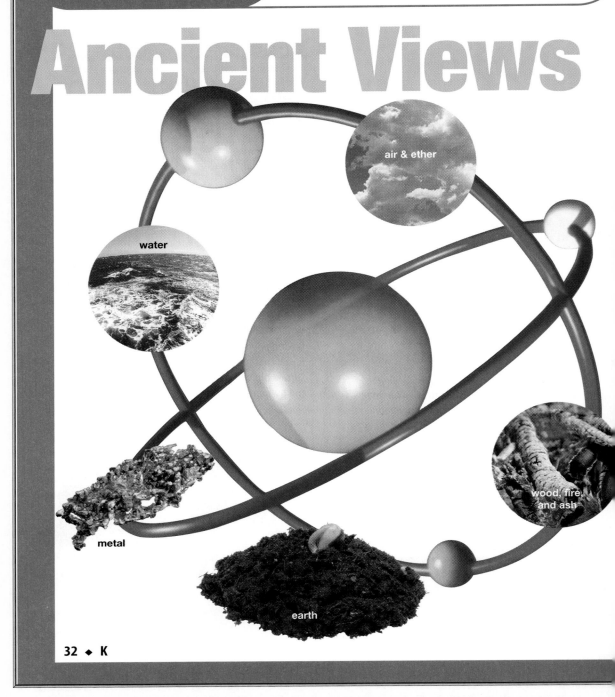

air & ether

water

metal

wood, fire, and ash

earth

Resources for Teachers and Students

Chemistry in Action, by Nina Morgan, Oxford University Press, 1995.

The Periodic Kingdom, by P.W. Atkins, Basic Books, 1995.

# of Matter

Two cultures observed the world around them differently

The world's earliest scientists were people who were curious about the world around them and who tried to develop explanations for the things they observed. This type of observation and inquiry flourished in ancient cultures such as those found in India and China. In some cases, their views of the world weren't so different from ours. Matter, for example, is defined today as anything that has mass and takes up space. Read on to see how the ancient Indians and Chinese defined matter.

Indian Ideas

To Indians living about 3,000 years ago, the world was made up of five elements: fire, air, earth, water, and ether, which they thought of as an unseen substance that filled the heavens. Building upon this concept, the early Indian philosopher Kashyapa (kah SHI ah pah) proposed that the five elements could be broken down into smaller units called parmanu (par MAH new). Parmanu were similar to atoms in that they were too small to be seen but still retained the properties of the original element. Kashyapa also believed that each type of parmanu had unique physical and chemical properties.

Parmanu of earth elements, for instance, were heavier than parmanu of air elements.

The different properties of the parmanu determined the characteristics of a substance. Kashyapa's ideas about matter are similar to those of the Greek philosopher Democritus, who lived centuries after Kashyapa. Historians are unsure as to whether the two men developed their views separately, or whether trade and communication with India influenced Greek thought.

Chinese Ideas

Ancient Chinese also broke matter down into five elements: fire, wood, metal, earth, and water. Unlike the early Indians, however, the Chinese believed that the elements constantly changed form. For example, wood can be burned and thus changes to fire. Fire eventually dies down and becomes ashes, or earth. Earth gives forth metals from the ground. Dew or water collects on these metals, and the water then nurtures plants that grow into trees, or wood.

This cycle of constant change was explained in the fourth century B.C. by the philosopher Tsou Yen. Yen, who is known as the founder of Chinese scientific thought, wrote that all changes that took place in nature were linked to changes in the five elements. In his writings, Yen also developed a classification system for matter.

Discussion

Do you think Kashyapa's ideas were known to Democritus when he developed his theory of the atom? Why or why not? Accept all well-supported answers. Point out to students on a globe the relative locations of Greece and India and remind them of the means of transportation and communication available at the time these two men lived.

Historical Significance

Both the Chinese and Indian philosophies presented here have roots reaching back in history. Encourage students to choose a current scientific theory and use a variety of research tools to trace the idea back to its earliest origins. Make sure students understand that a theory may have origins in ideas that arose independently in several different cultures. This activity will help students become aware that our modern theories have had a long history of development.

CONNECTIONS Research Write a brief paragraph that compares and contrasts the ancient Indian and Chinese views of matter. How are they different? Similar? Which is closer to the modern view of matter? Explain.

SCIENCE Online For more information, visit science.glencoe.com

CONNECTIONS Language Arts As a prewriting activity have students call out similarities and differences in the two theories presented here. Select a volunteer to record suggestions. Encourage students to use this information in their paragraphs, and to reexamine it as they compare the historical perspectives with the modern view of matter. Remind students that they studied the modern view of the atom earlier in the chapter.

SCIENCE Online

Internet Addresses
_____
_____
_____

Explore the Glencoe Science Web site at **science.glencoe.com** to find out more about topics in this feature.

Chapter ① Study Guide

Reviewing Main Ideas

Preview

Students can answer the questions in their Science Journals. Discuss the answers as you go through the chapter. **Linguistic**

Review

Students can write their answers, then compare them with those of other students. **Interpersonal**

Reteach

Students can look at the illustrations and describe details that support the main ideas of the chapter. **Visual-Spatial**

Answers to Chapter Review

SECTION 1

3. electrons

SECTION 2

4. metal

SECTION 3

2. heterogeneous mixture

Reviewing Main Ideas

Section 1 Models of the Atom

1. Matter is made up of very small particles called atoms. Different kinds of matter contain different kinds of atoms.

2. Many scientists have contributed to the understanding of the atom's structure through models and experimentation.

3. Atoms are made of smaller parts called protons, neutrons, and electrons. *Which particle was discovered using an apparatus like the one pictured?*

4. Many models of atoms have been created as scientists try to discover and define the atom's internal structure. Today's model has a central nucleus with the protons and neutrons, and an electron cloud surrounding it that contains the electrons.

Section 2 The Simplest Matter

1. Elements are the basic building blocks of matter.

2. An element's atomic number tells how many protons its atoms contain, and its atomic mass tells the average atomic mass of its atoms. The chemical symbol for each element is understood by scientists everywhere. Information about elements is displayed on the periodic table.

3. Isotopes are two or more atoms of the same element that have different numbers of neutrons.

4. Each element has a unique set of properties and is generally classified as a metal, metalloid, or nonmetal. *How would you classify the spool of wire in the picture?*

Section 3 Compounds and Mixtures

1. Compounds are substances that are produced when elements combine. Compounds contain specific proportions of the elements that make them up. A compound's properties are different from those of the elements from which it is formed.

2. Mixtures are combinations of compounds and elements that have not formed new substances. Their proportions can change. Homogeneous mixtures contain individual parts that cannot be seen. However, you can see the individual parts of heterogeneous mixtures. *Is the orange juice pictured a homogeneous or heterogeneous mixture?*

FOLDABLES Reading & Study Skills

After You Read

Under each tab of your Foldable, list several everyday examples of the atoms, elements, compounds and mixtures.

FOLDABLES Reading & Study Skills

After You Read

After students have read the chapter and completed the Foldable described in Before You Read, have them do the activity on the student page.

Dinah Zike

Visualizing Main Ideas

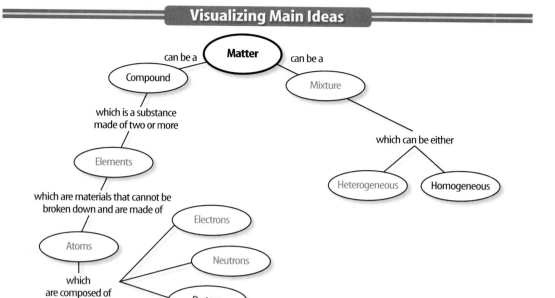

Vocabulary Review

Vocabulary Words

a. atomic mass
b. atomic number
c. compound
d. electron
e. electron cloud
f. element
g. isotope
h. mass number

i. metal
j. metalloid
k. mixture
l. neutron
m. nonmetal
n. proton
o. substance

THE PRINCETON REVIEW

Study Tip

Find out what concepts, objectives, or standards are being tested well before the test. Keep these concepts in mind as you answer the questions.

Using Vocabulary

Replace the underlined word or phrase with the correct vocabulary word.

1. The <u>neutron</u> is the particle in the nucleus of the atom that carries a positive charge and is counted to identify the atomic number.

2. The new substance formed when elements combine chemically is a <u>mixture</u>.

3. The <u>mass number</u> is equal to the number of protons in an atom.

4. The particles in the atom that account for most of the mass of the atom are protons and <u>electrons</u>.

5. Elements that are shiny, malleable, ductile, good conductors of heat and electricity, and make up most of the periodic table are <u>nonmetals</u>.

Vocabulary Review

Using Vocabulary

1. proton
2. compound
3. atomic number
4. neutrons
5. metals

Checking Concepts

1. D
2. C
3. B
4. C
5. D
6. B
7. C
8. A
9. B
10. C

Thinking Critically

11. one sulfur atom to two oxygen atoms
12. Nitrogen; the number of protons determines the identity of an atom.
13. The element loses its characteristics and a new substance is formed.
14. Cobalt-60 and cobalt-59 both have 27 protons in their nuclei, so they are both cobalt, but they have different numbers of neutrons so they have different mass numbers.
15. Rutherford's gold foil experiment told scientists that the atom contains a small, dense, positively charged structure. Rutherford called this structure the nucleus.

Chapter 1 Assessment

Checking Concepts

Choose the word or phrase that best answers the question.

1. What is a solution an example of?
   A) element
   B) heterogeneous mixture
   C) compound
   D) homogeneous mixture

2. The nucleus of one atom contains 12 protons and 12 neutrons, while the nucleus of another atom contains 12 protons and 16 neutrons. What are the atoms?
   A) chromium atoms
   B) two different elements
   C) two isotopes of an element
   D) negatively charged

3. What is a compound?
   A) a mixture of chemicals and elements
   B) a combination of two or more elements
   C) anything that has mass and occupies space
   D) the building block of matter

4. What does the atom consist of?
   A) electrons, protons, and alpha particles
   B) neutrons and protons
   C) electrons, protons, and neutrons
   D) elements, protons, and electrons

5. In an atom, where is an electron located?
   A) in the nucleus with the proton
   B) on the periodic table of the elements
   C) with the neutron
   D) in a cloudlike formation surrounding the nucleus

6. How is mass number defined?
   A) the negative charge in an atom
   B) the number of protons and neutrons in an atom
   C) the mass of the nucleus
   D) an atom's protons

7. What are two atoms that have the same number of protons called?
   A) metals
   B) nonmetals
   C) isotopes
   D) metalloids

8. What are the majority of the elements on the periodic table called?
   A) metals
   B) metalloids
   C) nonmetals
   D) compounds

9. Which element is a metalloid?
   A) bromine
   B) silicon
   C) potassium
   D) iron

10. Which is a heterogeneous mixture?
    A) air
    B) brass
    C) a salad
    D) apple juice

Thinking Critically

11. A chemical formula is written to indicate the makeup of a compound. What is the ratio of sulfur atoms to oxygen atoms in SO_2?

12. An atom contains seven electrons and seven protons. What element is this atom? Explain your answer.

13. What happens to an element when it becomes part of a compound?

14. Cobalt-60 and cobalt-59 are isotopes. How can they be the same element but have different mass numbers?

15. What did Rutherford's gold foil experiment tell scientists about atomic structure?

Developing Skills

16. **Predicting** Suppose Rutherford had bombarded aluminum foil with alpha particles instead of the gold foil he used in his experiment. What observations do you predict Rutherford would have made? Explain your prediction.

Chapter ✔Assessment Planner

Portfolio Encourage students to place in their portfolios one or two items of what they consider to be their best work. Examples include:
- Use Science Words, p. 14
- Science Journal, p. 14
- Extension, p. 21
- Curriculum Connection, p. 28

Performance Additional performance assessments, Performance Task Assessment Lists, and rubrics for evaluating these activities can be found in Glencoe's **Performance Assessment in the Science Classroom.**

17. Comparing and Contrasting Aluminum is close to carbon on the periodic table. List the properties that make aluminum a metal and carbon a nonmetal.

18. Drawing Conclusions You are shown a liquid that looks the same throughout. You're told that it contains more than one type of element and that the proportion of each varies throughout the liquid. Is this an element, a compound, or a mixture?

19. Interpreting Scientific Illustrations Look at the two carbon atoms below. Explain whether or not the atoms are isotopes.

Performance Assessment

20. Newspaper Article Research the source, composition, and properties of asbestos. Why was it used in the past? Why is it a health hazard now? What is being done about it? Write a newspaper article to share your findings.

TECHNOLOGY

Go to the Glencoe Science Web site at **science.glencoe.com** or use the **Glencoe Science CD-ROM** for additional chapter assessment.

THE PRINCETON REVIEW **Test Practice**

A researcher is analyzing four different compounds in the laboratory. The formulas for the compounds are listed below.

H_2O
Water

H_2O_2
Hydrogen peroxide

H_2SO_4
Sulfuric acid

SO_2
Sulfur dioxide

Study the formulas and answer the following questions.

1. Which of the compounds contains the most oxygen atoms?
   A) water
   B) sulfur dioxide
   C) sulfuric acid
   D) hydrogen peroxide

2. What is the ratio of oxygen to hydrogen in sulfuric acid?
   F) 2 to 1
   G) 1 to 2
   H) 1 to 1
   J) 2 to 4

3. What is the ratio of hydrogen to oxygen in a hydrogen peroxide?
   A) 2 to 1
   B) 4 to 2
   C) 1 to 1
   D) 2 to 4

THE PRINCETON REVIEW **Test Practice**

The Test-Taking Tip was written by The Princeton Review, the nation's leader in test preparation.
1. C
2. J
3. C

Developing Skills

16. If Rutherford used aluminum foil instead of gold foil, he would get the same results. This is because his conclusions about a dense nucleus surrounded by almost empty space were true for all types of atoms, including aluminum atoms.

17. Aluminum is a shiny, solid at room temperature, and can be pounded into different shapes without breaking. Carbon is dull and is not malleable or ductile.

18. The two samples of phosphorus are allotropes—different forms of the same element. Since allotropes have different molecular structures, their properties are different.

19. The atoms are isotopes because they have the same number of protons but different numbers of neutrons. The atom on the left has 6 protons and 6 neutrons whereas the one on the right has 6 protons and 8 neutrons.

Performance Assessment

20. Asbestos is a hydrous magnesium silicate—$Mg_3Si_2O_5(OH)_4$. It occurs as fibers, which are spun into yarn or mixed with other materials to form cement board or other fireproof building materials. When asbestos fibers become airborne, they can be inhaled. The sharp fibers penetrate the lungs, and can cause a form of lung cancer. Use **PASC,** p. 141.

✔*Assessment* **Resources**

 Reproducible Masters

Chapter Resources Booklet
   Chapter Review, pp. 33–34
   Chapter Tests, pp. 35–38
   Assessment Transparency Activity, p. 45

Glencoe Science Web site
   Interactive Tutor
   Chapter Quizzes

Glencoe Technology
   🖌 Assessment Transparency
   💿 Interactive CD-ROM Chapter Quizzes
   💿 ExamView Pro Test Bank
   💿 Vocabulary PuzzleMaker Software
   📀 MindJogger Videoquiz DVD/VHS

CHAPTER 2 STATES OF MATTER

Section/Objectives	Standards		Activities/Features
	National	**State/Local**	
Chapter Opener	See p. 7T for a Key to Standards.		**Explore Activity:** Experiment with a freezing liquid, p. 39 **Before You Read**, p. 39
Section 1 Matter 🕐 3 sessions 📦 1.5 blocks 1. **Recognize** that matter is made of particles in constant motion. 2. **Relate** the three states of matter to the arrangement of particles within them.	National Content Standards: UCP1, B1		**Earth Science Integration**, p. 42 **Science Online**, p. 43
Section 2 Changes of State 🕐 3 sessions 📦 1.5 blocks 1. **Define and compare** thermal energy and temperature. 2. **Relate** changes in thermal energy to changes of state. 3. **Explore** energy and temperature changes on a graph.	National Content Standards: UCP3, A1, B1, B3		**Physics Integration**, p. 46 **Visualizing States of Matter**, p. 48 **Science Online**, p. 49 **Problem-Solving Activity:** How can ice save oranges?, p. 49 **MiniLAB:** Explaining What You Feel, p. 50 **Science Online**, p. 51 **Activity:** A Spin Around the Water Cycle, p. 53
Section 3 Behavior of Fluids 🕐 5 sessions 📦 2.5 blocks 1. **Explain** why some things float but others sink. 2. **Describe** how pressure is transmitted through fluids.	National Content Standards: UCP3, A1, B1, D1, G2		**MiniLAB:** Predicting a Waterfall, p. 57 **Math Skills Activity:** Calculating Density, p. 59 **Science Online**, p. 61 **Activity:** Design Your Own Ship, pp. 62–63 **Oops! Accidents in Science:** The Incredible Stretching Goo, pp. 64–65

Activity Materials	Reproducible Resources	Section Assessment	Technology
Explore Activity: test tubes containing unidentified liquid, test tube rack, thermometer	**Chapter Resources Booklet** Foldables Worksheet, p. 15 Directed Reading Overview, p. 17 Note-taking Worksheets, pp. 31–33	GLENCOE'S **ASSESSMENT** ADVANTAGE	
Need materials? Contact Science Kit at 1-800-828-7777 or www.sciencekit.com on the Internet.	**Chapter Resources Booklet** Transparency Activity, p. 42 Enrichment, p. 28 Reinforcement, p. 25 Directed Reading, p. 18 Transparency Activity, pp. 45–46 Lab Activity, pp. 9–10	Portfolio Extension, p. 41 Assessment, p. 44 Performance Skill Builder Activities, p. 44 Content Section Assessment, p. 44	🔦 Section Focus Transparency 🔦 Teaching Transparency 💿 Interactive CD-ROM 🎧 Guided Reading Audio Program
MiniLAB: dropper, rubbing alcohol **Activity:** hot plate, ice cubes, Celsius thermometer, wall clock or watch with second hand, stirring rod, 250-mL beaker	**Chapter Resources Booklet** Transparency Activity, p. 43 MiniLAB, p. 3 Enrichment, p. 29 Reinforcement, p. 26 Directed Reading, p. 19 Activity Worksheet, pp. 5–6 Lab Activity, pp. 11–13 **Earth Science Critical Thinking/ Problem Solving,** p. 10 **Physical Science Critical Thinking/ Problem Solving,** p. 10 **Reading and Writing Skill Activities,** p. 17	Portfolio Extension, p. 47 Performance Problem-Solving Activity, p. 49 MiniLAB, p. 50 Skill Builder Activities, p. 52 Content Section Assessment, p. 52	🔦 Section Focus Transparency 💿 Interactive CD-ROM 🎧 Guided Reading Audio Program
MiniLAB: plastic cup, index card **Activity:** balance, 2 small plastic cups, graduated cylinder, metric ruler, scissors, cupful of marbles, sink or basin	**Chapter Resources Booklet** Transparency Activity, p. 44 MiniLAB, p. 4 Enrichment, p. 30 Reinforcement, p. 27 Directed Reading, pp. 19, 20 Activity Worksheet, pp. 7–8 **Lab Management and Safety,** p. 71 **Mathematics Skill Activities,** p. 31	Portfolio Science Journal, p. 55 Performance MiniLAB, p. 57 Math Skills Activity, p. 59 Skill Builder Activities, p. 61 Content Section Assessment, p. 61	🔦 Section Focus Transparency 💿 Interactive CD-ROM 🎧 Guided Reading Audio Program

GLENCOE'S ASSESSMENT ADVANTAGE — End of Chapter Assessment

Blackline Masters	Technology	Professional Series
Chapter Resources Booklet Chapter Review, pp. 35–36 Chapter Tests, pp. 37–40 **Standardized Test Practice by The Princeton Review,** pp. 15–18	📺 MindJogger Videoquiz 💿 Interactive CD-ROM 💿 Vocabulary PuzzleMakers 💿 ExamView Pro Test Bank 💿 Interactive Lesson Planner 💿 Interactive Teacher Edition	Performance Assessment in the Science Classroom (PASC)

Transparencies

Section Focus

Section Focus Transparency — Bummer

If you found a rock like one of these, what would you think? A lot of people would think they had found gold. Unfortunately, this rock is really a mineral called pyrite, or fool's gold.

1. What can you determine about pyrite from this picture?
2. How is pyrite similar to gold? How might pyrite and gold differ?

L2

Section Focus Transparency — Looking forward to some ice water, are you?

Be sure not to forget about any water you put in the freezer to cool quickly. You might come back to a big ice cube.

1. What state of matter was the water in before it was put into the freezer? What happened in the freezer?
2. Compared to liquid water, how much space does solid water take up?
3. What are some examples of the effects of water expanding as it freezes?

L2

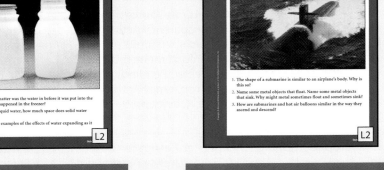

Section Focus Transparency — Up or Down?

Submarines have the ability to float on top of the ocean as well as dive beneath its surface. They accomplish this by taking water into holding tanks to dive and releasing it to surface.

1. The shape of a submarine is similar to an airplane's body. Why is this so?
2. Name some metal objects that float. Name some metal objects that sink. Why might metal sometimes float and sometimes sink?
3. How are submarines and hot air balloons similar in the way they ascend and descend?

L2

This is a representation of key blackline masters available in the Teacher Classroom Resources. See Resource Manager boxes within the chapter for additional information.

Assessment

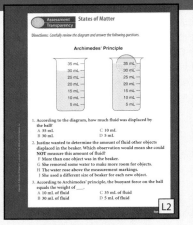

Assessment Transparency — States of Matter

Directions: Carefully review the diagram and answer the following questions.

Archimedes' Principle

1. According to the diagram, how much fluid was displaced by the ball?
   A 35 mL   C 10 mL
   B 30 mL   D 5 mL
2. Justine wanted to determine the amount of fluid other objects displaced in the beaker. Which observation would mean she could **NOT** measure this amount of fluid?
   F More than one object was in the beaker.
   G She removed some water to make more room for objects.
   H The water rose above the measurement markings.
   J She used a different size of beaker for each new object.
3. According to Archimedes' principle, the buoyant force on the ball equals the weight of ___.
   A 10 mL of fluid   C 35 mL of fluid
   B 30 mL of fluid   D 5 mL of fluid

L2

Teaching

Teaching Transparency — Solid, Liquid, Gas

Solid

Liquid

Gas

L2

Key to Teaching Strategies

The following designations will help you decide which activities are appropriate for your students.

L1 Level 1 activities should be appropriate for students with learning difficulties.

L2 Level 2 activities should be within the ability range of all students.

L3 Level 3 activities are designed for above-average students.

ELL ELL activities should be within the ability range of English Language Learners.

COOP LEARN Cooperative Learning activities are designed for small group work.

LS Multiple Learning Styles logos are used throughout to indicate strategies that address different learning styles.

P These strategies represent student products that can be placed into a best-work portfolio.

Hands-on Activities

Activity Worksheets

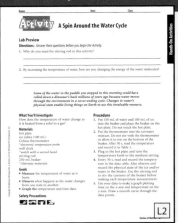

Activity — A Spin Around the Water Cycle

Lab Preview

Directions: Answer these questions before you begin the Activity.

1. Why do you need the stirring rod in this activity?

2. By increasing the temperature of water, how are you changing the energy of the water molecules?

Some of the water in the puddle you stepped in this morning could have rolled down a dinosaur's back millions of years ago because water moves through the environment in a never-ending cycle. Changes in water's physical state enable living things on Earth to use this invaluable resource.

What You'll Investigate
How does the temperature of water change as it is heated from a solid to a gas?

Materials
hot plate
ice cubes (100 mL)
Celsius thermometer
*electronic temperature probe
wall clock
*watch with a second hand
stirring rod
250-mL beaker
*Alternate materials

Goals
• **Measure** the temperature of water as it heats.
• **Observe** what happens as the water changes from one state to another.
• **Graph** the temperature and time data.

Safety Precautions

Procedure
1. Put 150 mL of water and 100 mL of ice into the beaker and place the beaker on the hot plate. Do not touch the hot plate.
2. Put the thermometer into the ice/water mixture. Do not stir with the thermometer or allow it to rest on the bottom of the beaker. After 30 s, read the temperature and record it in Table 1.
3. Plug in the hot plate and turn the temperature knob to the medium setting.
4. Every 30 s, read and record the temperature in the data table. Also observe and record the physical state of the ice and/or water in the beaker. Use the stirring rod to stir the contents of the beaker before making each temperature measurement.
5. Use your data to make a graph plotting time on the x-axis and temperature on the y-axis. Draw a smooth curve through the data points.

L2

Laboratory Activities

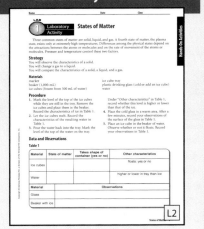

Laboratory Activity — States of Matter

Three common states of matter are solid, liquid, and gas. A fourth state of matter, the plasma state, exists only at extremely high temperatures. Differences among the physical states depend on the attractions between the atoms or molecules and on the rate of movement of the atoms or molecules. Pressure and temperature control these two factors.

Strategy
You will observe the characteristics of a solid.
You will change a gas to a liquid.
You will compare the characteristics of a solid, a liquid, and a gas.

Materials
marker
beaker (1,000 mL)
ice cubes (frozen from 500 mL of water)
ice cube tray
plastic drinking glass (cold or add an ice cube)
water

Procedure
1. Mark the level of the top of the ice cubes while they are still in the tray. Remove the ice cubes and place them in the beaker. Record the characteristics of ice in Table 1.
2. Let the ice cubes melt. Record the characteristics of the resulting water in Table 1.
3. Pour the water back into the tray. Mark the level of the top of the water in the tray.

Under "Other characteristics" in Table 1, record whether this level is higher or lower than that of the ice.
4. Place the cold glass in a warm area. After a few minutes, record your observations of the surface of the glass in Table 1.
5. Place an ice cube in the beaker of water. Observe whether or not it floats. Record your observations in Table 1.

Data and Observations

Table 1

Material	State of matter	Takes shape of container (yes or no)	Other characteristics
Ice cubes			floats: yes or no
Water			higher or lower in tray than ice

Material	Observations
Glass	
Beaker with ice	

L2

Meeting Different Ability Levels

Content Outline

Note-taking Worksheet — States of Matter

Section 1   Matter

A. _____—anything that takes up space and has mass; matter is composed of tiny particles.

1. Three usual _____ are solid, liquid, and gas.
2. _____, a fourth state, occurs only at very high temperatures and is not common on Earth.

B. _____—have definite shape and volume because particles are packed closely together and merely vibrate in place.

1. Solids in which particles are arranged in a repeating, three-dimensional pattern are called _____ or crystalline solids.
2. _____ solids have a random arrangement of particles.

C. Matter with a definite volume but no definite shape is a _____; a liquid's particles move more freely than those of a solid.

1. _____ is a liquid's resistance to flow and increases when particles are more strongly attracted to each other.
2. _____—uneven forces acting on the particles of a liquid's surface.

D. _____—matter that does not have a definite shape or volume; gas particles spread out evenly as far apart as possible.

Section 2   Changes of State

A. Particles are in constant motion; amount of movement depends on their _____.

1. _____—total energy of all the particles in a sample of matter.
2. The average kinetic energy of particles in a substance is its _____.
3. _____—movement of thermal energy from a substance with a higher temperature to one with a lower temperature.

L2

Reinforcement

Reinforcement — Matter

Directions: *Match the terms in Column I with the descriptions in Column I by writing the letter of the correct term in the blank at the left.*

Column I

_____ 1. Tar is hard to pour because it doesn't flow easily.
_____ 2. Energy from hot cocoa melts a marshmallow placed in it.
_____ 3. Like diamond, soot is made of carbon, but its atoms are arranged in a random manner.
_____ 4. Table salt changes to a liquid at 800°C.
_____ 5. Aluminum atoms are arranged in a repeating cubic pattern.
_____ 6. This sheet of paper is an arrangement of shaking particles.
_____ 7. A thermometer indirectly measures the average kinetic energy of particles.
_____ 8. Water changes to ice at 0°C.
_____ 9. The three physical states are liquid, solid, and gas.
_____ 10. A pin can float on the water in a cup.

Column II

a. amorphous solid
b. crystalline solid
c. freezing point
d. heat
e. matter
f. temperature
g. melting point
h. viscosity
i. solid
j. surface tension

Directions: *Answer the following questions on the lines provided.*

11. Why does water fill the bottom of a glass, rather than cling to the sides?
12. Why do beads of water often form on a slippery surface, such as a freshly waxed car?
13. What causes surface tension in water?
14. Explain why certain bugs can walk on water.
15. When does water begin entering the gaseous state?

L2

Directed Reading

Directed Reading for Content Mastery — *Overview* States of Matter

Directions: *Use the following terms to complete the concept map below.*

boiling point   liquid   decreases
increases   solid   condensation

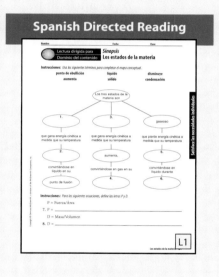

Directions: *For the following equations, define the letters P and D.*

P = Force/Area
7. P =
D = Mass/Volume
8. D =

L1

Assessment

Chapter Tests

Chapter Test — States of Matter

I. Testing Concepts

Directions: *In the blank at the left, write the letter of the term that best completes the statement or answers the question.*

_____ 1. Particles that make up matter are in a state of _____.
a. constant motion   c. ionization
b. flux   d. constant combination

_____ 2. When a warm object is brought near a cool object, the cool object will _____.
a. cool off   c. evaporate
b. remain unchanged   d. warm up

_____ 3. Which of the following is not a change between liquid and gas states?
a. vaporization   b. condensation   c. boiling   d. evaporation

_____ 4. A gas _____ fills its container.
a. partially   c. sometimes
b. most of the time   d. completely

_____ 5. The physical state of a type of matter depends mostly upon how its _____ are arranged and how they move.
a. pressures and densities   c. nucleus and protons
b. nucleus and neutrons   d. atoms and molecules

_____ 6. Different objects don't heat at the same rate because they have different _____.
a. specific heats   c. boiling points
b. energy   d. temperatures

_____ 7. The net upward force caused by displaced fluid is _____.
a. buoyant force   c. density force
b. Pascal's principle   d. pressure force

_____ 8. Solids made up of particles of matter arranged in repeating geometric patterns are _____.
a. geometric solids   c. triangular matter
b. tile solids   d. crystalline solids

_____ 9. The energy of moving particles is called _____.
a. kinetic energy   c. atomic energy
b. latent energy   d. potential energy

_____ 10. If an object's density is less than that of the fluid it is in, it will _____.
a. sink   b. float   c. melt   d. boil

_____ 11. When the attractive forces holding particles together are strong enough to hold them together as a group, but not in a fixed position, they form a _____.
a. solid   b. gas   c. liquid   d. crystal

_____ 12. The _____ remains constant when a liquid reaches its boiling point.
a. temperature   c. odor
b. sound   d. color

L2

Enrichment

Enrichment — Designing Scientific Models

As you learned in this section, each crystalline solid has a melting point and a freezing point. These are the same, whether measured in the Fahrenheit or Celsius system. For water, the freezing point is 32°F, or 0°C. When water reaches a temperature above 0°C, it exists either in the liquid or gaseous state, depending on how high the temperature goes. When the temperature of water falls below 0°C, it exists in a solid state. The molecules that make up ice are farther apart than the molecules that make up water.

This property makes water unique: as a solid it is less dense than as a liquid. This explains why ice cubes float in a glass of water.

Scientists use models to help them represent matter in its various states. The models can be created using a computer graphic program, by drawing them on paper, or be creating them out of three-dimensional objects. Using your knowledge that water in its solid state is less dense than water in its liquid state, create a model that would help explain to someone why ice cubes float in a glass of water.

1. What type of model did you choose to create?

2. Describe how your model represents water as a solid and as a liquid.

3. A copper penny will sink in molten copper. What can you infer about the differences in distance between the molecules in a copper penny and in molten copper?

L3

Spanish Directed Reading

Lectura dirigida para Dominio del contenido — *Sinopsis* Los estados de la materia

Instrucciones: *Usa los siguientes términos para completar el mapa conceptual.*

punto de ebullición   líquido   disminuye
aumenta   sólido   condensación

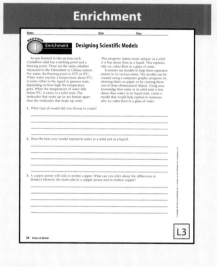

Instrucciones: *Para las siguientes ecuaciones, define las letras P y D.*

P = Fuerza/Área
7. P =
D = Masa/Volumen
8. D =

L1

Test Practice Workbook

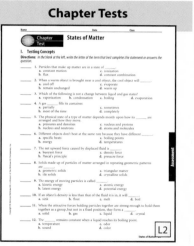

Standardized Test Practice
Teacher Edition
The Princeton Review

Glencoe Science

The Nature of Matter

NATIONAL GEOGRAPHIC SOCIETY

L2

Chapter Review

Chapter Review — States of Matter

Part A. Vocabulary Review

Directions: *Match the terms in Column II with the definitions in Column I. Write the letter of the correct term in the blank at the left.*

Column I

_____ 1. tells you whether a material is a solid, liquid or gas
_____ 2. anything that takes up space and has mass
_____ 3. thermal energy that flows from higher temperature to lower temperature
_____ 4. the temperature at which a substance changes from a solid to a liquid
_____ 5. the kinetic and potential energy of the particles of a substance
_____ 6. the temperature at which attractive forces begin to trap particles here and there, and crystals begin to form
_____ 7. temperature where some of a liquid begins to enter the gaseous state
_____ 8. the process by which individual particles of liquid escape from the surface and form a gas
_____ 9. the process by which particles move slowly enough for their attraction to bring them together to form a droplet of liquid
_____ 10. when a liquid changes to a gas
_____ 11. the amount of force applied per unit of area
_____ 12. the ability to do work or cause change
_____ 13. the term referring to the pressure applied at any point to a confined fluid being transmitted unchanged throughout the fluid
_____ 14. the term referring to mass divided by volume
_____ 15. When an object is placed in a fluid, the object weighs less by an amount equal to the weight of the displaced fluid.
_____ 16. the upward force of displaced fluid causing flotation

Column II

a. freezing point
b. evaporation
c. pressure
d. buoyant force
e. state of matter
f. vaporization
g. condensation
h. melting point
i. density
j. matter
k. Pascal's principle
l. energy
m. heat
n. Archimedes' principle
o. thermal energy
p. boiling point

L2

Science Content Background

Matter

Understanding Matter

Matter is made of tiny moving particles separated by space. The three states of matter that people mainly encounter are gases, liquids, and solids. In gases, the separation of the particles is the greatest because these particles are moving the fastest. Decreasing the spaces between gas molecules by decreasing the temperature or increasing the pressure can turn gases into liquids and liquids into solids.

Student Misconception

Matter does not include liquids or gases; matter includes energy such as heat and light.

Refer to the facing page for teaching strategies to address this misconception. Refer to pages 46–47 for content related to this topic.

Temperature

The Kelvin temperature scale is an absolute scale. It begins at absolute zero, or 0 K. Each degree on the Kelvin scale is the same magnitude as a degree on the Celsius temperature scale. The freezing point of water on the Celsius scale is 0°C; the freezing point of water on the Kelvin scale is 273 K. The average kinetic energy of the particles that make up a substance is directly proportional to its Kelvin temperature. Although particles should not be moving at absolute zero, they have a small amount of motion called the zero point energy.

Takehide Kazami/Peter Arnold, Inc.

Heat

Heat is energy transferred from matter at a higher temperature to matter at a lower temperature. Objects do not contain heat; they contain internal energy, which is the sum of the kinetic and potential energies of their particles. Heat can be transferred three ways: radiation is the emission of electromagnetic waves, conduction is the transfer of heat by direct contact, and convection is heat transfer by warmer matter flowing into regions of colder matter.

Changes of State

Forces Between Molecules

When a liquid is poured into a container such as a glass test tube, the liquid's surface is called the meniscus. The shape of the meniscus depends on the relative strength of the cohesive forces between liquid particles and the adhesive forces between particles of the liquid and the container. If the adhesive forces are greater, the meniscus is concave. Water in a glass tube has a concave meniscus. If the cohesive forces are greater, the meniscus is convex. Mercury in a glass tube has a convex meniscus.

Behavior of Fluids

Atmospheric Pressure

Air pressure decreases rapidly with altitude. At the top of Mount Everest, 8.85 km above sea level, the pressure is only 33% of atmospheric pressure at sea level. This difference in pressure demonstrates how effectively gravity contains Earth's atmosphere.

For additional content background on this topic, go to the Glencoe Science Web site at science.glencoe.com.

IDENTIFYING ▷ **Misconceptions**

Students may think that . . .

• **Matter does not include liquids or gases.**

• **Forms of energy such as heat and light are matter.**

Since solids are easy to see and feel, students usually understand easily that these materials are matter. Most gasses are not directly observed, either through vision or other senses, so students may have difficulty categorizing gases as matter. Some students, however, may have too inclusive a view of matter. They fail to realize that energy may affect particles but is not composed of particles. These misunderstandings about matter can interfere with acquisition of new concepts.

Discussion

Ask students to divide a page in their Science Journals into two columns, one headed "Matter" and the other headed "Not Matter". Read the following terms, and have students write each one in the appropriate column: *oxygen gas, orange juice, science book, pencil, electricity, carbon dioxide gas, water, heat,* and *light.*

Superstock

Promote Understanding

Demonstration

Explain that matter is composed of molecules.

• Hold up an ice cube, and establish that it is matter and is made of H_2O molecules.

• Allow the ice cube to melt. Point to the water. Is this matter? Establish that it is matter and that it is still made of H_2O molecules.

• Boil the water on a hot plate to produce steam. Is the steam matter? Establish that it is and that it is still made of H_2O molecules. Matter includes solids, liquids, and gases.

• Move your hand over the hot plate, and say that it feels warm. Is heat matter? Let students discuss this.

• Does heat have particles? Make sure students realize that heat affects particles but is not composed of particles. Heat is a form of energy, just as light and X rays are forms of energy. Energy is not matter.

Have students go back to their charts and move any terms that are not in the proper columns.

Assess

After completing the chapter, see *Identifying Misconceptions* in the Study Guide.

States of Matter

Chapter Vocabulary

What do you think?

Science Journal The photograph shows rain drops as they deflect off of an umbrella in a downpour. Rain is water in the liquid state.

States of Matter

Ahhh! A long, hot soak on a cold, snowy day. This Asian monkey called a macaque is experiencing one of the properties of matter—the transfer of thermal energy from a warmer object to a colder object. In this chapter, you will learn about other properties of solids, liquids, gases, and plasma—the four states of matter.

What do you think?

Science Journal Look at the picture below with a classmate. Discuss what you think is happening. Here's a hint: *Several of these bring flowers in May.* Write your answer or best guess in your Science Journal.

Theme Connection

Systems and Interactions The structure and motion of particles of matter can be analyzed to explain many properties of systems containing huge numbers of particles. Powerful changes can be caused when energy is absorbed or released by these systems. Earth's weather offers many examples of changes involving the absorption or release of energy.

I n a few short months, the lake that is now the solid surface supporting you on ice skates will be a liquid in which you can swim. Many substances, such as water, change as they become warm or cool.

Experiment with a freezing liquid

1. Make a table to record temperature and appearance. Obtain a test tube containing an unknown liquid from your teacher. Place the test tube in a rack.

2. Insert a thermometer into the liquid. **WARNING:** *Do not allow the thermometer to touch the bottom of the test tube.* Starting immediately, observe and record the substance's temperature and appearance every 30 s.

3. Continue making measurements and observations until you're told to stop.

Observe

In your Science Journal, describe your investigation and observations. Did anything unusual happen while you were observing? If so, what?

FOLDABLES
Reading & Study Skills

Before You Read

Making an Organizational Study Fold **Make the following Foldable to help you organize your thoughts into clear categories about states of matter.**

1. Place a sheet of paper in front of you so the short side is at the top. Fold the paper in half from the left side to the right side two times. Unfold all the folds.

2. Fold the paper in half from top to bottom. Then fold it in half again. Unfold all the folds and trace over all the fold lines.

3. Label the rows *Liquid Water, Water as a Vapor,* and *Water as a Solid (Ice).* Label the columns *Define States,* *+ Heat,* and *−Heat* as shown. As you read the chapter, define the states of matter listed on your Foldable in the *Define States* column.

	Define States	+ Heat	− Heat
Liquid Water			
Water as a Vapor			
Water as a Solid (Ice)			

Purpose Use the Explore Activity to help students discover that temperature remains constant as a substance freezes. L2

COOP LEARN **Kinesthetic**

Preparation When students arrive, have test tubes half-filled with molten stearic acid sitting in a hot water bath at a temperature of approximately 75°C.

Materials laboratory-grade stearic acid, glass test tube, Celsius thermometer, watch or clock with a second hand, test-tube rack or jar

Teaching Strategy Suggest that student groups divide the responsibilities of tracking time, taking temperature readings, and recording data. Students then can graph and analyze the data individually.

Observe

The liquid's temperature fell gradually, remained the same as the liquid formed a white solid, then fell again. Heat was given off by the freezing liquid.

✓Assessment

Performance Have students predict what would happen if they were given twice as much of the unknown liquid. Use **PASC,** p. 89.

Sample Data

Time (s)	Temperature (°C)
0	74.0
30	72.5
60	70.0
90	69.5
120	69.5
150	69.5
180	69.5
210	69.0
240	68.5

FOLDABLES
Reading & Study Skills

Before You Read

Dinah Zike Study Fold

Purpose Students will make and use a Foldable table to collect information about the states of matter and the changes these states experience when heat is added or taken away.

📁 For additional help, see Foldables Worksheet, p. 15 in **Chapter Resources Booklet,** or go to the Glencoe Science Web site at **science.glencoe.com.** See After You Read in the Study Guide at the end of this chapter.

SECTION

1

Matter

1 Motivate

Bellringer Transparency

Display the Section Focus Transparency for Section 1. Use the accompanying Transparency Activity Master. L2

ELL

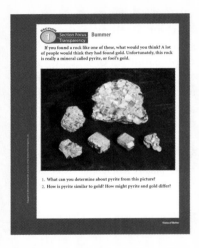

Tie to Prior Knowledge

Ask what happens to ice that is left out of a freezer. It melts. Explain that when ice melts, its state of matter changes.

Caption Answer

Figure 1 solid ice; liquid water; gaseous air; plasma in the Sun

✔ Reading Check

Answer the amount of motion the particles have and the strength of attraction between them

---

■ As You Read

What You'll Learn
- **Recognize** that matter is made of particles in constant motion.
- **Relate** the three states of matter to the arrangement of particles within them.

Vocabulary

matter   liquid
solid   gas

Why It's Important
Everything you can see, taste, and touch is matter. Without matter—well, nothing would matter!

Figure 1
Matter exists in all four states in this scene. *Identify the solid, liquid, gas, and plasma in this photograph.*

What is matter?

Take a look at the beautiful scene in **Figure 1.** What do you see? Perhaps you notice the water and ice. Maybe you are struck by the Sun in the background. All of these images show examples of matter. **Matter** is anything that takes up space and has mass. Matter doesn't have to be visible—even air is matter.

States of Matter All matter is made up of tiny particles, such as atoms, molecules, or ions. Each particle attracts other particles. In other words, each particle pulls other particles toward itself. These particles also are constantly moving. The motion of the particles and the strength of attraction between the particles determine a material's state of matter.

✔ Reading Check   *What determines a material's state of matter?*

There are three familiar states of matter—solid, liquid, and gas. A fourth state of matter known as plasma occurs only at extremely high temperatures. Plasma is found in stars, lightning, and neon lights. Although plasma is common in the universe, it is not common on Earth. For that reason, this chapter will focus only on the three states of matter that are common on Earth.

Section ✔ *Assessment* Planner

PORTFOLIO
Extension, p. 41
Assessment, p. 44
PERFORMANCE ASSESSMENT
Skill Builder Activities, p. 44
See page 68 for more options.

CONTENT ASSESSMENT
Section, p. 44
Challenge, p. 44
Chapter, pp. 68–69

Solids

What makes a solid a solid? Think about some solids that you are familiar with. Chairs, floors, rocks, and ice cubes are a few examples of matter in the solid state. What properties do all solids share? A **solid** is matter with a definite shape and volume. For example, when you pick up a rock from the ground and place it in a bucket, it doesn't change shape or size. A solid does not take the shape of a container in which it is placed. This is because the particles of a solid are packed closely together, as shown in **Figure 2**.

Particles in Motion The particles that make up all types of matter are in constant motion. Does this mean that the particles in a solid are moving too? Although you can't see them, a solid's particles are vibrating in place. The particles do not have enough energy to move out of their fixed positions.

 **Reading Check** *What motion do solid particles have?*

Crystalline Solids In some solids, the particles are arranged in a repeating, three-dimensional pattern called a crystal. These solids are called crystalline solids. In **Figure 3** you can see the arrangement of particles in a crystal of sodium chloride, which is table salt. The particles in the crystal are arranged in the shape of a cube. Diamond, another crystalline solid, is made entirely of carbon atoms that form crystals that look more like pyramids. Sugar, sand, and snow are other crystalline solids.

Solid

Figure 2
The particles in a solid vibrate in place, maintaining a constant shape and volume.

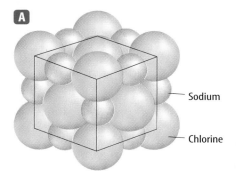

A

Sodium

Chlorine

Figure 3
A The particles in a crystal of sodium chloride (NaCl) are arranged in an orderly pattern. B This magnified image shows the cubic shape of sodium chloride crystals.

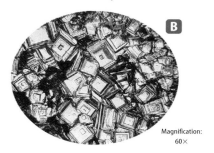

B

Magnification:
60×

SECTION 1 Matter   **K** ◆ **41**

Resource Manager

Chapter Resources Booklet
Transparency Activity, p. 42
Directed Reading for Content Mastery, p. 18
Note-taking Worksheets, pp. 31–33

What is matter?

Extension

Have students find out what plasma consists of and how it forms. Have them write a paragraph about what they find. Plasma consists of ions, electrons, and atomic nuclei that have lost all their electrons. Plasma forms at temperatures greater than 5,000°C. L3 ELL
LS **Linguistic** P

Solids

Teacher FYI

The arrangement of atoms and molecules in a solid determines its properties. For example, diamond and graphite are two forms of carbon in which the atoms are arranged differently. In diamonds, each carbon atom is bonded to four others to form a tetrahedron. Because this structure is extremely strong, the diamond is very hard. In graphite, the carbon atoms form layers of hexagonal rings that are held together by weak forces. Because these bonds are easily broken, the graphite layers can be made to slide easily past one another. Such inherent slipperiness makes graphite an excellent lubricant.

✔ **Reading Check**

Answer a vibratory motion

Make a Model

Have groups of students use **Figure 3** as a reference to make models of the sodium chloride crystal lattice. Provide colored marshmallows of different sizes and toothpicks. Discuss the features of the shape formed. L2
ELL COOP LEARN LS **Visual-Spatial**

Solids, continued

Use an Analogy

The particles in a crystalline solid occupy defined spaces, like eggs in an egg carton. In an amorphous solid the particles are in a random arrangement, more like lemons in a bowl.

✔ Reading Check

Answer The particles in amorphous solids have a random arrangement instead of an ordered arrangement as in a crystalline solid.

Earth Science
INTEGRATION

Explain to students that more than 97% of Earth's water is salt water found in the oceans. Have students make circle graphs showing the proportion of salt water to freshwater on Earth. L2
LS Logical-Mathematical

Liquids

Fun Fact

The physics department of the University of Queensland, Australia, has a funnel of pitch—the black, sticky material used in blacktopping roads and waterproofing basements—that is so viscous it takes about ten years for a drop to drip. Students can view it at the Glencoe Science Web site.

Earth Science
INTEGRATION

About 74.93 percent of Earth's freshwater is in the form of solid ice. Most of the remaining freshwater, about 25.04 percent, exists as a liquid in lakes, rivers, and in the ground. A small fraction, about 0.03 percent, of Earth's freshwater can be found in the air as water vapor, which is the gas state of water. Create a circle graph showing the states of Earth's freshwater.

Amorphous Solids Some solids come together without forming crystal structures. These solids often consist of large particles that are not arranged in a repeating pattern. Instead, the particles are found in a random arrangement. These solids are called amorphous (uh MOR fuhs) solids. Rubber, plastic, and glass are examples of amorphous solids.

✔ Reading Check
How is a crystalline solid different from an amorphous solid?

Liquids

From the orange juice you drink with breakfast to the water you use to brush your teeth at night, matter in the liquid state is familiar to you. How would you describe the characteristics of a liquid? Is it hard like a solid? Does it keep its shape? A **liquid** is matter that has a definite volume but no definite shape. When you pour a liquid from one container to another, the liquid takes the shape of the container. The volume of a liquid, however, is the same no matter what the shape of the container. If you pour 50 mL of juice from a carton into a pitcher, the pitcher will contain 50 mL of juice. If you then pour that same juice into a glass, its shape will change again but its volume will not.

Free to Move The reason that a liquid can have different shapes is because the particles in a liquid move more freely, as shown in **Figure 4,** than the particles in a solid. The particles in a liquid have enough energy to move out of their fixed positions but not enough to move far apart.

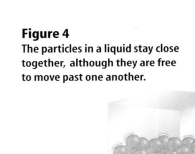

Figure 4
The particles in a liquid stay close together, although they are free to move past one another.

Liquid

Inclusion Strategies

Learning Disabled Have students make their own vocabulary flash cards. Using index cards, the students should write the word on one side of the card and the definition on the other side. English language learners may want to use both their native language and English initially. Students should save these cards and use them to study for chapter, unit, and semester exams. L1
ELL **LS** Linguistic

Resource Manager

Chapter Resources Booklet
Enrichment, p. 28
Reinforcement, p. 25
Transparency Activity, pp. 45–46
Lab Activity, pp. 9–10

Viscosity Do all liquids flow the way water flows? You know that honey flows more slowly than water and you've probably heard the phrase "slow as molasses." Some liquids flow more easily than others. A liquid's resistance to flow is known as the liquid's viscosity. Honey has a high viscosity. Water has a lower viscosity. The slower a liquid flows, the higher its viscosity is. The viscosity results from the strength of the attraction between the particles of the liquid. For many liquids, viscosity increases as the liquid becomes colder.

Surface Tension If you're careful, you can float a needle on the surface of water. This is because attractive forces cause the particles on the surface of a liquid to pull themselves together and resist being pushed apart. You can see in **Figure 5A** that particles beneath the surface of a liquid are pulled in all directions. Particles at the surface of a liquid are pulled toward the center of the liquid and sideways along the surface. No liquid particles are located above to pull on them. The uneven forces acting on the particles on the surface of a liquid are called surface tension. Surface tension causes the liquid to act as if a thin film were stretched across its surface. As a result you can float a needle on the surface of water. For the same reason, the water strider in **Figure 5B** can move around on the surface of a pond or lake. When a liquid is present in small amounts, surface tension causes the liquid to form small droplets, as shown in **Figure 5C**.

SCIENCE Online

Research Visit the Glencoe Science Web site at **science.glencoe.com** for more information about the states of matter. How does the fourth state of matter, plasma, differ from the others? Make a poster that describes and gives examples of the four states of matter.

Visual Learning

Figure 5 Explain the forces that are in effect in each photo and ask why surface tension is not a property of solids. The particles in solids are rigidly held in place and are not free to move. L2

IS Logical-Mathematical

Use an Analogy

One force of attraction that causes particles to pull toward each other is called cohesion. Cohesion between particles is similar to the force of gravity that pulls inward to produce the spherical shape of the planets and sun.

SCIENCE Online
Internet Addresses

_____

_____

_____

Explore the Glencoe Science Web site at **science.glencoe.com** to find out more about topics in this section.

Figure 5
A These arrows show the forces pulling on the particles of a liquid. Surface tension exists because the particles at the surface experience different forces than those at the center of the liquid. **B** Surface tension allows this strider to float on water as if the water had a thin film. **C** Water drops form on these blades of grass due to surface tension.

A

Side view

B

C

LAB DEMONSTRATION

Purpose to show how temperature affects the viscosity of a liquid

Materials 2 jars, syrup or molasses, refrigerator, 2 small beakers, stopwatch

Preparation Add 10 mL of syrup to each jar. Place one jar in a refrigerator overnight, and allow the other to stand at room temperature.

Procedure Have one student pour all the cold syrup into one beaker while another student pours all the room-temperature syrup into the other beaker. Have remaining students record the time it takes to empty each jar.

Expected Outcome The cold syrup takes longer to pour.

✓Assessment

Why does the cold syrup have higher viscosity than the warmer syrup? The particles in the cold syrup are closer together and exert a stronger force upon each other than do the warmer particles.

Gases

✔ Reading Check

Answer The helium will move out of the balloon in all directions to fill the room.

Quick Demo

Demonstrate that gases spread out to fill all available space by spraying a small amount of air freshener in one corner of the room. Have students raise their hands when they first smell the scent. Have students explain the movement of the particles.

③ Assess

Reteach

Blow up a balloon and tie it closed at the neck. Use the balloon to illustrate to students that a gas can be compressed. Ask students what happens to the gas in the balloon if you twist the balloon at the center. Some gas moves into each end of the balloon, where it is compressed into a smaller space. L1 IS **Visual-Spatial**

Challenge

Have students explain why motor oil is made in a wide range of viscosities. Motor oil must remain fluid enough to protect a car engine in a wide range of weather conditions. L2
IS **Logical-Mathematical**

✔ Assessment

Content Have students prepare posters that compare and contrast the properties of solids, liquids, and gases. Use **PASC**, p. 145. P

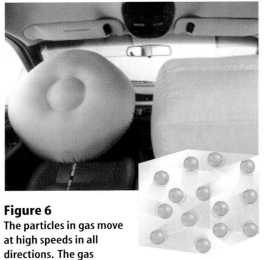

Figure 6
The particles in gas move at high speeds in all directions. The gas inside these air bags spreads out to fill the entire volume of the bag.

Gases

Unlike solids and liquids, most gases are invisible. The air in the air bags in **Figure 6** and the helium in some balloons are examples of gases. **Gas** is matter that does not have a definite shape or volume. The particles in gas are much farther apart than those in a liquid or solid. Gas particles move at high speeds in all directions. They will spread out evenly, as far apart as possible. If you poured a small volume of a liquid into a container, the liquid would stay in the bottom of the container. However, if you poured the same volume of a gas into a container, the gas would fill the container completely. A gas can expand or be compressed. Decreasing the volume of the container squeezes the gas particles closer together.

✔ Reading Check *How will the shape and volume of helium gas change when it escapes from a balloon?*

You sometimes will hear the term *vapor* applied to gases. A vapor is matter that exists in the gas state but is generally a liquid or solid at room temperature. Water, for example, is a liquid at room temperature. Steam, the gas state of water, is called water vapor.

Section ① Assessment

1. Define matter in your own words and provide at least three examples.
2. Describe the movement of particles within solids, liquids, and gases.
3. Why do liquids flow?
4. A scientist places 25 mL of a yellow substance into a 50-mL container. The substance quickly fills the entire container. In which state of matter is the substance? Why?
5. **Think Critically** Two of the three common states of matter can be grouped together. Which two states share a similar property? Explain your reasoning.

Skill Builder Activities

6. **Concept Mapping** Using what you have read, draw a Venn diagram in your Science Journal and fill in the characteristics of the states of matter. Add information that you've gained from experience. **For more help, refer to the** Science Skill Handbook.
7. **Communicating** You are surrounded by solids, liquids, and gases all the time. In your Science Journal, make a table with three columns. List several examples of each state of matter. **For more help, refer to the** Science Skill Handbook.

Answers to Section Assessment

1. Matter is anything that takes up space and has mass. It is composed of tiny particles. Salt, water, and oxygen are three examples of matter.
2. Solids: particles are very close together and vibrate back and forth; liquids: particles are farther apart and individual particles can flow past each other; gases: particles are very far apart and move quickly in all directions.
3. The attraction between the particles is strong enough to hold them together, but not strong enough to hold them in fixed positions, so the liquid can flow. The attraction between the particles pulls additional particles along.
4. Gas state; the particles take the shape and volume of their container.
5. Liquids and gases both take the shape of their containers.
6. Diagrams should show that a solid has a definite shape and a gas has no definite volume. Both solid and liquid have definite volume. Both liquid and gas have no definite shape.
7. Check students' work.

SECTION 2 Changes of State

Thermal Energy and Heat

Shards of ice fly from the sculptor's chisel. As the crowd looks on, a swan slowly emerges from a massive block of ice. As the day wears on, however, drops of water begin to fall from the sculpture. Drip by drip, the sculpture is transformed into a puddle of liquid water. What makes matter change from one state to another? To answer this question, you need to take another look at the particles that make up matter.

Energy Simply stated, energy is the ability to do work or cause change. The energy of motion is called kinetic energy. Particles within matter are in constant motion. The amount of motion of these particles depends on the kinetic energy they possess. Particles with more kinetic energy move faster and farther apart. Particles with less energy move more slowly and stay closer together.

The total energy of all the particles in a sample of matter is called thermal energy. Thermal energy depends on the number of particles in a substance as well as the amount of energy each particle has. If either the number of particles or the amount of energy each particle in a sample has increases, the thermal energy of the sample increases. The hot water and snow in **Figure 7** have different amounts of energy.

As You Read

What You'll Learn
- **Define** and **Compare** thermal energy and temperature.
- **Relate** changes in thermal energy to changes of state.
- **Explore** energy and temperature changes on a graph.

Vocabulary
temperature   freezing
heat   vaporization
melting   condensation

Why It's Important
Matter changes state as it heats up or cools down.

Figure 7
You know how it feels to be hot and cold. This hot spring, for example, feels much hotter than the snow around it. *How is hot matter different from cold matter?*

SECTION 2 Changes of State   **K** ◆ **45**

SECTION 2

Changes of State

1 Motivate

Bellringer Transparency
Display the Section Focus Transparency for Section 2. Use the accompanying Transparency Activity Master. L2
ELL

Tie to Prior Knowledge
Remind students of the differences in particle arrangement and movement in solids, liquids, and gases.

Caption Answer
Figure 7 Hot matter has more kinetic energy than cold matter.

Resource Manager

Chapter Resources Booklet
Transparency Activity, p. 43
Directed Reading for Content Mastery, p. 19

Section ✓Assessment Planner

PORTFOLIO
Extension, p. 47
PERFORMANCE ASSESSMENT
MiniLAB, p. 50
Skill Builder Activities, p. 52
See page 68 for more options.

CONTENT ASSESSMENT
Section, p. 52
Challenge, p. 52
Chapter, pp. 68–69

Thermal Energy and Heat

IDENTIFYING Misconceptions

Students may think that matter does not include liquids or gases. They may also think that forms of energy, such as heat and light, are matter. Refer to page 38F for teaching strategies that address these misconceptions.

Physics INTEGRATION

Possible answer: mechanical energy used in riding bike, chemical energy in digesting food, electrical energy in flashlight batteries

✔ Reading Check

Answer When a substance is heated, it gains thermal energy; therefore, its particles move faster and its temperature rises.

Figure 8
The particles in hot tea move faster than those in iced tea. The temperature of hot tea is higher than the temperature of iced tea.

Physics INTEGRATION

Thermal energy is one of several different forms of energy. Other forms include the chemical energy in chemical compounds, the electrical energy used in appliances, the electromagnetic energy of light, and the nuclear energy stored in the nucleus of an atom. Make a list of examples of energy that you are familiar with.

Temperature Not all of the particles in a sample of matter have the same amount of energy. Some have more energy than others. The average kinetic energy of the individual particles is the **temperature** of the substance. You can find an average by adding up a group of numbers and dividing the total by the number of items in the group. For example, the average of the numbers 2, 4, 8, and 10 is $(2 + 4 + 8 + 10) \div 4 = 6$. Temperature is different from thermal energy because thermal energy is a total and temperature is an average.

You know that the iced tea is colder than the hot tea, as shown in **Figure 8.** Stated differently, the temperature of iced tea is lower than the temperature of hot tea. You also could say that the average kinetic energy of the particles in the iced tea is less than the average kinetic energy of the particles in the hot tea.

Heat When a warm object is brought near a cooler object, thermal energy will be transferred from the warmer object to the cooler one. The movement of thermal energy from a substance at a higher temperature to one at a lower temperature is called **heat.** When a substance is heated, it gains thermal energy. Therefore, its particles move faster and its temperature rises. When a substance is cooled, it loses thermal energy, which causes its particles to move more slowly and its temperature to drop.

✔ Reading Check   *How is heat related to temperature?*

Science Journal

Thermal Energy on the Move Ask students to pay attention to the transfer of thermal energy around them and record all the examples they observe in one 24-hour period. Have them write their observations in their Science Journals, including for each example where the thermal energy came from and where it went. L2 IS **Naturalist**

Teacher FYI

Two systems at the same temperature can have different amounts of thermal energy. For example, a cup of boiling water and a pot of boiling water may have the same temperature, but the pot of water has more thermal energy and can transfer more heat.

Specific Heat

If you walk from the grass to the pavement on a hot summer day, you know that the pavement is much hotter than the grass. Both surfaces were heated by the Sun and therefore received the same amount of thermal energy. Why does the temperature of one increase faster than the temperature of the other? The reason is that each surface has a different specific heat. The specific heat of a substance is the amount of heat needed to raise the temperature of 1 g of a substance 1°C.

Substances that have a low specific heat, such as most metals, heat up quickly because they require only small amounts of heat to cause their temperatures to rise. A substance with a high specific heat, such as the water in **Figure 9,** heats up slowly because a much larger quantity of heat is required to cause its temperature to rise by the same amount.

Figure 9
One reason the water in this lake is much colder than the surrounding sand is because the specific heat of water is higher than that of sand.

Changes Between the Solid and Liquid States

Matter can change from one state to another when thermal energy is absorbed or released. A change from one physical state of matter to another is known as change of state. The graph in **Figure 11** shows the changes in temperature and thermal energy that occur as you gradually heat a container of ice.

Figure 10
Rather than melting into a liquid, glass gradually softens. Glass blowers use this characteristic to shape glass into beautiful vases while it is hot.

Melting As the ice in **Figure 11** is heated, it absorbs thermal energy and its temperature rises. At some point, the temperature stops rising and the ice begins to change into liquid water. The change from the solid state to the liquid state is called **melting.** The temperature at which a substance changes from a solid to a liquid is called the melting point. The melting point of water is 0°C.

Amorphous solids, such as rubber and glass, don't melt in the same way as crystalline solids. Because they don't have crystal structures to break down, these solids get softer and softer as they are heated, as you can see in **Figure 10.**

Specific Heat

Extension

Between 0°C and 100°C the specific heat of water is about 4.18 J/g °C. Ask students to find the specific heats of several metals and compare them with the specific heat of water. Have them make a table from their findings. The specific heat of silver between these temperatures is 0.235 J/g°C. Between 20°C and 100°C the specific heat of aluminum is 0.903 J/g°C, the specific heat of copper is 0.385 J/g°C, and the specific heat of iron is 0.449 J/g°C. These range from about one-twentieth that of water to about one-fifth that of water. L3

IS Logical-Mathematical P

Changes Between the Solid and Liquid States

IDENTIFYING Misconceptions

Students may think particles of a substance can change state only at the melting point or boiling point of the substance. In fact, at any temperature different particles of a substance have different amounts of kinetic energy and may have enough energy to change state. Melting and boiling occur when the number of particles with enough energy to change state is great enough that the average kinetic energy of the particles is at the melting point or the boiling point of the substance.

Resource Manager

Chapter Resources Booklet
   Lab Activity, pp. 11–13

Earth Science Critical Thinking/Problem
   Solving, p. 10

Curriculum Connection

Geography Earth's temperature has increased during the past few decades. Have students research how this increase could cause changes in the state of water and the effects these changes could have on a specific geographic region. For example, melting of the polar ice caps is causing erosion along coastlines. L3 **IS Linguistic**

Visualizing States of Matter

Have students examine the pictures and read the captions. Then ask the following questions.

During the melting and vaporization process the temperature remains constant. Look at the graph and identify which factor continues to increase. thermal energy

What changes in molecular attraction occur as water goes from a solid to a liquid to a gas? As a solid, the molecules have the most attraction for each other. As a liquid, the molecular attraction has decreased. As a gas, the particles are very far apart and are moving quickly enough to completely overcome the attractive forces.

During condensation, what must be removed from the gas in order for the gas to become a liquid? thermal energy

Activity

Have students write poems about the life of a water molecule as it goes from a solid to a gas. The poems should contain information about changes in molecular attraction and thermal energy. L2 **IS** **Linguistic**

Extension

Challenge students to research the energy changes that occur during the refrigeration cycle. Have them also find the properties of good refrigerants and share the information that they find with the class. L3
IS **Linguistic**

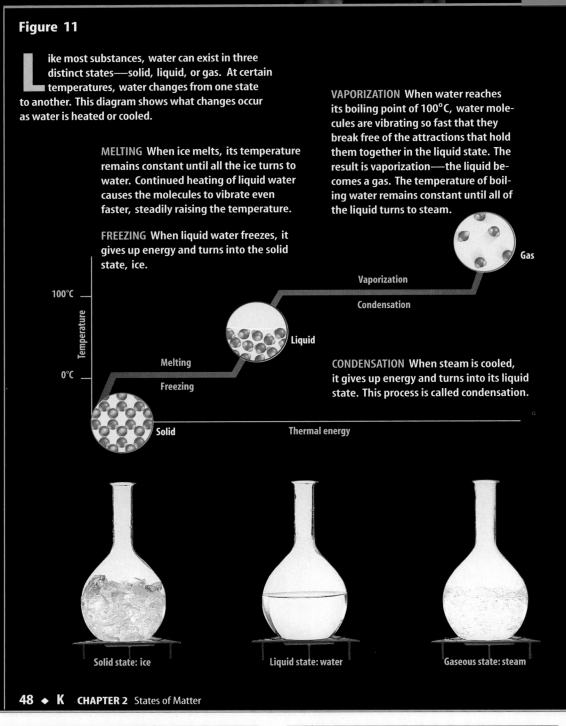

Figure 11

Like most substances, water can exist in three distinct states—solid, liquid, or gas. At certain temperatures, water changes from one state to another. This diagram shows what changes occur as water is heated or cooled.

MELTING When ice melts, its temperature remains constant until all the ice turns to water. Continued heating of liquid water causes the molecules to vibrate even faster, steadily raising the temperature.

FREEZING When liquid water freezes, it gives up energy and turns into the solid state, ice.

VAPORIZATION When water reaches its boiling point of 100°C, water molecules are vibrating so fast that they break free of the attractions that hold them together in the liquid state. The result is vaporization—the liquid becomes a gas. The temperature of boiling water remains constant until all of the liquid turns to steam.

CONDENSATION When steam is cooled, it gives up energy and turns into its liquid state. This process is called condensation.

Gas

Vaporization

Condensation

Liquid

Melting

Freezing

Solid

100°C

0°C

Temperature

Thermal energy

Solid state: ice

Liquid state: water

Gaseous state: steam

Resource Manager

Chapter Resources Booklet
  Enrichment, p. 29

Physical Science Critical Thinking/Problem Solving, p. 10

✓ Active Reading

Quickwrites This strategy will help students identify what they already know about thermal energy, temperature, and changes in state. Have students list ideas about these topics, and then share their ideas with the class. Students can write their ideas freely in a paragraph and share them with the class during or after a learning experience on the states of matter.

Freezing The process of melting a crystalline solid can be reversed if the liquid is cooled. As the liquid cools, it loses thermal energy. As a result, its particles slow down and come closer together. Attractive forces begin to trap particles, and the crystals of a solid begin to form. The change from the liquid state to the solid state is called **freezing**. As you can see in **Figure 11,** freezing and melting are opposite processes.

The temperature at which a substance changes from the liquid state to the solid state is called the freezing point. The freezing point of the liquid state of a substance is the same temperature as the melting point of the solid state. For example, solid ice melts at 0°C and liquid water freezes at 0°C.

During freezing, the temperature of a substance remains constant while the particles in the liquid form a crystalline solid. Because particles in a liquid have more energy than particles in a solid, energy is released during freezing. This energy is released into the surroundings. After all of the liquid has become a solid, the temperature begins to decrease again.

SCIENCE Online

Research Visit the Glencoe Science Web site at **science.glencoe.com** for more information about freezing. Make a list of several substances and the temperatures at which they freeze. Find out how the freezing point affects how the substance is used. Share your findings with the class.

Problem-Solving Activity

How can ice save oranges?

During the spring, Florida citrus farmers carefully watch the fruit when temperatures drop close to freezing. When the temperatures fall below 0°C, the liquid in the cells of oranges can freeze and expand. This causes the cells to break, making the oranges mushy and the crop useless for sale. To prevent this, farmers spray the oranges with water just before the temperature reaches 0°C. How does spraying oranges with water protect them?

Identifying the Problem

Using the diagram in **Figure 11,** consider what is happening to the water at 0°C. Two things occur. What are they?

Solving the Problem

1. What change of state and what energy changes occur when water freezes?
2. How does the formation of ice on the orange help the orange?

Teacher FYI

The field of low-temperature physics is called cryogenics. Scientists working in this area have been able to reach temperatures as low as 0.0001 K.

Discussion

Since temperature doesn't change as a substance is freezing, the kinetic energy of its particles doesn't change. But the substance is losing energy. **What kind of energy is the substance losing?** It is losing the potential energy of the attraction between the particles.
L3 IS **Logical-Mathematical**

Problem-Solving Activity

Teaching Strategies

Show students an orange that has been frozen below 0°C (−2.2°C) and one that has not been frozen. The layer of ice around the orange protects it from cold air temperatures. Point out that this is also what occurs when a lake freezes over. The ice on top protects the water beneath, so fish can survive.

Answers

1. The two changes that occur are the phase change from water to ice and the loss of energy (exothermic) when the phase change occurs.
2. The ice forms at 0°C, coating the orange and acting as insulation against the colder air temperature. Some of the energy that is released when the ice forms goes into the orange.

SCIENCE Online
Internet Addresses

Explore the Glencoe Science Web site at **science.glencoe.com** to find out more about topics in this section.

Inclusion Strategies

Learning Disabled Help students analyze the questions posed in the Problem-Solving Activity by breaking down the process that occurs as the water sprayed on the oranges freezes. Draw diagrams and use arrows to show the energy transfers involved and relate them to the illustration on the previous page. L2 IS **Logical-Mathematical**

Changes Between the Liquid and Gas States

Purpose Students observe that a liquid absorbs heat from its surroundings as it evaporates. [L1] [IS] **Kinesthetic**

Materials dropper, rubbing alcohol

Teaching Strategy Prevent waste by providing students with small amounts of alcohol.

Safety Precautions Students should wear goggles when performing this MiniLAB. Alcohol is flammable. There should be no open flames in the lab.

Analysis
1. The alcohol evaporated.
2. The hand felt cool where the alcohol was located. The alcohol removed heat from the skin as it evaporated, and then the hand warmed up again.

✔ Assessment

Content Explain how the body is cooled by perspiration. Heat from the body is absorbed as perspiration evaporates from the skin. Use **Performance Assessment in the Science Classroom**, p. 89. [L2]

Visual Learning ⎯○

 Figure 12 Discuss with students the difference between evaporation and boiling. **Could both occur at the same time?** Yes; while some particles are becoming gas inside the liquid, other gas particles can escape from the surface. [L2]
[IS] **Logical-Mathematical**

Mini LAB

Explaining What You Feel

Procedure
1. Use a **dropper** to place one drop of **rubbing alcohol** on the back of your hand.
2. Describe how your hand feels during the next 2 min.
3. Wash your hands.

Analysis
1. What changes in the appearance of the rubbing alcohol did you notice?
2. What sensation did you feel during the 2 min? How can you explain this sensation?

Figure 12
During boiling, liquid changes to gas, forming bubbles in the liquid that rise to the surface.

Changes Between the Liquid and Gas States

After an early morning rain, you and your friends enjoy stomping through the puddles left behind. But later that afternoon when you head out to run through the puddles once more, the puddles are gone. The liquid water in the puddles changed into a gas. Matter changes between the liquid and gas states through vaporization and condensation.

Vaporization As liquid water is heated, its temperature rises until it reaches 100°C. At this point, liquid water changes into water vapor. The change from a liquid to a gas is known as **vaporization** (vay puhr uh ZAh shun). You can see in **Figure 11** that the temperature of the substance does not change during vaporization. However, the substance absorbs thermal energy. The additional energy causes the particles to move faster until they have enough energy to escape the liquid as gas particles.

Two forms of vaporization exist. Vaporization that takes place below the surface of a liquid is called boiling. When a liquid boils, bubbles form within the liquid and rise to the surface, as shown in **Figure 12**. The temperature at which a liquid boils is called the boiling point. The boiling point of water is 100°C.

Vaporization that takes place at the surface of a liquid is called evaporation. Evaporation, which occurs at temperatures below the boiling point, explains how puddles dry up. Imagine that you could watch individual water molecules in a puddle. You would notice that the molecules move at different speeds. Although the temperature of the water is constant, remember that temperature is a measure of the average kinetic energy of the molecules. Some of the fastest-moving molecules overcome the attractive forces of other molecules and escape from the surface of the water.

Resource Manager

Chapter Resources Booklet
   MiniLAB, p. 3

Reading and Writing Skill Activities, p. 17

Teacher FYI

At a given temperature, the motions of the particles in a substance vary according to a well-defined distribution of particle speeds called the Maxwell-Boltzmann distribution. This distribution looks similar to a bell curve but is not as symmetrical. The limit on the fastest speeds is the speed of light, while zero is the lowest speed a particle can have.

Figure 13
The drops of water on these glasses and pitcher of lemonade were formed when water vapor in the air lost enough energy to return to the liquid state. This process is called condensation.

Location of Molecules It takes more than speed for water molecules to escape the liquid state. During evaporation, these faster molecules also must be near the surface, heading in the right direction, and they must avoid hitting other water molecules as they leave. With the faster particles evaporating from the surface of a liquid, the particles that remain are the slower, cooler ones. Evaporation cools the liquid and anything near the liquid. You experience this cooling effect when perspiration evaporates from your skin.

Condensation Pour a nice, cold glass of lemonade and place it on the table for a half hour on a warm day. When you come back to take a drink, the outside of the glass will be covered by drops of water, as shown in **Figure 13.** What happened? As a gas cools, its particles slow down. When particles move slowly enough for their attractions to bring them together, droplets of liquid form. This process, which is the opposite of vaporization, is called **condensation.** As a gas condenses to a liquid, it releases the thermal energy it absorbed to become a gas. During this process, the temperature of the substance does not change. The decrease in energy changes the arrangement of particles. After the change of state is complete, the temperature continues to drop, as you saw in **Figure 11.**

✔ **Reading Check** *What energy change occurs during condensation?*

Condensation formed the droplets of water on the outside of your glass of lemonade. In the same way, water vapor in the atmosphere condenses to form the liquid water droplets in clouds. When the droplets become large enough, they can fall to the ground as rain.

SCIENCE *Online*

Research Visit the Glencoe Science Web site at **science.glencoe.com** for more information about how condensation is involved in weather. Find out how condensation is affected by the temperature as well as the amount of water in the air.

SECTION 2 Changes of State **K ◆ 51**

Visual Learning

Figure 13 Have students describe the various places that heat transfer is occurring in **Figure 13.** L2 IS **Visual-Spatial**

SCIENCE *Online*
Internet Addresses

_____

_____

_____

Explore the Glencoe Science Web site at **science.glencoe.com** to find out more about topics in this section.

✔ **Reading Check**

Answer During condensation, a gas releases energy as its particles become more ordered.

Curriculum Connection

Geography Have students research how changes of state contribute to the formation of deserts near the Tropic of Cancer. Ask students to make posters with diagrams illustrating their findings. Warm moist air from the equator rises and flows northward and southward. As this moist air cools it loses its moisture. This dry air then decends over the Tropics of Capricorn and Cancer pulling moisture out of the ground by evaporation and drying out the land. This pattern has produced a belt of deserts along the Tropics of Capricorn and Cancer. L2 IS **Linguistic**

3 Assess

Reteach

Have students explain the difference between evaporation and boiling. Boiling occurs when particles below the surface of a liquid change from liquid to gas. Evaporation occurs when particles at the surface of a liquid change from liquid to gas. L1

IS Logical-Mathematical

Challenge

If you have an automatic ice-cube maker in your freezer, you may have noticed that the older ice cubes at the bottom of the tray are much smaller than the newer cubes at the top. Use what you have learned to explain why. The faster molecules on the surface of an ice cube can escape from the cube and become a gas. Over time, the ice cube will completely sublimate away. L2 **IS Logical-Mathematical**

✓Assessment

Performance Have students hypothesize what would happen if the unknown substance from the Explore Activity were reheated. The substance would melt at the same temperature at which it froze. The temperature would remain constant while the substance was melting, then increase gradually. Use **PASC,** p. 93.

Figure 14
The solid dry ice at the bottom of this beaker of water is changing directly into gaseous carbon dioxide. This process is called sublimation.

Changes Between the Solid and Gas States

Some substances can change from the solid state to the gas state without ever becoming a liquid. During this process, known as sublimation, the surface particles of the solid gain enough energy to become a gas. One example of a substance that undergoes sublimation is dry ice. Dry ice is the solid form of carbon dioxide. It often is used to keep materials cold and dry. At room temperature and pressure, carbon dioxide does not exist as a liquid. Therefore, as dry ice absorbs thermal energy from the objects around it, it changes directly into a gas. When dry ice becomes a gas, it absorbs thermal energy from water vapor in the air. As a result, the water vapor cools and condenses into liquid water droplets, forming the fog you see in **Figure 14.**

Section Assessment

1. How are thermal energy and temperature similar? How are they different?
2. How does a change in thermal energy cause matter to change from one state to another? Give an example.
3. During which three changes of state is energy absorbed?
4. What are two types of vaporization?
5. **Think Critically** How can the temperature of a substance remain the same even if the substance is absorbing thermal energy?

Skill Builder Activities

6. **Making and Using Graphs** Using the data you collected in the Explore Activity, plot a temperature-time graph. Describe your graph. At what temperature does the graph level off? What was the liquid doing during this time period? **For more help, refer to the** Science Skill Handbook.
7. **Communicating** In your Science Journal, explain why you can step out of the shower into a warm bathroom and begin to shiver. **For more help, refer to the** Science Skill Handbook.

Answers to Section Assessment

1. Thermal energy is the total amount of energy contained in a body whereas temperature measures the average kinetic energy of the particles in the body. Both deal with the amount of energy something has.
2. As thermal energy changes, the kinetic energy of the particles

changes. If their kinetic energy increases, particles can overcome the attractive forces holding them together. If their kinetic energy decreases, particles can become subject to the forces pulling them together. Examples will vary.

3. melting, vaporization, and sublimation
4. boiling and evaporation
5. The temperature remains the same because the absorbed energy is being used to break attractive forces between the particles of a substance as it changes state.

6. Check students' work. Sample data can be found on page 39.
7. The water on your skin absorbs heat from your body and evaporates, cooling the skin and causing you to shiver.

Activity

A Spin Around the Water Cycle

Some of the water in the puddle you stepped in this morning could have rolled down a dinosaur's back millions of years ago because water moves through the environment in a never-ending cycle. Changes in water's physical state enable living things to use this resource.

What You'll Investigate
How does the temperature of water change as it is heated from a solid to a gas?

Materials
hot plate	wall clock
ice cubes (100 mL)	*watch with second hand
Celsius thermometer	stirring rod
*electronic	250-mL beaker
temperature probe	*Alternate materials

Goals
- **Measure** the temperature of water as it heats.
- **Observe** what happens as the water changes from one state to another.
- **Graph** the temperature and time data.

Safety Precautions

Procedure
1. Copy the data table shown.
2. Put 150 mL of water and 100 mL of ice into the beaker and place the beaker on the hot plate. Do not touch the hot plate.
3. Put the thermometer into the ice/water mixture. Do not stir with the thermometer or allow it to rest on the bottom of the beaker. After 30 s, read the temperature and record them in your data table.

Characteristics of Water Sample

Time (min)	Temperature (°C)	Physical State
0.0		
0.5		
1.0	Answers will vary.	
1.5		
2.0		

4. Plug in the hot plate and turn the temperature knob to the medium setting.
5. Every 30 s, read and record the temperature and physical state of the water until it begins to boil. Use the stirring rod to stir the contents of the beaker before making each temperature measurement. Stop recording. Allow the water to cool.
6. Use your data to make a graph plotting time on the x-axis and temperature on the y-axis. Draw a smooth curve through the data points.

Conclude and Apply
1. How did the temperature of the ice/water mixture change as you heated the beaker?
2. How did the state of water change as you heated the beaker?
3. **Describe** the shape of the graph during any changes of state.

Communicating Your Data
Add captions to your graph. Use the detailed graph to explain to your class how water changes state. **For more help, refer to the Science Skill Handbook.**

ACTIVITY **K ◆ 53**

Resource Manager

Chapter Resources Booklet
Reinforcement, p. 26
Activity Worksheet, pp. 5–6

Communicating Your Data
Encourage students to compare graphs with other students and discuss possible reasons for inconsistent data.

Purpose Students observe the solid and liquid states of water.
L1 LS **Kinesthetic**

Process Skills measuring, observing, making and using tables, using numbers, making and using graphs, inferring

Time 30 minutes

Alternate Materials electronic temperature probe

Safety Precautions Caution students not to use the thermometer as a stirrer or allow it to rest on the bottom of the beaker during heating.

Teaching Strategy Crushed ice or small pieces will give quicker results.

Answers to Questions
1. The temperature increased, stayed the same for a period of time, then increased again.
2. The ice changed from the solid state to the liquid state.
3. During changes of state, the graph leveled off.

Assessment

Performance How would the graphs change if twice as much ice were used? The temperature would rise more slowly and the plateau would be longer. Use **Performance Assessment in the Science Classroom**, p. 101. L2
LS **Logical-Mathematical**

SECTION

3

Behavior of Fluids

1 Motivate

Bellringer Transparency

Display the Section Focus Transparency for Section 3. Use the accompanying Transparency Activity Master. L2

ELL

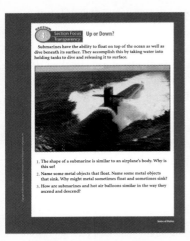

Tie to Prior Knowledge

Ask students whether they have ever pumped up bicycle tires. Have a volunteer describe what happens during the process. More and more air molecules are pushed into the tire, increasing the pressure inside. Explain that in this section students will explore how the motion of particles of matter is related to different kinds of pressure occurring in fluids.

Behavior of Fluids

As You Read

What You'll Learn
- **Explain** why some things float but others sink.
- **Describe** how pressure is transmitted through fluids.

Vocabulary
pressure
buoyant force
Archimedes' principle
density
Pascal's principle

Why It's Important
Pressure enables you to squeeze toothpaste from a tube, and buoyant force helps you float in water.

Pressure

It's a beautiful summer day when you and your friends go outside to play volleyball, much like the kids in **Figure 15.** There's only one problem—the ball is flat. You pump air into the ball until it is firm. The firmness of the ball is the result of the motion of the air particles in the ball. As the air particles in the ball move, they collide with one another and with the inside walls of the ball. As each particle collides with the inside walls, it exerts a force, pushing the surface of the ball outward. A force is a push or a pull. The forces of all the individual particles add together to make up the pressure of the air.

Pressure is equal to the force exerted on a surface divided by the total area over which the force is exerted.

$$(P) \text{ pressure} = (F) \text{ force}/(A) \text{ area}$$

When force is measured in newtons (N) and area is measured in square meters (m^2), pressure is measured in newtons per square meter (N/m^2). This unit of pressure is called a pascal (Pa). A more useful unit when discussing atmospheric pressure is the kilopascal (kPa), which is 1,000 pascals.

Figure 15
Without the pressure of air inside this volleyball, the ball would be flat.

Section ✓ Assessment Planner

PORTFOLIO
Science Journal, p. 55
PERFORMANCE ASSESSMENT
Try at Home MiniLAB, p. 57
Skill Builder Activities, p. 61
See page 68 for more options.

CONTENT ASSESSMENT
Section, p. 61
Challenge, p. 61
Chapter, pp. 68–69

Figure 16
The force of the dancer's weight on pointed toes results in a higher pressure than the same force on flat feet. *Why is the pressure different?*

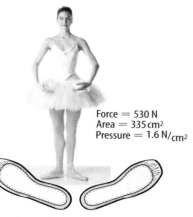

Force = 530 N
Area = 335 cm²
Pressure = 1.6 N/cm²

Force = 530 N
Area = 37 cm²
Pressure = 14 N/cm²

Force and Area You can see from the equation on the opposite page that pressure depends on the quantity of force exerted and the area over which the force is exerted. As the force increases over a given area, pressure increases. If the force decreases, the pressure will decrease. However, if the area changes, the same amount of force can result in different pressure. **Figure 16** shows that if the force of the ballerina's weight is exerted over a smaller area, the pressure increases. If that same force is exerted over a larger area, the pressure will decrease.

 **Reading Check** *What variables does pressure depend on?*

Atmospheric Pressure You can't see it and you usually can't feel it, but the air around you presses on you with tremendous force. The pressure of air also is known as atmospheric pressure because air makes up the atmosphere around Earth. Atmospheric pressure is 101.3 kPa at sea level. This means that air exerts a force of about 101,000 N on every square meter it touches. This is approximately equal to the weight of a large truck.

It might be difficult to think of air as having pressure when you don't notice it. However, you often take advantage of air pressure without even realizing it. Air pressure, for example, enables you to drink from a straw. When you first suck on a straw, you remove the air from it. As you can see in **Figure 17,** air pressure pushing down on the liquid in your glass then forces liquid up into the straw. If you tried to drink through a straw inserted into a sealed, airtight container, you would not have any success because the air would not be able to push down on the surface of the drink.

Figure 17
The downward pressure of air pushes the juice up into the straw.

Air pressure

SECTION 3 Behavior of Fluids **K ◆ 55**

Resource Manager

Chapter Resources Booklet
Transparency Activity, p. 44
Directed Reading for Content Mastery, pp. 19, 20

Science Journal

Pressure Applied Have each student make a drawing of a sports ball in his or her Science Journal and show the molecular forces that are keeping the ball inflated. Ask students to include captions that explain why the ball stays inflated. After completing the section, have students compare their drawings and explanations with **Figure 15.** L2 [S] **Visual-Spatial** P

---

② Teach

Pressure

Caption Answer

Figure 16 The area is smaller.

Extension

Some bicycle tires are inflated to a pressure of 90 lb/in². Have students convert this pressure to kilopascals. There are 9.8 N in 1 kg, and 2.2 lb in 1 kg. Therefore, there are 9.8 ÷ 2.2 = 4.45 N in 1 lb. In 90 lb there are 4.45 × 90 = 400.5 N. There are 0.0254 m in 1 in. so there are 0.000645 m² in 1 in². Therefore 90 lb/in² = 400.5 N ÷ 0.000645 m² = 620,930 Pa = 621 kPa. L2 [S] **Logical-Mathematical**

✓ Reading Check

Answer force and area

Visual Learning

Figure 17 Have students explain how a drinking straw works. Sucking on the straw creates a difference between the air pressure on the liquid in the cup and the air pressure on the liquid in the straw. The higher pressure outside the straw pushes the liquid up the straw. L2 [S] **Visual-Spatial**

Discussion

How does using snow skis or snowshoes enable a person to ski or walk on soft snow? The skis or snowshoes distribute the force of the person's weight over a larger area, decreasing the pressure exerted on the surface of the snow. L2 [S] **Logical-Mathematical**

Pressure, continued

Use Science Words

Word Meaning The word *atmosphere* is formed from the word parts *atmos*, which is Greek for "vapor," and *sphaera*, the Latin word for "sphere." Ask students to explain how these word parts are related to the meaning of *atmosphere*. The atmosphere is the gases (or vapors) that surround Earth (a spherical body). L2 IS **Linguistic**

Extension

Changes in atmospheric pressure cause problems for people who climb high mountains such as Mount Everest. Have students find out what mountain climbers do to adjust to the situation. Mountain climbers rest a few days at camps at successively higher altitudes to allow their bodies time to adjust. L3 IS **Linguistic**

Discussion

Suppose that instead of a balloon you had a sealed box of air. **What would happen to the particles of air as you carried the box up the mountain? Explain.** Nothing would happen as long as the box was sealed, because the rigid walls of the box would keep the particles in the box isolated from the changes in air pressure outside the box. L3 IS **Logical-Mathematical**

Caption Answer

Figure 18 The pressure of fluids in her body balances atmospheric pressure.

Figure 18
Atmospheric pressure exerts a force on all surfaces of this dancer's body. *Why can't she feel this pressure?*

Balanced Pressure If air is so forceful, why don't you feel it? The reason is that the pressure exerted outward by the fluids in your body balances the pressure exerted by the atmosphere on the surface of your body. Look at **Figure 18.** The atmosphere exerts a pressure on all surfaces of the dancer's body. She is not crushed by this pressure because the fluids in her body exert a pressure that balances atmospheric pressure.

Variations in Atmospheric Pressure
Atmospheric pressure changes with altitutde. Altitude is the height above sea level. As altitude increases atmospheric pressure decreases. This is because fewer air particles are found in a given volume. Fewer particles have fewer collisions and, therefore, exert less pressure. This idea was tested in the seventeenth century by a French physician named Blaise Pascal. He designed an experiment in which he filled a balloon only partially with air. He then had the balloon carried to the top of a mountain. **Figure 19** shows that as Pascal predicted, the balloon expanded while being carried up the mountain. Although the amount of air inside the balloon stayed the same, the air pressure pushing in on it from the outside decreased. Consequently, the particles of air inside the balloon were able to spread out further.

Figure 19
Notice how the balloon expands as it is carried up the mountain. The reason is because atmospheric pressure decreases with altitude. With less pressure pushing in on the balloon, the gas particles within the balloon are free to expand.

Visual Learning

Figure 19 Discuss with students how the balloon would change if the amount of air pressure exerted on it were increased. The gas inside the balloon would be compressed as it was squeezed by increased air pressure acting on the balloon. This would make the balloon get smaller. L2 IS **Logical-Mathematical**

Teacher FYI

Blaise Pascal lived from 1623 to 1662. As part of his work with fluids, he formulated Pascal's principle, which will be studied later in this chapter. The unit of pressure, the pascal, was named for him.

Air Travel If you travel to higher altitudes, perhaps flying in an airplane or driving up a mountain, you might feel a popping sensation in your ears. As the air pressure drops, the air pressure in your ears becomes greater than the air pressure outside your body. The release of some of the air trapped inside your ears is heard as a pop. Airplanes are pressurized so that the air pressure within the cabin does not change dramatically throughout the course of a flight.

Changes in Gas Pressure

In the same way that atmospheric pressure can vary as conditions change, the pressure of gases in confined containers also can change. The pressure of a gas in a closed container changes with volume and temperature.

Pressure and Volume If you squeeze a portion of a filled balloon, as shown in **Figure 20A,** the remaining portion of the balloon becomes more firm. By squeezing it, you decrease the volume of the balloon, forcing the same number of gas particles into a smaller space. As a result, the particles collide with the walls more often, thereby producing greater pressure. This is true as long as the temperature of the gas remains the same. You can see the change in the motion of the particles in **Figure 20B.** What will happen if the volume of a gas increases? If you make a container larger without changing its temperature, the gas particles will collide less often and thereby produce a lower pressure.

TRY AT HOME
Mini LAB

Predicting a Waterfall

Procedure
1. Fill a **plastic cup** to the brim with **water.**
2. Cover the top of the cup with an **index card.**
3. Predict what will happen if you turn the cup upside down.
4. While holding the index card in place, turn the cup upside down over a sink. Then let go of the card.

Analysis
1. What happened to the water when you turned the cup?
2. How can you explain your observation in terms of the concept of fluid pressure?

Figure 20
Pressure changes in a way that is opposite to a change in volume. As volume decreases, pressure increases.

A When this girl squeezes on the balloon, the air is forced into a smaller space. As a result, the pressure increases and the balloon becomes more firm.

B As the piston is moved down, the gas particles have less room and collide more often. This means that the pressure increases.

SECTION 3 Behavior of Fluids **K** ◆ **57**

Changes in Gas Pressure

TRY AT HOME
Mini LAB

Purpose to observe how air pressure produces enough force to hold water in a cup.

L2 ELL COOP LEARN
K **Kinesthetic**

Materials plastic cup, water index card

Teaching Strategy Tell students to try not to let any water out of the cup as they turn it over.

Troubleshooting The card must be able to make a tight seal with the cup in order for this experiment to work. Any cup used should have a continuously smooth rim.

Analysis
1. The water remained in the cup.
2. The pressure of the molecules in the air pushing up on the card was greater than the pressure of the water pushing down on the card.

✓ *Assessment*

Process Ask students to form a hypothesis concerning what will happen if some air is included in the cup. Have them try the experiment As long as the cup contains enough water to make a seal between the rim and the card, the card will remain in place. Use **Performanc Assessment in the Science Classroom,** p. 93.

Resource Manager

Chapter Resources Booklet
MiniLAB, p. 4

Physical Science Critical Thinking/Problem Solving, p. 3

Teacher **FYI**

Relationships among temperature, pressure, and volume in a gas sample were defined by Jacques Charles and Robert Boyle. Charles's law relates temperature and volume. Boyle's law relates pressure and volume.

Changes in Gas Pressure, continued

Activity

Provide students with balloons. Have them blow up the balloons and tie them shut. Ask each student to measure the circumference of his or her balloon at its widest point, then hold it over a lit lightbulb for a few minutes and measure the circumference again. **What happened to the balloon as it was warmed by the lightbulb?** The gas particles inside it started moving faster, pushing out on the balloon and causing it to expand. Extend the activity by placing one or two balloons in the freezer for a short while. L2 **Kinesthetic**

Caption Answer

Figure 21 The container will explode.

✔ Reading Check

Answer As temperatures decreases, pressure decreases. This makes the pressure inside the container lower that the pressure outside the container. The external pressure pushes the container inward.

Float or Sink

Discussion

What do you think will happen if the buoyant force in a fluid is equal to the weight of an object in it? The object will remain suspended in the fluid, neither rising nor falling. L3 **Logical-Mathematical**

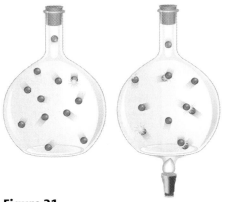

Figure 21
Even though the volume of this container does not change, the pressure increases as the substance is heated. *What will happen if the substance is heated too much?*

Figure 22
A The pressure pushing up on an immersed object is greater than the pressure pushing down on it. This difference results in the buoyant force. **B** Weight is a force in the downward direction. The buoyant force is in the upward direction. An object will float if the upward force is equal to the downward force.

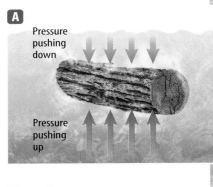

A

Pressure pushing down

Pressure pushing up

Pressure and Temperature When the volume of a confined gas remains the same, the pressure can change as the temperature of the gas changes. You have learned that temperature rises as the kinetic energy of the particles in a substance increases. The greater the kinetic energy is, the faster the particles move. The faster the speed of the particles is, the more they collide and the greater the pressure is. If the temperature of a confined gas increases, the pressure of the gas will increase, as shown in **Figure 21.**

✔ **Reading Check** *Why would a sealed container of air be crushed after being frozen?*

Float or Sink

You may have noticed that you feel lighter in water than you do when you climb out of it. While you are under water, you experience water pressure pushing on you in all directions. Just as air pressure increases as you walk down a mountain, water pressure increases as you swim deeper in water. Water pressure increases with depth. As a result, the pressure pushing up on the bottom of an object is greater than the pressure pushing down on it because the bottom of the object is deeper than the top.

The difference in pressure results in an upward force on an object immersed in a fluid, as shown in **Figure 22A.** This force is known as the **buoyant force.** But if the buoyant force is equal to the weight of an object, the object will float. If the buoyant force is less than the weight of an object, the object will sink.

B

Weight   Buoyant force

Inclusion Strategies

Gifted Have students construct a neutrally buoyant helium balloon and gondola—one that has the same density as air. When you test the balloon, make sure there are no drafts in the room. Students will have succeeded if the balloon and gondola remain stationary between the ceiling and floor of a room for several minutes or if they ascend or descend slowly. L3 **Kinesthetic**

Archimedes' Principle What determines the buoyant force? According to **Archimedes'** (ar kuh MEE deez) **principle,** the buoyant force on an object is equal to the weight of the fluid displaced by the object. In other words, if you place an object in a beaker that already is filled to the brim with water, some water will spill out of the beaker, as in **Figure 23.** If you weigh the spilled water, you will find the buoyant force on the object.

Density Understanding density can help you predict whether an object will float or sink. **Density** is mass divided by volume.

$$density = \frac{mass}{volume}$$

An object will float in a fluid that is more dense than itself and sink in a fluid that is less dense than itself. If an object has the same density as the fluid, the object will neither sink nor float but instead stay at the same level in the fluid. An iceberg floats on water because the density of ice is less than the density of water. A helium balloon rises in air because the density of helium is less than the density of air.

Figure 23
When the golfball was dropped in the large beaker, it displaced some of the water, which was collected and placed into the smaller beaker. *What do you know about the weight and the volume of the displaced water?*

Math Skills Activity

Calculating Density

Example Problem

You are given a sample of a solid that has a mass of 10.0 g and a volume of 4.60 cm³. Will it float in liquid water, which has a density of 1.00 g/cm³?

Solution

1 *This is what you know:*
    mass = 10.0 g
    volume = 4.60 cm³
    density of water = 1.00 g/cm³

    A sample will float in a substance that is more dense than itself.

2 *This is what you need to find:*   the density of the sample

3 *This is the equation you need to use:*   density = mass/volume

4 *Substitute the known values:*   density = 10.0 g/4.60 cm³ = 2.17 g/cm³

    The density of the sample is greater than the density of water. The sample will sink.

> **Practice Problem**
>
> A 7.40-cm³ sample of mercury has a mass of 102 g. Will it float in water?

For more help, refer to the Math Skill Handbook.

Resource Manager

Chapter Resources Booklet
  Enrichment, p. 30
Mathematics Skill Activities, p. 31
Performance Assessment in the Science Classroom, p. 39

Curriculum Connection

History Archimedes was one of history's most gifted mathematicians. He very nearly invented calculus, but did not have the notation to describe his ideas. According to legend, he came to an unfortunate end when he yelled at an invading Roman soldier for ruining calculations he was writing in the dirt. The unappreciative soldier killed him with his sword. Have students find out when Archimedes lived. 287–212 B.C. [L2]

Caption Answer

Figure 23 The volume of the displaced water equals the volume of the golf ball. The weight of the displaced water is less than the weight of the golf ball.

Activity

Obtain unopened aluminum cans of regular and diet versions of a soft drink. Show the class that the volumes of the cans are equal. Have students predict what will happen when the cans are placed in a sink or aquarium filled with water. Place the cans into the water and observe. The can of diet drink floats, while the can of regular drink sinks. Divide the class in half and have each group measure the masses of the cans with a balance. Ask how the masses compare. The regular drink is heavier. Discuss with students the idea that equal volumes of different substances can have different masses. Explain that the difference in mass is due to sugar. [L2] ELL **Kinesthetic**

Math Skills Activity

National Math Standards
Correlation to Mathematics Objectives
6, 8, 9

Teaching Strategy

This is what you know: mass = 102 g; volume = 7.40 cm³, density of water = 1.00 g/cm³

This is what you need to find: density of the sample.

This is the equation you need to use: density = mass/volume

Substitute in the known values: density = 102 g/7.40 cm³ = 1.36 cm³

Answer

No; the density of mercury is greater than the density of water.

Teacher FYI

Pascal's principle led to the development of hydraulics, in which a small force is multiplied to create a much larger force that can be used to lift heavy objects, such as an automobile in a repair shop. Pressure is the same throughout the hydraulic fluid. Because you cannot derive more work from a system than you put into the system, the small force must be applied over a greater distance.

Visual Learning

Figure 25 Review with students the process shown in this figure. Remind students that work equals force times distance. In a hydraulic lift, the force applied to the smaller piston is small, but it is applied over a long distance, so the work done on each side of the lift is the same. [L2]
[JS] **Visual-Spatial**

Discussion

Challenge students to use Pascal's principle to explain why their ears may hurt when they swim to the bottom of the deepest part of a swimming pool. The weight of the water above makes the pressure at the bottom of the pool greater than that at the surface. [L2]

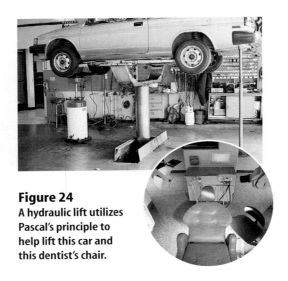

Figure 24
A hydraulic lift utilizes Pascal's principle to help lift this car and this dentist's chair.

Pascal's Principle

What happens if you squeeze a plastic container filled with water? If the container is closed, the water has nowhere to go. As a result, the pressure in the water increases by the same amount everywhere in the container—not just where you squeeze or near the top of the container. When a force is applied to a confined fluid, an increase in pressure is transmitted equally to all parts of the fluid. This relationship is known as **Pascal's principle.**

Hydraulic Systems You witness Pascal's principle when a car is lifted up to have its oil changed or if you are in a dentist's chair as it is raised or lowered, as shown in **Figure 24.** These devices, known as hydraulic (hi DRAW lihk) systems, use Pascal's principle to increase force. Look at the tube in **Figure 25.** The force applied to the piston on the left increases the pressure within the fluid. That increase in pressure is transmitted to the piston on the right. Recall that pressure is equal to force divided by area. You can solve for force by multiplying pressure by area.

$$\text{pressure} = \frac{\text{force}}{\text{area}} \quad \text{or} \quad \text{force} = \text{pressure} \times \text{area}$$

If the two pistons on the tube have the same area, the force will be the same on both pistons. If, however, the piston on the right has a greater surface area than the piston on the left, the resulting force will be greater. The same pressure multiplied by a larger area equals a greater force. Hydraulic systems enable people to lift heavy objects using relatively small forces.

Figure 25
By increasing the area of the piston on the right side of the tube, you can increase the force exerted on the piston. In this way a small force pushing down on the left piston can result in a large force pushing up on the right piston. The force can be great enough to lift a car.

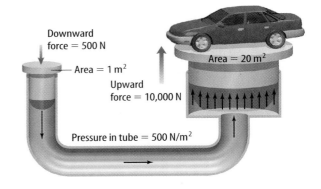

Downward force = 500 N
Area = 1 m²
Area = 20 m²
Upward force = 10,000 N
Pressure in tube = 500 N/m²

Resource Manager

Chapter Resources Booklet
Reinforcement, p. 27
Activity Worksheet, pp. 7–8
Lab Management and Safety, p. 71

Cultural Diversity

Force Pumps Simple piston-type force pumps were known throughout the ancient world. The more efficient double-acting piston bellows was developed by the Chinese, and did not reach Europe until the 1500s. In this device, fluid is pulled in through intake valves on either side and pushed out through a nozzle on both strokes of the piston.

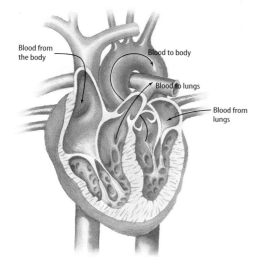

Blood from the body
Blood to body
Blood to lungs
Blood from lungs

Figure 26
The heart is responsible for moving blood throughout the body. Two force pumps work together to move blood to and from the lungs and to the rest of the body.

Force Pumps If an otherwise closed container has a hole in it, any fluid in the container will be pushed out the opening when you squeeze it. This arrangement, known as a force pump, makes it possible for you to squeeze toothpaste out of a tube or mustard from a plastic container.

Life Science
INTEGRATION

Your heart has two force pumps. One pump pushes blood to the lungs, where it picks up oxygen. The other force pump pushes the oxygen-rich blood to the rest of your body. These pumps are shown in **Figure 26.**

SCIENCE
Online

Research Visit the Glencoe Science Web site at **science.glencoe.com** for more information about blood pressure. Find out what the term means, how it changes throughout the human body, and why it is unhealthy to have high blood pressure. Communicate to your class what you learn.

Section ③ Assessment

1. What happens to pressure as the force exerted on a given area increases?

2. How does atmospheric pressure change as altitude increases?

3. State Pascal's principle in your own words.

4. An object floats in a fluid. What do you know about the buoyant force on the object? How does the density of the object compare with the density of the fluid?

5. **Think Critically** All of the air is removed from a sealed metal can. After the air has been removed, the can looks as if it were crushed. Why?

Skill Builder Activities

6. **Recognizing Cause and Effect** On a hot summer day, you buy a bunch of balloons in a store. But when you take the balloons out of the air-conditioned store, some of them pop. How can you explain this? **For more help, refer to the Science Skill Handbook.**

7. **Solving One-Step Equations** What pressure is created when 5.0 N of force are applied to an area of 2.0 m²? How does the pressure change if the force is increased to 10.0 N? What about if instead the area is decreased to 1.0 m²? **For more help, refer to the Math Skill Handbook.**

SCIENCE
Online
Internet Addresses

Explore the Glencoe Science Web site at **science.glencoe.com** to find out more about topics in this section.

③ Assess

Reteach

Organize the class into five groups. Assign each group pressure, density, Archimedes' principle, Bernoulli's principle, or Pascal's principle. Have each group present to the class its understanding of the assigned term. Each group should be able to define the term and give examples illustrating it. L2
COOP LEARN **IS Interpersonal**

Challenge

Have students predict what would happen if a rock punched a small hole in the bottom of an airtight compartment in a ship. As long as no air escaped, the pressure of the air in the compartment would allow little water into the compartment. L3
IS Logical-Mathematical

✔Assessment

Process Place a beaker of water, a beaker of alcohol, and a beaker of ethylene glycol in front of the class. Challenge students to use buoyancy to put the liquids in order from lowest density to highest density. Students may immerse objects in the liquids to determine the relative densities of the liquids. Use **PASC,** p. 97.

Answers to Section Assessment

1. Pressure increases.
2. Atmospheric pressure decreases.
3. When a force is applied to a confined fluid, an increase in pressure is transmitted equally to all parts of the fluid.
4. The buoyant force is greater than the weight of the object. The density

of the object is less than the density of the fluid.
5. After the air is removed, the atmospheric pressure on the outside of the can is greater than the pressure on the inside of the can, so the can collapses.
6. As the temperature increased, the movement of the gas particles in

the balloons increased, which increased the pressure inside the balloons and caused them to pop.
7. 2.5 Pa; the pressure increases to 5 Pa. If the force is 5.0 N and the area is decreased to 1.0 m² the pressure increases to 5 Pa.

Activity
BENCH TESTED

Recognize the Problem

Purpose
Students apply Archimedes' principle to shipbuilding. L2
ELL COOP LEARN
IS **Logical-Mathematical**

Process Skills
observing and inferring, designing an experiment to test a hypothesis, interpreting data, separating and controlling variables, predicting, using numbers

Time Required
90 minutes

Materials
balance, 2 small plastic cups, graduated cylinder into which the cups will fit, metric ruler, scissors, marbles, sink

Alternate Materials
basin, pan, or bucket

Form a Hypothesis

Possible Hypothesis
Students might hypothesize that a boat floats when the displaced water weighs the same as or more than the boat and its cargo.

Test Your Hypothesis

Possible Procedure
Find the mass of the cup and the marbles. Use the density of water (1.00 g/mL) to calculate the volume of water that has the same mass as the cup and marbles, which is the volume of water the boat must displace. Fill the cup with the amount of

---

Activity Design Your Own Experiment

Design Your Own Ship

I t is amazing to watch ships that are taller than buildings float easily on water. Passengers and cargo are carried on these ships in addition to the tremendous weight of the ship itself. How can you figure out how much cargo a ship can carry before it sinks? Can you design a ship to hold a specific amount of cargo?

Cargo Ship

Recognize the Problem

How can you determine the size of a ship needed to keep a certain mass of cargo afloat?

Form a Hypothesis

Think about Archimedes' principle and how it relates to buoyant force. Form a hypothesis about how the volume of water displaced by a ship relates to the mass of cargo the ship can carry.

Possible Materials
balance
small plastic cups (2)
graduated cylinder
metric ruler
scissors
marbles (cupful)
sink
*basin, pan, or bucket
*Alternate materials

Safety Precautions

Goals
■ **Design** an experiment that uses Archimedes' principle to determine the size of ship needed to carry a given amount of cargo in such a way that the top of the ship is even with the surface of the water.

---

water that has the same mass as the cup and marbles or submerge the cup so that it displaces this volume. Draw a line around the cup at the water line, trim the cup to size, and dry the cup. Put the cup into the water in the sink or basin and carefully load the marbles and the trimmed pieces of cup into the floating cup.

Test Your Hypothesis

Plan

1. Obtain a set of marbles or other items from your teacher. This is the cargo that your ship must carry. Think about the type of ship you will design. Consider the types of materials you will use. Decide how your group is going to test your hypothesis.

2. **List** the steps you need to follow to test your hypothesis. Include in your plan how you will measure the mass of your ship and cargo, calculate the volume of water your ship must displace in order to float with its cargo, and measure the volume and mass of the displaced water. Also explain how you will design your ship so that it will float with the top of the ship even with the surface of the water.

3. **Prepare** a data table in your Science Journal so that it is ready to use as your group collects data.

Do

1. Make sure your teacher approves your plan before you start.

2. Carry out your experiment as planned. Be sure to follow all proper safety procedures. In particular, clean up any spilled water immediately.

3. While doing the experiment, record your observations carefully and complete the data table in your Science Journal.

Analyze Your Data

1. **Write** your calculations showing how you determined the volume of displaced water needed to make your ship and cargo float.

2. Did your ship float at the water's surface, sink, or float above the water's surface? Draw a diagram of your ship in the water.

Draw Conclusions

1. If your ship sank, how would you change your experiment or calculations to correct the problem? What changes would you make if your ship floated too high in the water?

2. What does the density of a ship's cargo have to do with the volume of cargo the ship can carry? What about the density of the water?

*C*ommunicating

Your Data

Compare your results with other students' data. Prepare a combined data table or summary showing how the calculations affect the success of the ship. **For more help, refer to the** Science Skill Handbook.

Teaching Strategies

- Before conducting the experiment, review density and its relationship to buoyancy.
- Students should not put the marbles into the boats until they are ready to test their boats.

Expected Outcome

Students' data tables should include spaces for the mass of the cup and marbles, the volume of water the cup must displace, measurements of the cup, any calculations of the cup's volume, and the results of the experiment.

Analyze Your Data

1. Typical calculations will involve relating the mass of the cargo and boat to the volume of the water displaced.
2. Results will vary.

Error Analysis

Students should explain why the boat sank or floated too high in the water and identify the problems.

Draw Conclusions

1. Answers will vary. Either way, students should check their measurements and calculations.
2. A ship can carry only a certain mass of cargo safely. Therefore, the ship can carry less high-density cargo than low-density cargo.

✓*Assessment*

Oral Have students explain why a ship designer always designs ships to be taller than needed to just float the anticipated cargo. If the ship has no excess height, waves could wash over the ship's side easily or excess cargo could be loaded onto the ship, sinking the ship. Use **Performance Assessment in the Science Classroom,** p. 89. L2

*C*ommunicating

Your Data

Suggest students use a spreadsheet program for preparing combined data tables.

Content Background

Silicon is the second most abundant element in Earth's crust. Rubber is a natural carbon-based polymer that comes from trees. Polymers are large molecules made from many small molecules linked together. During World War II, scientists were trying to replace carbon in organic molecules such as rubber with silicon. Silicones are polymers made up of silicon atoms linked to oxygen atoms. Various organic compounds are often attached to the polymer to control and change its physical properties. Some silicones form rubbery elastic compounds, while others are designed to act as lubricants.

Discussion

Why wasn't the goo a good substitute for synthetic rubber? Possible answer: If strong pressure is applied, the goo breaks apart and rubber doesn't. For that reason, it wouldn't work well on vehicle tires.

Why do you think the toy maker decided to package the goo in plastic eggs? Possible answers: It could easily be shipped to toy stores in egg cartons, which are inexpensive and were readily available.

The Incredible

A boric acid and silicone oil mix is sometimes packaged in a plastic egg.

During World War II, when natural resources were scarce and needed for the war effort, the U.S. government asked an engineer to come up with an inexpensive alternative to synthetic rubber. While researching the problem and looking for solutions, the engineer dropped boric acid into silicone oil. The result of these two substances mixing together was—a goo!

Because of its molecular structure, the goo could bounce and stretch in all directions. The engineer also discovered the goo could break into pieces. When strong pressure is applied to the substance, it reacts like a solid and breaks apart. Even though the combination was versatile—and quite amusing, the U.S. government decided the new substance wasn't a good substitute for synthetic rubber.

64 ◆ K

Resources for Teachers and Students

They All Laughed...From Light Bulbs to Lasers: The Fascinating Stories Behind Great Inventions That Have Changed Our Lives, by Ira Flatow, Harper Perennial, 1992.

Super Science Concoctions, by Jill Frankel Hauser, Williamson Publishing, 1997.

A serious search turns up a toy

Stretching Goo

A few years later, the recipe for the stretch material fell into the hands of a businessperson, who saw the goo's potential—as a toy. The toymaker paid $147 for rights to the boric acid and silicone oil mixture. And in 1949 it was sold at toy stores for the first time. The material was packaged in a plastic egg and it took the U.S. by storm. Today, the acid and oil mixture comes in a multitude of colors and almost every child has played with it at some time.

The substance can be used for more than child's play. Its sticky consistency makes it good for cleaning computer keyboards and removing small specks of lint from fabrics.

People use it to make impressions of newspaper print or comics. Athletes strengthen their grips by grasping it over and over. Astronauts use it to anchor tools on spacecraft in zero gravity. All in all, a most *eggs-cellent* idea!

CONNECTIONS Research As a group, examine a sample of the colorful, sticky, stretch toy made of boric acid and silicone oil. Then brainstorm some practical—and impractical—uses for the substance.

SCIENCE *Online*
For more information, visit science.glencoe.com

Activity

Allow small groups of students to investigate how the addition of a compound can change the properties of a polymer. Dissolve 2 mL of borax in 125 mL of water in a beaker. Have students pour 15 mL of white glue (a polymer) into a paper cup. Then have them add 15 mL of the borax solution to the glue and stir it with a craft stick. The borax cross-links the glue polymers, making the resulting compound thicker and more rubbery. Tell students to remove the polymer from the cup and knead it for a few minutes. As a class, discuss the properties of the new polymer. L2 IS **Kinesthetic**

Analyze the Event

Ask students to brainstorm possible reasons scientists tried unusual experiments when working to come up with an inexpensive alternative to synthetic rubber.

CONNECTIONS Ask students in each group to describe the list of uses they came up with for the goo. Ask students in other groups to comment on whether or not they think the proposed uses would actually work. If possible, allow students to demonstrate some of the uses they brainstormed.

SCIENCE *Online*

Internet Addresses

_____

_____

_____

Explore the Glencoe Science Web site at **science.glencoe.com** to find out more about topics in this feature.

Preview

Students can answer the questions in their Science Journals. Discuss the answers as you go through the chapter. **Ⓛ Linguistic**

Review

Students can write their answers, then compare them with those of other students. **Ⓛ Interpersonal**

Reteach

Students can look at the illustrations and describe details that support the main ideas of the chapter. **Ⓛ Visual-Spatial**

Answers to Chapter Review

SECTION 1

3. Liquids take the shape of their containers.

SECTION 2

1. the sample in the pot

SECTION 3

4. Squeezing the tube transfers pressure throughout the tube. Since the tube has an opening, toothpaste is pushed out.

Section 1 Matter

1. All matter, which includes anything that takes up space and has mass, is composed of tiny particles that are in constant motion.

2. In the solid state, the attractive forces between particles hold them in place to vibrate. Solids have definite shapes and volumes.

3. Particles in the liquid state have defined volumes and are free to move about within the liquid. *What property of liquids is shown in the photo?*

4. Particles in the gas state move about freely and completely fill their containers. Gases have neither definite shapes nor volumes.

Section 2 Changes of State

1. Thermal energy is the total energy of the particles in a sample of matter. The average kinetic energy of the particles is temperature. *At 85°C, which of these samples has a greater amount of thermal energy?*

2. For a change of state to occur, matter must gain or lose thermal energy.

3. An object gains thermal energy during melting when it changes from a solid to a liquid or during vaporization when it changes from a liquid to a gas.

4. An object loses thermal energy during condensation when it changes from a gas into a liquid or during freezing when it changes from a liquid to a solid.

Section 3 Behavior of Fluids

1. Pressure is force divided by area.

2. Fluids exert a buoyant force in the upward direction on objects immersed in them. Archimedes' principle states that the buoyant force on an object is equal to the weight of the fluid displaced by the object.

3. An object will float in a fluid that is more dense than itself. Density is equal to mass divided by volume.

4. Pressure applied to a liquid is transmitted evenly throughout the liquid. This is known as Pascal's principle. *How does Pascal's principle relate to this tube of toothpaste?*

FOLDABLES
Reading & Study Skills

After You Read

Use what you learned to write about what happens when heat is added to or lost from the three states of matter on your Organizational Study Fold.

FOLDABLES
Reading & Study Skills

After You Read

After students have read the chapter and completed the Foldable described in Before You Read, have them do the activity on the student page.

Dinah Zike

Visualizing Main Ideas

Complete the following concept map on matter.

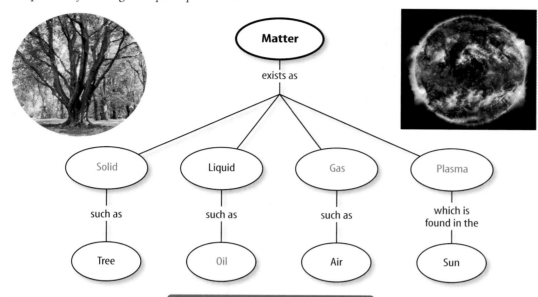

Visualizing Main Ideas

See student page.

Vocabulary Review

Using Vocabulary

1. gas
2. liquid
3. Heat
4. Temperature
5. condensation
6. vaporization
7. Density
8. Pressure

Vocabulary Review

Vocabulary Words

a. Archimedes' principle
b. buoyant force
c. condensation
d. density
e. freezing
f. gas
g. heat
h. liquid
i. matter
j. melting
k. Pascal's principle
l. pressure
m. solid
n. temperature
o. vaporization

THE PRINCETON REVIEW — Study Tip

Find a quiet place to study, whether at home or school. Turn off the television or radio, and give your full attention to your lessons.

Using Vocabulary

Replace the underlined words with the correct vocabulary words.

1. A <u>liquid</u> can change shape and volume.

2. A <u>solid</u> has a different shape but the same volume in any container.

3. <u>Matter</u> is thermal energy moving from one substance to another.

4. <u>Heat</u> is a measure of the average kinetic energy of the particles of a substance.

5. A substance changes from a gas to a liquid during the process of <u>melting</u>.

6. A liquid becomes a gas during <u>freezing</u>.

7. <u>Pressure</u> is mass divided by volume.

8. <u>Density</u> is force divided by area.

CHAPTER STUDY GUIDE   K ◆ 67

IDENTIFYING ▷ Misconceptions

Assess

Use the assessment as follow-up to page 38F after students have completed the chapter.

Materials paper, pencil

Procedure Have students work in groups to make cartoon posters of sporting events in which the Matter Team plays the Non-Matter Team. Students should choose a team sport and create each team. For instance in a baseball game there can be an Iron Infielder and Plastic Pitcher on the Matter Team and Light Left fielder and Kinetic Energy Catcher on the Non-Matter Team.

Expected Outcome Students should realize that matter includes solids, liquids, and gases and does not include types of energy.

Chapter ❷ Assessment

Checking Concepts

1. A
2. B
3. C
4. D
5. B
6. C
7. D
8. B
9. C
10. B

Thinking Critically

11. Steam has more thermal energy than boiling water.
12. The melting and boiling points would remain the same. However, the temperature would rise more slowly and the time required for melting and boiling would increase. Therefore, the slopes during the temperature increases would be less.
13. Some of the hot water from the shower evaporates into the air. It condenses on the mirror because the mirror is cooler than the air.
14. As air pressure decreases, the boiling point decreases.
15. No; $1,800 \div 110 = 16.3$; the crown is not dense enough to be pure gold.

Checking Concepts

Choose the word or phrase that best answers the question.

1. Which description best describes a solid?
   A) It has a definite shape and volume.
   B) It has a definite shape but not a definite volume.
   C) It adjusts to the shape of its container.
   D) It can flow.

2. Which of these is a crystalline solid?
   A) glass   C) rubber
   B) sugar   D) plastic

3. What property enables you to float a needle on water?
   A) viscosity   C) surface tension
   B) temperature   D) crystal structure

4. What happens to an object as its kinetic energy increases?
   A) It holds more tightly to nearby objects.
   B) Its mass increases.
   C) Its particles move more slowly.
   D) Its particles move faster.

5. During which process do particles of matter release energy?
   A) melting   C) sublimation
   B) freezing   D) boiling

6. How does water vapor in air form clouds?
   A) melting   C) condensation
   B) evaporation   D) sublimation

7. Which is a unit of pressure?
   A) N   C) g/cm^3
   B) kg   D) N/m^2

8. Which change results in an increase in gas pressure in a sealed, flexible container?
   A) decrease in temperature
   B) decrease in volume
   C) increase in volume
   D) increase in altitude

9. In which case will an object float on a fluid?
   A) Buoyant force is greater than weight.
   B) Buoyant force is less than weight.
   C) Buoyant force equals weight.
   D) Buoyant force equals zero.

10. Which is equal to the buoyant force on an object?
    A) volume of the object
    B) weight of the displaced fluid
    C) weight of object
    D) volume of fluid

Thinking Critically

11. Why does steam cause more severe burns than boiling water?

12. How would this graph change if a greater volume of water were heated? How would it stay the same? Explain.

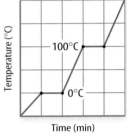

13. Why does the bathroom mirror become fogged while you are taking a shower?

14. The boiling point of a substance decreases as altitude increases. Based on this information, infer the relationship between boiling point and air pressure. Draw a graph.

15. A king's crown has a volume of 110 cm^3 and a mass of 1,800 g. The density of gold is 19.3 g/cm^3. Is the crown pure gold?

Developing Skills

16. **Forming Operational Definitions** Write operational definitions that explain the properties of and differences among solids, liquids, and gases.

Chapter ✔Assessment Planner

Portfolio Encourage students to place in their portfolios one or two items of what they consider to be their best work. Examples include:
• Extension, p. 41
• Assessment, p. 44
• Extension, p. 47
• Science Journal, p. 55

Performance Additional performance assessments, Performance Task Assessment Lists, and rubrics for evaluating these activities can be found in Glencoe's **Performance Assessment in the Science Classroom.**

17. Concept Mapping Prepare a sequence chart to show the events that occur as a solid changes into a liquid and then into a gas.

18. Drawing Conclusions Why do some balloons pop when they are left in sunlight for too long?

19. Calculating A hydraulic device has two pistons. How much force do you have to apply to the piston with an area of 10 cm^2 to lift an object weighing 2,000 N on a piston with an area of 50 cm^2?

20. Making and Using Graphs In January of 2000, Francisco "Pipin" Ferreras of Cuba dove to a depth of 150 m without any scuba equipment. Make a depth-pressure graph for the data below. Based on your graph, how does water pressure vary with depth? Note: The pressure at sea level, 101.3 kPa, is called one atmosphere (atm).

Water Pressure			
Depth (m)	Pressure (atm)	Depth (m)	Pressure (atm)
0	1.0	100	11.0
25	3.5	125	13.5
50	6.0	150	16.0
75	8.5	175	18.5

Performance Assessment

21. Storyboard Create a visual-aid storyboard to show ice changing to steam. There should be a minimum of five frames.

TECHNOLOGY

Go to the Glencoe Science Web site at **science.glencoe.com** or use the **Glencoe Science CD-ROM** for additional chapter assessment.

 **Test Practice**

Seth is studying the forces exerted on objects in water and has drawn the following illustration of his experiment.

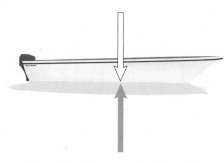

Study the diagram and answer the following questions:

1. The most likely reason the boat is floating rather than sinking is that
  A) the boat's weight is pushing it down
  B) the boat's weight is greater than the buoyant force
  C) the buoyant force is greater than the boat's weight
  D) the boat's weight is equal to the buoyant force

2. Seth wanted to find out how shape affects buoyancy. To compare these two variables, he should _____.
  F) use boats of different sizes
  G) use different-shaped objects of the same weight
  H) use similarly shaped objects of different weights
  J) use objects with different textures

 Test Practice

The Test-Taking Tip was written by The Princeton Review, the nation's leader in test preparation.
1. D
2. G

Developing Skills

16. Solids are materials with particles that are very close together. Solids have a definite shape and volume and can be crystalline or amorphous. Liquids are materials in which particles are farther apart than in solids. The individual particles in liquids can flow past each other and have an attraction to each other that gives liquids viscosity and surface tension. Liquids have a definite volume and take the shape of their containers. Gases have particles that are very far apart, move quickly, and lack an attraction to each other. Gases have no definite shape or volume.

17. Check students' work.

18. The pressure of the gas inside the balloon increases as the air in the balloon heats up.

19. 2,000 N/50 cm^2 = F/10 cm^2; F = 400N

20. Water pressure increases as the depth increases.

Performance Assessment

21. Ice should change first to liquid water, then to steam as heat is added to the system and the water molecules move faster. Use **PASC**, p. 135.

✓*Assessment* Resources

📁 Reproducible Masters

Chapter Resources Booklet
 Chapter Review, pp. 35–36
 Chapter Tests, pp. 37–40
 Assessment Transparency Activity, p. 47

Glencoe Science Web site
 Interactive Tutor
 Chapter Quizzes

Glencoe Technology
 Assessment Transparency
 Interactive CD-ROM Chapter Quizzes
 ExamView Pro Test Bank
 Vocabulary PuzzleMaker Software
 MindJogger Videoquiz DVD/VHS

Section/Objectives	Standards		Activities/Features
	National	**State/Local**	
Chapter Opener	See p. 7T for a Key to Standards.		**Explore Activity:** Compare properties, p. 71 **Before You Read,** p. 71
Section 1 Physical and Chemical Properties ⏱ 3 sessions ▦ 1.5 blocks 1. **Identify** physical and chemical properties of matter.	National Content Standards: UCP3, A1, B1		**MiniLAB:** Measuring Properties, p. 74 **Earth Science Integration,** p. 75 **Science Online,** p. 76 **Activity:** Finding the Difference, p. 77
Section 2 Physical and Chemical Changes ⏱ 5 sessions ▦ 2.5 blocks 1. **Compare** several physical and chemical changes. 2. **Identify** examples of physical and chemical changes.	National Content Standards: UCP3, A1, B1, F5, G2		**MiniLAB:** Comparing Changes, p. 81 **Science Online,** p. 81 **Astronomy Integration,** p. 83 **Math Skills Activity,** p. 84 **Visualizing Recycling,** p. 86 **Activity:** Battle of the Toothpastes, pp. 88–89 **Science Stats:** Strange Changes, pp. 90–91

Activity Materials	Reproducible Resources	Section Assessment	Technology
Explore Activity: samples of obsidian and pumice, clear container	**Chapter Resources Booklet** Foldables Worksheet, p. 17 Directed Reading Overview, p. 19 Note-taking Worksheets, pp. 31–32	GLENCOE'S ASSESSMENT ADVANTAGE	
MiniLAB: 10-mL graduated cylinder, balance **Activity:** meterstick, spring scale, block of wood, metal bar or ruler, plastic bin, drinking glass, water, rubber ball, paper, carpet, magnet, feather, rock, plant or flower, soil, sand, a vegetable, apple, slice of bread, dry cereal, egg	**Chapter Resources Booklet** Transparency Activity, p. 42 MiniLAB, p. 3 Enrichment, p. 29 Reinforcement, p. 27 Directed Reading, p. 20 Activity Worksheet, pp. 5–6 Lab Activity, pp. 9–12 **Reading and Writing Skill Activities,** p. 17	**Portfolio** Assessment, p. 76 **Performance** MiniLAB, p. 74 Skill Builder Activities, p. 76 **Content** Section Assessment, p. 76	🔖 Section Focus Transparency 💿 Interactive CD-ROM 🎧 Guided Reading Audio Program
MiniLAB: a piece of fine steel wool, paper plate, tap water **Activity:** 2 or 3 different brands of toothpaste, drinking glasses or bowls, hard boiled eggs, concentrated lemon juice, apple juice water, artist's paint brush *Need materials?* Contact Science Kit at 1-800-828-7777 or www.sciencekit.com on the Internet.	**Chapter Resources Booklet** Transparency Activity, p. 43 MiniLAB, p. 4 Enrichment, p. 30 Reinforcement, p. 28 Directed Reading, pp. 21, 22 Transparency Activity, pp. 45–46 Activity Worksheet, pp. 7–8 Lab Activity, pp. 13–16 **Mathematics Skill Activities,** p. 9 **Science Inquiry Labs,** pp. 25, 51 **Home and Community Involvement,** p. 27 **Cultural Diversity,** p. 5 **Life Science Critical Thinking/ Problem Solving,** p. 8 **Lab Management and Safety,** p. 67	**Portfolio** Assessment, p. 81 **Performance** MiniLAB, p. 81 Skill Builder Activities, p. 87 **Content** Section Assessment, p. 87	🔖 Section Focus Transparency 🔖 Teaching Transparency 💿 Interactive CD-ROM 🎧 Guided Reading Audio Program

End of Chapter Assessment

GLENCOE'S ASSESSMENT ADVANTAGE

Blackline Masters	Technology	Professional Series
Chapter Resources Booklet Chapter Review, pp. 35–36 Chapter Tests, pp. 37–40 **Standardized Test Practice by The Princeton Review,** pp. 19–22	📼 MindJogger Videoquiz 💿 Interactive CD-ROM 💿 Vocabulary PuzzleMakers 💿 ExamView Pro Test Bank 💿 Interactive Lesson Planner 💿 Interactive Teacher Edition	Performance Assessment in the Science Classroom (PASC)

Transparencies

Section Focus

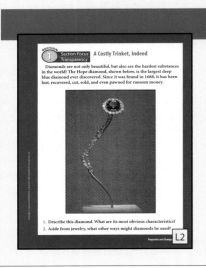

Section Focus Transparency 1 — A Costly Trinket, Indeed

Diamonds are not only beautiful, but also are the hardest substances in the world! The Hope diamond, shown below, is the largest deep blue diamond ever discovered. Since it was found in 1688, it has been lost, recovered, cut, sold, and even pawned for ransom money.

1. Describe this diamond. What are its most obvious characteristics?
2. Aside from jewelry, what other ways might diamonds be used?

L2

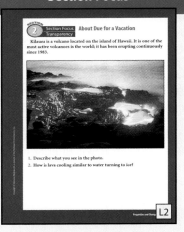

Section Focus Transparency 2 — About Due for a Vacation

Kilauea is a volcano located on the island of Hawaii. It is one of the most active volcanoes is the world; it has been erupting continuously since 1983.

1. Describe what you see in the photo.
2. How is lava cooling similar to water turning to ice?

L2

This is a representation of key blackline masters available in the Teacher Classroom Resources. See Resource Manager boxes within the chapter for additional information.

Key to Teaching Strategies

The following designations will help you decide which activities are appropriate for your students.

- **L1** Level 1 activities should be appropriate for students with learning difficulties.
- **L2** Level 2 activities should be within the ability range of all students.
- **L3** Level 3 activities are designed for above-average students.
- **ELL** ELL activities should be within the ability range of English Language Learners.
- **COOP LEARN** Cooperative Learning activities are designed for small group work.
- **LS** Multiple Learning Styles logos are used throughout to indicate strategies that address different learning styles.
- **P** These strategies represent student products that can be placed into a best-work portfolio.

Assessment

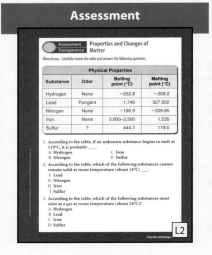

Assessment Transparency — Properties and Changes of Matter

Directions: Carefully review the table and answer the following questions.

Physical Properties

Substance	Odor	Boiling point (°C)	Melting point (°C)
Hydrogen	None	−252.8	−259.2
Lead	Pungent	1,740	327.502
Nitrogen	None	−195.9	−209.95
Iron	None	3,000–3,500	1,535
Sulfur	?	444.7	119.0

1. According to the table, if an unknown substance begins to melt at 119°C, it is probably ___.
   A Hydrogen   C Iron
   B Nitrogen   D Sulfur
2. According to the table, which of the following substances cannot remain solid at room temperature (about 24°C) ___.
   F Lead
   G Nitrogen
   H Iron
   J Sulfur
3. According to the table, which of the following substances must exist as a gas at room temperature (about 24°C)?
   A Hydrogen
   B Lead
   C Iron
   D Sulfur

L2

Teaching

Teaching Transparency 2 — Chemical Changes

L2

Hands-on Activities

Activity Worksheets

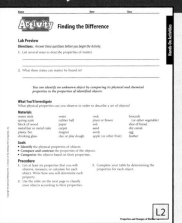

Activity — Finding the Difference

Lab Preview
Directions: Answer these questions before you begin the Activity.

1. List several ways to describe properties of matter.

2. What three states can matter be found in?

You can identify an unknown object by comparing its physical and chemical properties to the properties of identified objects.

What You'll Investigate
What physical properties can you observe in order to describe a set of objects?

Materials
meter stick   water   rock   broccoli
spring scale   rubber ball   plant or flower (or other vegetable)
block of wood   paper   soil   slice of bread
metal bar or metal ruler carpet   sand   dry cereal
plastic bin   magnet   seeds   egg
drinking glass   clay or play dough apple (or other fruit) feather

Goals
- **Identify** the physical properties of objects.
- **Compare and contrast** the properties of the objects.
- **Categorize** the objects based on their properties.

Procedure
1. List at least six properties that you will observe, measure, or calculate for each object. Write how you will determine each property.
2. Use the table on the next page to classify your objects according to their properties.
3. Complete your table by determining the properties for each object.

L2

Laboratory Activities

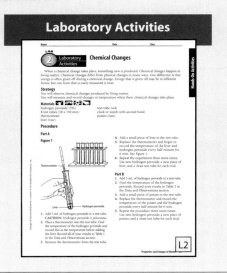

Laboratory Activities 2 — Chemical Changes

When a chemical change takes place, something new is produced. Chemical changes happen in living matter. Chemical changes differ from physical changes in many ways. One difference is that energy is often given off during a chemical change. Energy that is given off may be in different forms, but one form that is easily measured is heat.

Strategy
You will observe chemical changes produced by living matter.
You will measure and record changes in temperature when these chemical changes take place.

Materials
hydrogen peroxide (3%)   test-tube rack
8 test tubes (18 × 150 mm)   clock or watch with second hand
thermometer   potato (raw)
liver (raw)

Procedure

Part A
Figure 1

1. Add 5 mL of hydrogen peroxide to a test tube.
   CAUTION: Hydrogen peroxide is poisonous.
2. Place a thermometer into the test tube. Find the temperature of the hydrogen peroxide and record this as the temperature before adding the liver. Record all of your results in Table 1 in the Data and Observations section.
3. Remove the thermometer from the test tube.

4. Add a small piece of liver to the test tube.
5. Replace the thermometer and begin to record the temperature of the liver and hydrogen peroxide every half minute for 6 min. See Figure 1.
6. Repeat the experiment three more times. Use new hydrogen peroxide, a new piece of liver, and a clean test tube for each trial.

Part B
1. Add 5 mL of hydrogen peroxide to a test tube.
2. Find temperature of the hydrogen peroxide. Record your results in Table 2 in the Data and Observations section.
3. Add a small piece of potato to the test tube.
4. Replace the thermometer and record the temperature of the potato and the hydrogen peroxide every half minute for 6 min.
5. Repeat the procedure three more times. Use new hydrogen peroxide, a new piece of potato, and a clean test tube for each trial.

L2

Meeting Different Ability Levels

Content Outline

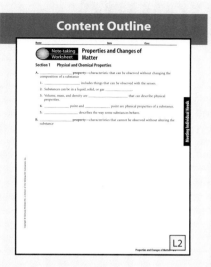

Reinforcement

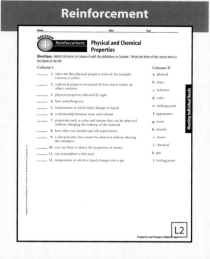

Directed Reading

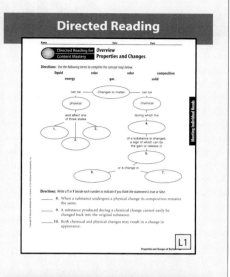

Assessment

Chapter Tests

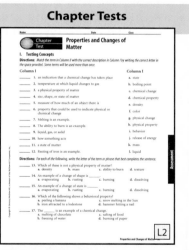

Enrichment

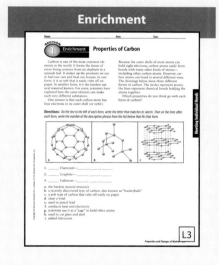

Spanish Directed Reading

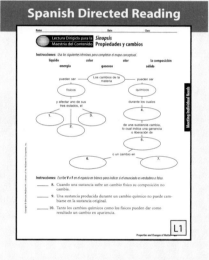

Test Practice Workbook

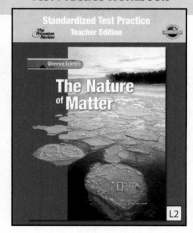

Chapter Review

Science Content Background

Physical and Chemical Properties

Physical Properties

You must be careful in describing some physical properties, particularly properties such as solubility. Describing solubility can involve a reaction and, for that reason, may not be a true physical property. For example, if you say that sodium is soluble in water that would imply that the sodium simply dissolves in water. Instead, sodium reacts with water to form hydrogen gas and an aqueous sodium hydroxide solution.

Chemical Properties

A substance's chemical properties describe its ability to react with other substances or to decompose. For example, one chemical property of limestone, or calcium carbonate, is its ability to react with hydrochloric acid, producing carbon dioxide, water, and calcium chloride.

> ## Fun Fact
>
> In black and white photographic film, a chemical change occurs when silver bromide (AgBr) is exposed to light and turns dark.

Another chemical property of calcium carbonate is the ability to decompose, forming calcium oxide and carbon dioxide when heated.

The ability to corrode many metals is a chemical property of some acids. For example, when sulfuric acid corrodes aluminum, the aluminum atoms are oxidized (lose electrons) to form positively charged aluminum ions, while the hydrogen ions in the sulfuric acid are reduced (gain electrons) to form hydrogen atoms.

Intensive and Extensive Properties

Properties can also be classified as either intensive or extensive, depending on whether their value changes with the size of the sample. Intensive properties, like melting point and temperature, have values that do not depend on the amount of the sample. Extensive properties, like mass, length, and volume, have values that do depend on the sample size. Density is an intensive physical property that relates the mass of an object to its volume. Density is temperature dependent because most substances change in volume when heated or cooled.

Jeff Greenberg/PhotoEdit

SECTION
②

Physical and Chemical Changes

Physical Changes

Knowledge of physical changes and the circumstances under which they occur can be used to separate mixtures. Distillation is a change-of-state operation that is used to separate substances with different boiling points. Distillation is used to separate drinking water from seawater and hydrocarbons, such as gasoline and kerosene, from petroleum.

Chemical Changes

Chemical reaction is another term for chemical change. In a chemical change, atoms are rearranged. If a precipitate, gas, color change, or energy change occurs, a chemical change probably has taken place. Almost all chemical changes involve either taking in (endothermic) or giving off (exothermic) energy. However, not all changes that absorb or release energy are chemical. A cold pack is an example of physical change (dissolution) that absorbs heat.

Conservation of Mass

The French chemist, Antoine Lavoisier (1743–1794), found that when a chemical reaction was carried out in a closed system, the total mass of the system was not changed. Perhaps the most important chemical reaction Lavoisier performed was the decomposition of the red oxide of mercury to form metallic mercury and a gas he named oxygen. This reaction had been carried out by other scientists, but he was the first to weigh all the substances present before and after the reaction. He was also the first to interpret the reaction correctly. Lavoisier carried out many quantitative experiments, even those with animals. Lavoisier summarized all of his findings in the law of conservation of mass.

SCIENCE *Online*

For additional content background on this topic, go to the Glencoe Science Web site at science.glencoe.com.

Fun Fact

Photochromic sunglasses darken when exposed to light because of the chemical change in the silver chloride (AgCl) embedded in the glass.

Charles D. Winters/Photo Researchers, Inc.

Properties and Changes of Matter

Properties and Changes of Matter

Chapter Vocabulary

physical property, p. 72
chemical property, p. 76
physical change, p. 78
chemical change, p. 80
law of conservation of mass,
    p. 87

What do you think?

Science Journal The photo shows pumice, an igneous rock formed when lava cools on or near Earth's surface. Pumice is actually volcanic glass.

At very high temperatures deep within Earth, solid rock melts. When a volcano erupts, the liquid lava cools and turns back to rock. One of the properties of rock is its state—solid, liquid, or gas. Other properties include color, shape, texture, and weight. As lava changes from a liquid to a solid, what happens to its properties? In this chapter, you will learn about physical and chemical properties and changes of matter.

What do you think?

Science Journal Look at the picture below with a classmate. Discuss what you think this might be. Here's a hint: *It can keep your feet smooth.* Write your answer or best guess in your Science Journal.

Theme Connection

Stability and Change Matter can be described by its physical and chemical properties. These properties determine the physical and chemical changes that different types of matter can undergo.

When a volcano erupts, it spews lava and gases. Lava is hot, melted rock from deep within Earth. After it reaches Earth's surface, the lava cools and hardens into solid rock. The minerals and gases within the lava, as well as the rate at which it cools, determine the characteristics of the resulting rocks. In this activity, you will compare two types of volcanic rock.

Compare properties

1. Obtain samples of the rocks obsidian (uhb SIH dee un) and pumice (PUH mus) of about the same size from your teacher.

2. Compare the colors of the two rocks.

3. Decide which sample is heavier.

4. Look at the surfaces of the two rocks. How are the surfaces different?

5. Place each rock in water and observe.

Observe

What things are different about these rocks? In your Science Journal, make a table that compares the observations you made about the rocks.

Purpose Use the Explore Activity to help students understand that obsidian and pumice, two rocks formed from volcanic lava, have different properties. L1
ELL LS **Kinesthetic**

Preparation Obtain pumice and obsidian samples and a clear container.

Materials pumice and obsidian samples, a clear cup or container that will hold each sample, water

Teaching Strategy In Step 5, advise students to lower the obsidian and pumice samples into the cup slowly to avoid splashing.

Observe

Tables should show that pumice has a rough surface while obsidian is smooth. For a similar-sized sample, the obsidian is much heavier. Pumice floats in water (or at least is more buoyant) while obsidian sinks.

✓ *Assessment*

Process Have students use a balance to determine the mass of their rock samples and use water displacement in a graduated cylinder to determine the volume of each rock sample. Explain what density is, and show students how to calculate the densities of the pumice and obsidian. Use **Performance Assessment in the Science Classroom**, p. 89.

FOLDABLES
Reading & Study Skills

Before You Read

Making an Organizational Study Fold Make the following Foldable to help you organize your thoughts into clear categories about properties and changes.

1. Place a sheet of paper in front of you so the short side is at the top. Fold the paper in half from the top to the bottom two times. Unfold all the folds.

2. Trace over all the fold lines and label the folds *Physical Properties, Physical Changes, Chemical Properties,* and *Chemical Changes* as shown.

3. As you read the chapter, write information about matter's physical and chemical properties and changes on your Foldable.

Physical Properties

Physical Changes

Chemical Properties

Chemical Changes

FOLDABLES
Reading & Study Skills

Before You Read

Dinah Zike Study Fold

Purpose Students make and use a Foldable table to collect information on the physical and chemical properties and changes of matter, and use the data to compare and contrast physical and chemical changes and physical and chemical properties.

For additional help, see Foldables Worksheet, p. 17 in **Chapter Resources Booklet,** or go to the Glencoe Science Web site at **science.glencoe.com.** See After You Read in the Study Guide at the end of this chapter.

SECTION

1

Physical and Chemical Properties

1 Motivate

Bellringer Transparency

Display the Section Focus Transparency for Section 1. Use the accompanying Transparency Activity Master. L2 ELL

Tie to Prior Knowledge

Have students recall occasions when they had to describe an object using their senses.

✔ Reading Check

Answer a characteristic that can be observed without changing the composition of a substance

Caption Answer

Figure 1 Answers will vary.

Physical and Chemical Properties

As You Read

What You'll Learn
■ Identify physical and chemical properties of matter.

Vocabulary
physical property
chemical property

Why It's Important
Understanding the different properties of matter will help you to better describe the world around you.

Physical Properties

It's a busy day at the state fair as you and your classmates navigate your way through the crowd. While you follow your teacher, you can't help but notice the many sights and sounds that surround you. Eventually, you fall behind the group as you spot the most amazing ride you have ever seen. You inspect it from one end to the other. How will you describe it to the group when you catch up to them? What features will you use in your description?

Perhaps you will mention that the ride is large, blue, and made of wood. These features are all physical properties, or characteristics, of the ride. A **physical property** is a characteristic you can observe without changing or trying to change the composition of the substance. How something looks, smells, sounds, or tastes are all examples of physical properties. Look at **Figure 1.** You can describe all types of matter and differentiate between them by observing their properties.

✔ Reading Check   *What is a physical property of matter?*

Figure 1
All matter can be described by physical properties that can be observed using the five senses. *What types of matter do you think you could see, hear, taste, touch, and smell at the fair?*

Section ✔ *Assessment* Planner

PORTFOLIO
Assessment, p. 76
PERFORMANCE ASSESSMENT
MiniLAB, p. 75
Skill Builder Activities, p. 76
See page 94 for more options.

CONTENT ASSESSMENT
Section, p. 76
Challenge, p. 76
Chapter, pp. 94–95

Using Your Senses Some physical properties describe the appearance of matter. You can detect many of these properties with your senses. For example, you can see the color and shape of the ride at the fair. You can also touch it to feel its texture. You can smell the odor or taste the flavor of some matter. (You should never taste anything in the laboratory.) Consider the physical properties of the items in **Figure 2.**

State To describe a sample of matter, you need to identify its state. Is the ride a solid, a liquid, or a gas? This property, known as the state of matter, is another physical property that you can observe. The ride, your chair, a book, and a pen are examples of matter in the solid state. Milk, gasoline, and vegetable oil are examples of matter in the liquid state. The helium in a balloon, air in a tire, and neon in a sign are examples of matter in the gas state. You can see examples of solids, liquids, and gases in **Figure 3.**

Perhaps you are most familiar with the three states of water. You can drink or swim in liquid water. You use the solid state of water, which is ice, when you put the solid cubes in a drink or skate on a frozen lake. Although you can't see it, water in the gas state is all around you in the air.

Figure 2
A Some matter has a characteristic color, such as this sulfur pile.
B You can use a characteristic smell or taste to identify these fruits. **C** Even if you didn't see it, you could probably identify this sponge by feeling its texture.

Figure 3
The state of a sample of matter is an important physical property.

A This rock formation is in the solid state.

B The oil flowing out of a bottle is in the liquid state.

C This colorful sign uses the element neon, which is generally found in the gas state.

---

2 Teach

Physical Properties

Make a Model

Have each student make a model of a water molecule by using a large circle to represent oxygen and two small circles to represent hydrogen. Direct them to connect the small circles to the large circle with chenille stems and glue. As you discuss solids, liquids, and gases, collect students' molecules and arrange them on a large piece of construction paper. Glue some of them closely together in a hexagonal arrangement to represent the molecules in solid ice. Arrange the next set more randomly and with spaces between them to represent liquid water. Then lay out a few molecules with large spaces between them to represent gaseous water vapor. Keep these models on the wall to remind students that the molecule for water did not change; instead the arrangement of the molecules determined state. L1 ELL IS **Kinesthetic**

Visual Learning

Figure 3 Have students describe the physical properties shown in the pictures. rock formation: brown, orange, sharp, sandy, solid; oil: brown, thick, liquid; neon sign: bright, colorful, yellow

---

Teacher FYI

In addition to solid, liquid, and gas, there is a state of matter called plasma. Plasma exists when high energies strip electrons from atomic nuclei, so the nuclei and the electrons exist separately. Matter in the Sun is in the plasma state, as is matter in lightning. Most of the matter in the universe is in the plasma state.

Resource Manager

Chapter Resources Booklet
Transparency Activity, p. 42
Directed Reading for Content Mastery, pp. 19, 20
Note-taking Worksheets, pp. 31–32

Physical Properties,
continued

Purpose Students measure mass and volume of a water sample and determine its density.

Materials 10-mL graduated cylinder, balance

Teaching Strategy • Review with students how to read the volume of a liquid in a graduated cylinder using the meniscus.

Analysis

1. The mass of the water could not be measured unless the water is in a container. The mass of the container is subtracted from the total mass.

2. It would be greater.

Assessment

Performance Using their calculated density, have students calculate the mass of water that would have a volume of 7.5 mL and perform an experiment to confirm the answer. Use **PASC,** p. 93.

Activity

Give students classroom objects that are rectangular solids, such as a chalkboard eraser, and have them calculate the volume of each by finding the product of the width, height, and depth. L2 IS **Logical-Mathematical**

Mini LAB

Measuring Properties

Procedure

1. Measure the mass of a **10-mL graduated cylinder.**
2. Fill the graduated cylinder with **water** to the 10-mL mark and measure the mass of the graduated cylinder and water.
3. Determine the mass of the water by subtracting the mass of the graduated cylinder from the mass of the graduated cylinder and water.
4. Determine the density of water by dividing the mass of the water by the volume of the water.

Analysis

1. Why did you need to measure the mass of the empty graduated cylinder?
2. How would your calculated density be affected if you added more than 10-mL of water?

Figure 4

A spring scale is used to measure an object's weight.

Size Dependent Properties Some physical properties depend on the size of the object. Suppose you need to move a box. The size of the box would be important in deciding if you need to use your backpack or a truck. You can begin by measuring the width, height, and depth of the box. If you multiply them together, you calculate the box's volume. The volume of an object is the amount of space it occupies.

Another physical property that depends on size is mass. Recall that the mass of an object is a measurement of how much matter it contains. A bowling ball has more mass than a basketball. Weight is a measurement of force. Weight depends on the mass of the object and on gravity. If you were to travel to other planets, your weight would change but your size and mass would not. Weight is measured using a spring scale like the one in **Figure 4.**

Size Independent Properties Another physical property, density, does not depend on the size of an object. Density measures the amount of mass in a given volume. To calculate the density of an object, divide its mass by its volume. The density of water is the same in a glass as it is in a tub. Another property, solubility, also does not depend on size. Solubility is the number of grams of one substance that will dissolve in 100 g of another substance at a given temperature. The amount of drink mix that can be dissolved in 100 g of water is the same in a pitcher as it is when it is poured into a glass. Size dependent and independent properties are shown in **Table 1.**

Melting and Boiling Point Melting and boiling point also do not depend upon an object's size. The temperature at which a solid changes into a liquid is called its melting point. The temperature at which a liquid changes into a gas is called its boiling point. The melting and boiling points of several substances, along with some of their other physical properties, are shown in **Table 2.**

Table 1 Properties of Matter	
	Physical Properties
Dependent on sample size	mass, weight, volume
Independent of sample size	density, melting/boiling point, solubility, ability to attract a magnet, state of matter, color.

Purpose to measure the melting and boiling points of water

Materials large beaker, several ice cubes made from distilled water, thermometer, hot plate, hot pad

Procedure Place the ice in the container, then measure the temperature of the ice. Heat the ice. Measure the temperature of

the water and ice mixture. Continue to heat the water until it boils, and then measure the temperature of the boiling water. Write all three temperatures on the board.

Expected Outcome Students observe the temperatures for the melting and boiling points of water.

Assessment

What happened to the ice between the first and second temperature checks? Its molecules gained energy and broke apart to change the ice to a liquid. **What is the second temperature called?** melting point **What happened to water at its boiling point?** It turned to gas.

Table 2   Physical Properties of Several Substances
(at atmospheric temperature and pressure)

Substance	Color	State	Density (g/cm³)	Melting Point (°C)	Boiling Point (°C)
Bromine	Red-brown	Liquid	3.12	−7	59
Chlorine	Yellowish	Gas	0.0032	−101	−34
Mercury	Silvery-white	Liquid	13.5	−39	357
Neon	Colorless	Gas	0.0009	−249	−246
Oxygen	Colorless	Gas	0.0014	−219	−183
Sodium chloride	White	Solid	2.17	801	1,413
Sulfur	Yellow	Solid	2.07	115	445
Water	Colorless	Liquid	1.00	0	100

Behavior   Some matter can be described by the specific way in which it behaves. For example, some materials pull iron toward them. These materials are said to be magnetic. The lodestone in **Figure 5** is a rock that is naturally magnetic.

Other materials can be made into magnets. You might have magnets on your refrigerator or locker at school. The door of your refrigerator also has a magnet within it that holds the door shut tightly.

 **Reading Check**   *What are some examples of physical properties of matter?*

 **Earth Science**
INTEGRATION

Scientists can learn about the history of the Moon by analyzing the properties of moon rocks. The properties of some moon rocks, for example, are similar to those of rocks produced by volcanoes on Earth. In this way, scientists learned that the Moon once had volcanic activity. Make a list of questions to ask about the properties of a moon rock.

Figure 5
This lodestone attracts certain metals to it. Lodestone is a natural magnet.

Visual Learning

Table 2 Have students work in groups to make graphs from the density, boiling point, and melting point data. Ask students what type of graph they will make and how they will organize the substances on the graph. Have groups compare and discuss their graphs and work out reasons for any discrepancies. L2 COOP LEARN

✔ **Reading Check**

Answer appearance, state (solid, liquid, gas), size, melting point and boiling point, magnetism

 Earth Science
INTEGRATION

The dark-colored flat regions of the Moon are called *maria* (MAHR ee uh, the plural of *mare*). Maria formed when ancient lava flows from the Moon's interior filled large craters on the surface. Those craters were created when meteorites, asteroids, and comets struck the Moon's surface. The impacts caused the formation of cracks that allowed lava to flow upward and fill in the craters, where it solidified into maria. Accept all reasonable questions.

Use an Analogy

Describing physical properties of matter is like providing a witness statement for a police officer. You want to include as much accurate information as possible to ensure that others will know exactly what you observed.

Science Journal

Physical Properties Have students select five items from their homes and describe the physical properties of each. Some properties to describe include color, shape, smell, texture, and state. Have them write their descriptions in their Science Journals. L2 ⟦LS⟧ **Linguistic**

Resource Manager

Chapter Resources Booklet
  MiniLAB, p. 3
  Enrichment, p. 29
  Lab Activity, pp. 9–12

Chemical Properties

SCIENCE *Online*
Internet Addresses

_____

_____

_____

_____

Explore the Glencoe Science Web site at **science.glencoe.com** to find out more about topics in this section.

3 Assess

Reteach
Ask students which of the following properties of a liquid would be physical and which chemical: color physical, ability to burn chemical, nutritional value chemical, volume physical, thickness physical, boiling point physical, smell physical, whether it is poisonous chemical. L2
LS Logical-Mathematical

Challenge
Have students work in small groups to make picture books that explain physical and chemical properties to students who have not studied these concepts.
L2 COOP LEARN **LS Visual-Spatial**

Assessment

Portfolio Have students make miniposters on 5 × 7 index cards explaining physical properties and chemical properties. Encourage them to put their miniposters in their portfolios. Use **Performance Assessment in the Science Classroom,** p. 145. P

Figure 6
Notice the difference between the new matches and the matches that have been burned. The ability to burn is a chemical property of matter.

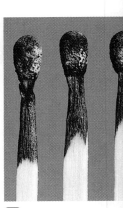

A **B** **C**

SCIENCE *Online*

Research Visit the Glencoe Science Web site at **science.glencoe.com** for more information about methods of measuring matter. Make a poster showing how to make measurements involving several different samples of matter.

Chemical Properties

Some properties of matter cannot be identified just by looking at a sample. For example, nothing happens if you look at the matches in **Figure 6A.** But if someone strikes the matches on a hard, rough surface they will burn, as shown in **Figure 6B.** The ability to burn is a chemical property. A **chemical property** is a characteristic that cannot be observed without altering the substance. As you can see in **Figure 6C,** the matches are permanently changed after they are burned. Therefore this property can be observed only by changing the composition of the match. Another way to define a chemical property, then, is the ability of a substance to undergo a change that alters its identity. You will learn more about changes in matter in the following section.

Section 1 Assessment

1. What physical properties could you use to describe a baseball?
2. How are your senses important to identifying physical properties of matter?
3. How is density related to mass and volume? Explain and write an equation.
4. Describe a chemical property in your own words. Give an example.
5. **Think Critically** Explain why density and solubility are size-independent physical properties of matter.

Skill Builder Activities

6. **Comparing and Contrasting** How is a chemical property different from a physical property? **For more help, refer to the** Science Skill Handbook.
7. **Solving One-Step Equations** You need to fill a bucket with water. The volume of the bucket is 5 L and you are using a cup with a volume of 50 mL. How many cupfuls will you need? There's a hint: *1 L = 1000 mL.* **For more help, refer to the** Math Skill Handbook.

Answers to Section Assessment

1. Possible answers: state (solid), shape (spherical), texture, color, mass, volume, density
2. It is through the senses that you gather information about the world around you. For example, you use your senses to detect an object's shape, color, texture, taste, sound, temperature, smell, weight, state, and behavior, as well as to make measurements.
3. Density is calculated by dividing the mass of an object by its volume.
4. characteristic that determines a substance's ability to interact with other substances in a way that changes its identity; ability to burn
5. Density and solubility are size independent because they are a ratio of two size-dependent properties. As one property increases, so does the other. The ratio doesn't change.
6. A physical property can be observed without changing the composition of the substance. A chemical property cannot be observed without altering the composition of the sample.
7. 100 cups

Activity

Finding the Difference

Y ou can identify an unknown object by comparing its physical and chemical properties to the properties of identified objects.

What You'll Investigate
What physical properties can you observe in order to describe a set of objects?

Materials
meterstick	rock
spring scale	plant or flower
block of wood	soil
metal bar or metal ruler	sand
plastic bin	apple (or other fruit)
drinking glass	vegetable
water	slice of bread
rubber ball	dry cereal
paper	egg
carpet	feather
magnet	

Goals
- ■ **Identify** the physical properties of objects.
- ■ **Compare and Contrast** the properties.
- ■ **Categorize** the objects based on their properties.

Safety Precautions

Procedure
1. List at least six properties that you will observe, measure, or calculate for each object. Describe how to determine each property.

2. In your Science Journal, create a data table with a column for each property and rows for the objects.

3. Complete your table by determining the properties for each object.

Conclude and Apply
1. Which properties were you able to observe easily? Which required making measurements? Which required calculations?

2. **Compare and contrast** the objects based on the information in your table.

3. Choose a set of categories and group your objects into those categories. Some examples of categories are large/medium/small, heavy/moderate/light, bright/moderate/dull, solid/liquid/gas, etc. Were the categories you chose useful for grouping your objects? Why or why not?

𝒞ommunicating
Your Data

Compare your results with those of other students in your class. **Discuss** the properties of objects that different groups included on their tables. Make a large table including all of the objects that students in the class studied.

𝒞ommunicating
Your Data

Students may want to use a computer database to organize their class table.

Resource Manager

Chapter Resources Booklet
  Activity Worksheet, pp. 5–6
  Reinforcement, p. 27
Reading and Writing Skill Activities, p. 17

Activity

BENCH TESTED

Purpose Students will identify physical characteristics and classify objects based on these characteristics. L2 IS **Kinesthetic**

Process Skills collecting data, observing, classifying, comparing and contrasting, making and using tables, drawing conclusions

Time Required 40 minutes

Safety Precautions Students should wear goggles and aprons during this lab.

Teaching Strategies Set up an area where students can get a few items at a time.

Answers to Questions
1. Easy to identify: possible answers: color, texture, physical state. Required measurements: possible answers: mass, length. Required calculations: possible answer: density.
2. Answers will vary.
3. Answers will vary.

✓Assessment

Oral Ask students the following questions. **What are some physical properties that depend on the amount of material present?** Possible answers: mass, length, volume **What are some physical properties that are independent of the amount of material present?** Possible answers: density, boiling point, melting point. Use **PASC**, p. 89.

Physical and Chemical Changes

1 Motivate

Bellringer Transparency

Display the Section Focus Transparency for Section 2. Use the accompanying Transparency Activity Master. L2

ELL

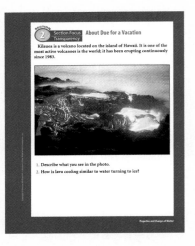

About Due for a Vacation

Kilauea is a volcano located on the island of Hawaii. It is one of the most active volcanoes is the world; it has been erupting continuously since 1983.

1. Describe what you see in the photo.
2. How is lava cooling similar to water turning to ice?

Tie to Prior Knowledge

Review the concepts of physical properties and chemical properties. Ask students to give an example of each. Explain that in this section they will learn some ways to distinguish between physical and chemical changes.

As You Read

What You'll Learn
- **Compare** several physical and chemical changes.
- **Identify** examples of physical and chemical changes.

Vocabulary
physical change
chemical change
law of conservation of mass

Why It's Important
Physical and chemical changes affect your life every day.

Figure 7
Although each sample looks quite different after it experiences a change, the composition of the matter remains the same. These changes are examples of physical changes.

Physical Changes

What happens when the artist turns the lump of clay shown in **Figure 7** into a work of art? The composition of the clay does not change. Its appearance, however, changes dramatically. The change from a lump of clay to a work of art is a physical change. A **physical change** is one in which the form or appearance of matter changes, but not its composition. The lake in **Figure 7** also experiences a physical change. Although the water changes state due to a change in temperature, it is still made of the elements hydrogen and oxygen.

Changing Shape Have you ever crumpled a sheet of paper into a ball? If so, you caused physical change. Whether it exists as one flat sheet or a crumpled ball, the matter is still paper. Similarly, if you cut fruit into pieces to make a fruit salad, you do not change the composition of the fruit. You change only its form. Generally, whenever you cut, tear, grind, or bend matter, you are causing a physical change.

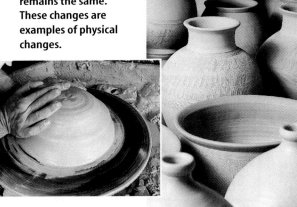

Section ✔Assessment Planner

PORTFOLIO
Assessment, p. 81
PERFORMANCE ASSESSMENT
Try at Home MiniLAB, p. 81
Math Skills Activity, p. 84
Skill Builder Activities, p. 87
See page 94 for more options.

CONTENT ASSESSMENT
Section, p. 87
Challenge, p. 87
Chapter, pp. 94–95

Dissolving What type of change occurs when you add sugar to iced tea, as shown in **Figure 8?** Although the sugar seems to disappear, it does not. Instead, the sugar dissolves. When this happens, the particles of sugar spread out in the liquid. The composition of the sugar stays the same, which is why the iced tea tastes sweet. Only the form of the sugar has changed.

Figure 8
Physical changes are occurring constantly. The sugar blending into the iced tea is an example of a physical change.

Changing State Another common physical change occurs when matter changes from one state to another. When an ice cube melts, for example, it becomes liquid water. The solid ice and the liquid water have the same composition. The only difference is the form.

Matter can change from any state to another. Freezing is the opposite of melting. During freezing, a liquid changes into a solid. A liquid also can change into a gas. This process is known as vaporization. During the reverse process, called condensation, a gas changes into a liquid. **Figure 9** summarizes these changes.

In some cases, matter changes between the solid and gas states without ever becoming a liquid. The process in which a solid changes directly into a gas is called sublimation. The opposite process, in which a gas changes into a solid, is called deposition.

Figure 9
Look at the photographs below to identify the different physical changes that bromine undergoes as it changes from one state to another.

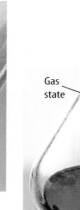

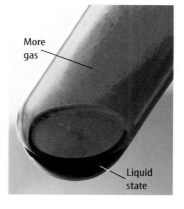

Solid state

Gas state

Liquid state

More gas

Liquid state

2 Teach

Physical Changes

Use Science Words
Word Usage Have students use the word *dissolve* in a sentence that describes its meaning and type of change. Possible answer: A substance dissolves when its particles spread out in a liquid; this is a physical change. L2 ELL IS **Linguistic**

Quick Demo
Weigh out a 20–30 g sample of dry ice. Place the sample in a zipper-closure plastic bag and allow students to observe it. Release gas from the bag periodically as students observe. Ask students to list the physical properties and physical changes they observe. physical properties: mass, white, solid; physical changes: sublimates into a gas L2 ELL
IS **Visual-Spatial**

Curriculum Connection

History Heat hardens clay into a form that can be used for pottery. Intense heating causes a chemical, as well as physical, change to the clay. Because pottery does not easily decompose, historians have used pottery remains to study ancient civilizations. Ask students to research one early civilization and give a short presentation about the pottery it produced. Civilizations include Maya, Toltec, Inca, Aztec, Cush, Olmec, Cretan, and those in Egypt, Mesopotamia, and the Indus Valley. L3

Resource Manager

Chapter Resources Booklet
  Transparency Activity, p. 43
  Directed Reading for Content Mastery, pp. 21, 22
Cultural Diversity, p. 5

Chemical Changes

Caption Answer

Figure 10 a change that causes substances to be changed into different substances

Visual Learning

Figure 10 Explain to students that in fireworks, different compounds react with oxygen to produce bright colors. Copper acetoarsenate produces blue, anhydrous strontium carbonate produces red, and barium chloride produces green. L2
Visual-Spatial

✔ Reading Check

Answer A chemical change alters the composition of the matter, while a physical change alters appearance but not composition.

Fun Fact

In order for iron to rust, it must be exposed not only to oxygen in air, but also to water, often as humidity in air. The chemical formula for rust is $Fe_2O_3 \cdot H_2O$. Once some rust has formed, it catalyzes the reaction, and causes additional rust to form faster.

Quick Demo

Bring to class a tarnished piece of silver and some silver polish. Polish the silver in front of the class. Discuss whether the process of cleaning the silver is a physical change or a chemical change. **That is, does silver polish remove tarnish by rubbing it off, or does it react with the tarnish so that the silver is restored?** Most silver polishes remove tarnish by rubbing it off. This is a physical change. L2 **Visual-Spatial**

Figure 10
These brilliant fireworks result from chemical changes. *What is a chemical change?*

Chemical Changes

It's the Fourth of July in New York City. Brilliant fireworks are exploding in the night sky. When you look at fireworks, such as these in **Figure 10,** you see dazzling sparkles of red and white trickle down in all directions. The explosion of fireworks is an example of a chemical change. During a **chemical change,** substances are changed into different substances. In other words, the composition of the substance changes.

You are familiar with another chemical change if you have ever left your bicycle out in the rain. After a while, a small chip in the paint leads to an area of a reddish, powdery substance. This substance is rust. When iron in steel is exposed to oxygen and water in air, iron and oxygen atoms combine to form the principle component in rust. In a similar way, coins tarnish when exposed to air. These chemical changes are shown in **Figure 11.**

✔ Reading Check
How is a chemical change different from a physical change?

Figure 11
Each of these examples shows the results of a chemical change. In each case, the substances that are present after the change are different from those that were present before the change.

🔵 Cultural Diversity

Alchemists Greek, Arabic, and Chinese alchemists began studying chemical changes more than 2,000 years ago. Their work contributed greatly to the understanding of chemical substances and changes. Have students investigate different aspects of alchemy and present their findings to the class. Possible subjects include the processing of metals and the transmutation of metals into gold, the use of minerals and other chemicals for healing, chemical apparatuses developed by alchemists, elements identified by alchemists, and the making of cosmetics and perfumes. L3 **Linguistic**

Figure 12
The brilliant colors of autumn result from a chemical change.

Signs of Chemical Changes

Physical changes are relatively easy to identify. If only the form of a substance changes, you have observed a physical change. How can you tell whether a change is a chemical change? If you think you are unfamiliar with chemical changes, think again.

You have witnessed a spectacular change if you have seen the leaves of trees change colors in autumn, but you are not seeing a chemical change. Chemicals called pigments give tree leaves their color. In **Figure 12,** the pigment that is responsible for the green color you see during the summer is chlorophyll (KLOHR uh fihl). Two other pigments result in the colors you see in the red tree. Throughout the spring and summer, chlorophyll is present in much greater amounts than these other pigments, so you see leaves as green. In autumn, however, changes in temperature and rainfall amounts cause trees to stop producing chlorophyll. The chlorophyll that is already present undergoes a chemical change in which it loses its green color. Without chlorophyll, the red and yellow pigments, which are always present, can be seen.

Color Perhaps you have found that a half-eaten apple turns brown. The reason is that a chemical change occurs when food spoils. Maybe you have toasted a marshmallow or a slice of bread and watched them turn black. In each case, the color of the food changes as it is cooked because a chemical change occurs.

SCIENCE Online

Research Visit the Glencoe Science Web site at **science.glencoe.com** for more information about how to recognize chemical changes. Choose one example not mentioned in the chapter and present it to the class as a poster or in an oral report.

TRY AT HOME
Mini LAB

Comparing Changes

Procedure
1. Separate a piece of **fine steel wool** into two halves.
2. Dip one half in **tap water.**
3. Place each piece of steel wool on a separate **paper plate** and let them sit overnight.
4. Repeat step two with the same half of steel wool for five days.

Analysis
1. Did you observe any changes in the steel wool? If so, describe them.
2. If you observed changes, were they physical or chemical? How do you know?

Signs of Chemical Changes

Life Science INTEGRATION

The plant pigments that are responsible for the yellow and orange colors of leaves are carotenoids. The pigments responsible for red and purple colors are called anthocyanins. Anthocyanins change color depending on the acidity of the cell sap in the plant.

TRY AT HOME
Mini LAB

Purpose Students will observe a chemical change in a piece of steel wool. L1 ELL
Kinesthetic
Materials piece of fine steel wool, tap water, paper plate
Teaching Strategy Have students tear the steel wool or cut it with tin snips.
Analysis
1. The steel wool dipped in water turned orange.
2. chemical, because the color changed

Assessment

Portfolio Have each student prepare a series of drawings of the steel wool over a two-week period. Students should include descriptions of the chemical changes with the drawings. Use **PASC,** p. 127.

SCIENCE Online
Internet Addresses
_____
_____
_____

Explore the Glencoe Science Web site at **science.glencoe.com** to find out more about topics in this section.

Resource Manager

Chapter Resources Booklet
 MiniLAB, p. 4
Life Science Critical Thinking/Problem Solving, p. 8
Home and Community Involvement, p. 27

Visual Learning

Figure 14 Discuss with students the physical and chemical properties of each item. On the board, make a listing of the class's observations. L2 ELL
IS Visual-Spatial

Discussion

What evidence do you have that chemical changes occur as fruits and vegetables ripen? Possible answers: apples and tomatoes turn red, pears and bananas become yellow, oranges turn from green to orange

Extension

Tell students that reactions that give off energy are called exothermic, while those that require energy are called endothermic. Limestone buildings and statues are chemically changed by acid rain. Have students find out what the chemical changes are and whether the reaction is exothermic or endothermic. Calcium carbonate reacts with sulfuric acid to produce water and calcium sulfate, which wash away, and carbon dioxide gas. The reaction is exothermic. L3
IS Logical-Mathematical

Figure 13
Cake batter undergoes a chemical change as it absorbs energy during cooking.

Figure 14
A Energy is released when a firefly glows, **B** when fuel is burned in a camping stove, and **C** when sodium and chlorine undergo a chemical change to form table salt.

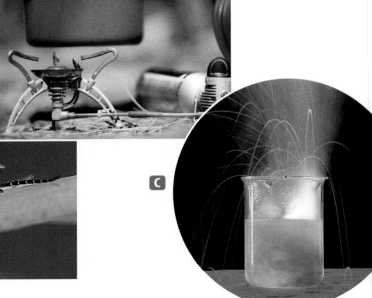

Energy Another sign of a chemical change is the release or gain of energy by an object. Many substances must absorb energy in order to undergo a chemical change. For example, energy is absorbed during the chemical changes involved in cooking. When you bake a cake or make pancakes, energy is absorbed by the batter as it changes from a runny mix into what you see in **Figure 13.**

Another chemical change in which a substance absorbs energy occurs during the production of cement. This process begins with the heating of limestone. Ordinarily, limestone will remain unchanged for centuries. But when it absorbs energy during heating, it undergoes a chemical change in which it turns into lime and carbon dioxide.

Energy also can be released during a chemical change. The fireworks you read about earlier released energy in the form of light that you can see. As shown in **Figure 14A,** a chemical change within a firefly releases energy in the form of light. Fuel burned in the camping stove shown in **Figure 14B** releases energy you see as light and feel as heat. You also can see that energy is released when sodium and chlorine are combined and ignited in **Figure 14C.** During this chemical change, the original substances change into sodium chloride, which is ordinary table salt.

Science Journal

Energy in Physical and Chemical Changes
Ask students to list all the changes they can think of that involve the absorption or release of energy and classify each as a chemical or physical change. Changes might include cooking (chemical), boiling water (physical), burning fuel (chemical), cooling your hand by putting it in cold water (physical). L2
IS Logical-Mathematical

Teacher FYI

Adding energy does not necessarily produce a chemical change. Adding heat to substances can cause them to warm up or to change state, neither of which is a chemical change. In the same way, the release of energy does not necessarily indicate that a chemical change has occurred.

Odor It takes only one experience with a rotten egg to learn that they smell much different than fresh eggs. When eggs and other foods spoil, they undergo chemical change. The change in odor is a clue to the chemical change. This clue can be used to save lives. When you smell an odd odor in foods, such as chicken, pork, or mayonnaise, you know that the food has undergone a chemical change. You can use this clue to avoid eating spoiled food and protect yourself from becoming ill.

Gases or Solids Look at the antacid tablet in **Figure 15A.** You can produce similar bubbles if you pour vinegar on baking soda. The formation of a gas is a clue to a chemical change. What other products undergo chemical changes and produce bubbles?

Figure 15B shows another clue to a chemical change—the formation of a solid. A solid that separates out of a solution during a chemical change is called a precipitate. The precipitate in the photograph forms when a solution containing sodium iodide is mixed with a solution containing lead nitrate.

Astronomy
INTEGRATION

A meteoroid is a chunk of metal or stone in space. Every day, meteoroids enter Earth's atmosphere. When this happens, the meteoroid burns as a result of friction with gases in the atmosphere. A streak of light produced during this chemical change is known as a meteor or shooting star. In your Science Journal, infer why most meteoroids never reach Earth's surface.

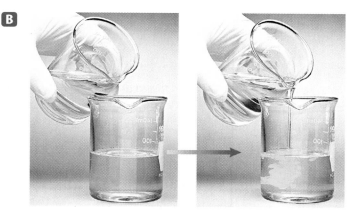

Astronomy
INTEGRATION

When a meteoroid burns up in Earth's atmosphere, it is called a meteor; when it strikes Earth, it is called a meteorite. Most meteoroids are debris from asteroid collisions or broken-up comets. *Answers will vary but should include that during the chemical change that occurs in the atmosphere, most meteors burn up.*

Quick Demo

Pour 10 mL of vinegar into a large glass container. Measure and record the temperature of the vinegar. Add 5 mL of baking soda to the vinegar, and take the temperature again. The heat and gas produced are evidence that a chemical reaction has occurred. Explain that in this reaction, the baking soda reacted with the vinegar to form sodium acetate, water, and the gas, carbon dioxide. [L2] ELL
[LS] **Visual-Spatial**

Figure 15
A The bubbles of gas formed when this antacid tablet is dropped into water indicate a chemical change. **B** The solid forming from two liquids is another sign that a chemical change has taken place.

IDENTIFYING
Misconceptions

The production of bubbles of gas does not necessarily mean a chemical change has taken place. In carbonated soft drinks, carbon dioxide gas dissolved in the liquid forms bubbles when the bottle or can is opened. Bubbles also form when a liquid changes state to a gas by boiling.

Teacher FYI

The main ingredient in car air bags is sodium azide, NaN_3. Upon impact at speeds above 10–15 mph, a sensor transmits an electrical signal that ignites a detonator compound in the bag. Heat from the detonator causes the sodium azide to decompose into sodium and nitrogen gas, which, in 0.03 seconds, inflates the bag.

Resource Manager

Chapter Resources Booklet
    Lab Activity, pp. 13–16
Science Inquiry Labs, p. 25
Earth Science Critical Thinking/Problem Solving, p. 15

Signs of Chemical Changes, continued

Caption Answer

Figure 16 No; the ashes are the result of a chemical change.

✔ Reading Check

Answer Possible answers: change in color, loss or gain of energy, odor, production of a gas or solid, the change is not easily reversible

Math Skills Activity

National Math Standards

Correlation to Mathematics Objectives
1, 2, 4, 6, 8, 9

Answer to Problem

This is what you know:
temperature = 156° F
This is what you want to find:
temperature in degrees Celsius
This is the equation you need to use:
(°C × 1.8) + 32 = °F
Rearrange the equation to solve for °C.
°C = (°F − 32)/1.8
Then substitute the known value for °F.
°C = (156 − 32)/1.8 = 68.9°C

Figure 16
As wood burns, it turns into a pile of ashes and gases that rise into the air. *Can you turn ashes back into wood?*

Not Easily Reversed How do physical and chemical changes differ from one another? Think about ice for a moment. After solid ice melts into liquid water, it can refreeze into solid ice if the temperature drops enough. Freezing and melting are physical changes. The substances produced during a chemical change cannot be changed back into the original substances by physical means. For example, the wood in **Figure 16** changes into ashes and gases that are released into the air. After wood is burned, it cannot be restored to its original form as a log.

Think about a few of the chemical changes you just read about to see if this holds true. An antacid tablet cannot be restored to its original form after being dropped in water. Rotten eggs cannot be made fresh again, and pancakes cannot be turned back into batter. The substances that existed before the chemical change no longer exist.

✔ **Reading Check** *What signs indicate a chemical change?*

Math Skills Activity

Converting Temperatures

Fahrenheit is a non-SI temperature scale. Because it is used so often, it is useful to be able to convert from Fahrenheit to Celsius. The equation that relates Celsius degrees to Fahrenheit degrees is:

(°C × 1.8) + 32 = °F

Using this information, what is 15°F on the Celsius scale?

Solution

1. *This is what you know:* temperature = 15°F
2. *This is what you want to find:* temperature in degrees Celsius
3. *This is the equation you need to use:* (°C × 1.8) + 32 = °F
4. *Rearrange the equation to solve for °C.* (°C × 1.8) + 32 = °F
   °C = (°F − 32)/1.8

Then substitute the known value for °F. °C = (15 − 32)/1.8 = −9.4° C

Check your answer by substituting the Celsius temperature into the original equation. Did you calculate the Fahrenheit temperature that was given in the question?

Practice Problem

Water is being heated on the stove at 156°F. What is this temperature on the Celsius scale?

For help refer to the Math Skill Handbook.

84 ◆ K   CHAPTER 3 Properties and Changes of Matter

Inclusion Strategies

Gifted Have students investigate what must occur to change the ashes left after a piece of wood has burned into new wood and identify each as a chemical or physical change. The ashes must become part of soil (physical). A tree must grow in the soil (chemical). The tree must absorb the minerals in the ash (physical), and incorporate them in its wood (chemical). L3
IS **Logical-Mathematical**

✔ Active Reading

Reflective Journal In this strategy, students identify what they have learned about the nature of physical and chemical changes. Have students divide sheets of paper into several columns and record their thoughts under headings such as "What I learned," "What surprises did I experience," "What questions do I have," and "Overall response." Have students then write a Reflective Journal entry for an activity in this section.

Chemical Versus Physical Change

Now you have learned about many different physical and chemical changes. You have read about several characteristics that you can use to distinguish between physical and chemical changes. The most important point for you to remember is that in a physical change, the composition of a substance does not change and in a chemical change, the composition of a substance does change. When a substance undergoes a physical change, only its form changes. In a chemical change, both form and composition change.

When the wood and copper in **Figure 17** undergo physical changes, the original wood and copper still remain after the change. When a substance undergoes a chemical change, however, the original substance is no longer present after the change. Instead, different substances are produced during the chemical change. When the wood and copper in **Figure 17** undergo chemical changes, wood and copper have changed into new substances with new physical and chemical properties.

Physical and chemical changes are used to recycle or reuse certain materials. **Figure 18** discusses the importance of some of these changes in recycling.

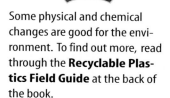

Some physical and chemical changes are good for the environment. To find out more, read through the **Recyclable Plastics Field Guide** at the back of the book.

Figure 17
When a substance undergoes a physical change, its composition stays the same. When a substance undergoes a chemical change, it is changed into different substances.

Chemical change

Physical change

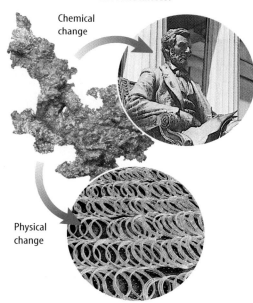

Chemical change

Physical change

Chemical Versus Physical Change

IDENTIFYING Misconceptions

There are situations in which each of the signs of a chemical change discussed in these pages occurs during a physical change. This can cause confusion. A chemical change has occurred only if new substances have been created. Make sure students understand that changes in color and odor, the production of gases or precipitates, the absorption or release of energy, and the fact that a change is difficult to reverse are indications that they should look further to see whether a new substance has been produced.

Use an Analogy

Tell students that chemical changes occur and new substances form when electrons interact to form bonds between different kinds of atoms. Discuss the following analogy. Think of the members of a basketball team as electrons associated with a basketball atom. They practice together and play games with other basketball teams. These are analogous to physical changes. The basketball players interact but no new substance is formed. Suppose some of the players decide to join with players from a soccer team to form a sports club. These players are like electrons that have formed bonds with a different kind of atom to form a new substance.

Inclusion Strategies

Visually Impaired Describe and discuss in detail with these students each of the photographs in **Figure 17.** Ask another student to describe the observable physical properties in each photo and tell how he or she knows which shows a physical change and which shows a chemical change. L2 **Visual-Spatial**

Resource Manager

Chapter Resources Booklet
  Enrichment, p. 30

Mathematics Skill Activities, p. 9

Physical Science Critical Thinking/Problem Solving, p. 10

Visualizing Recycling

Have students examine the pictures and read the captions. Then ask the following questions.

What are some examples of physical changes described in this feature? Possible answer: Pulverizing or crushing of glass; melting of plastics and re-forming them; the shredding of plastics; shredding of rubber; crushing, flattening, and chopping apart of car bodies; separating iron and steel from other materials with a magnet.

Why is it better to remove steel wires from rubber tires? Possible answer: It would prevent pieces of wire from sticking out of pavement where it could damage vehicles tires or from playground surfaces where it could cause injuries. Also, the steel could then be recycled with the other metal car parts.

Activity

Have small groups of students research making new glass bottles from cullet. Have each group make a poster that illustrates the chemical and physical changes that are involved in the process. [L2] COOP LEARN
[IS] **Visual-Spatial and Interpersonal**

Extension

Students can write poems or songs about physical and chemical changes involved in recycling. Ask volunteers to read their poems or sing their songs for the class. [L3]
[IS] **Auditory-Musical**

Figure 18

Recycling is a way to separate wastes into their component parts and then reuse those components in new products. In order to be recycled, wastes need to be both physically—and sometimes chemically—changed. The average junked automobile contains about 62 percent iron and steel, 28 percent other materials such as aluminum, copper, and lead, and 10 percent rubber, plastics, and various materials.

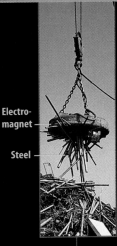

Electromagnet

Steel

◀ Rubber tires can be shredded and added to asphalt pavement and playground surfaces. New recycling processes make it possible to supercool tires to a temperature at which the rubber is shattered like glass. A magnet can then draw out steel from the tires and parts of the car.

▼ After being crushed and flattened, car bodies are chopped into small pieces. Metals are separated from other materials using physical processes. Some metals are separated using powerful magnets. Others are separated by hand.

◀ Glass can be pulverized and used in asphalt pavement, new glass, and even artwork. This sculpture named *Groundswell,* was created by artist Maya Lin, using windshield glass.

▲ Some plastics can be melted and formed into new products. Others are ground up or shredded and used as fillers or insulating materials.

86 ◆ K CHAPTER 3 Properties and Changes of Matter

Resource Manager

Chapter Resources Booklet
   Reinforcement, p. 28
   Transparency Activity, pp. 45–46
Performance Assessment in the Science Classroom, p. 44

Conservation of Mass

During a chemical change, the form or the composition of the matter changes. The particles within the matter rearrange to form new substances, but they are not destroyed and new particles are not created. The number and type of particles remains the same. As a result, the total mass of the matter is the same before and after a physical or chemical change. This is known as the **law of conservation of mass.**

This law can sometimes be difficult to believe, especially when the materials remaining after a chemical change might look different from those before it. In many chemical changes in which mass seems to be gained or lost, the difference is often due to a gas being given off or taken in. The difference, for example, before and after the candle in **Figure 19** is burned is in the gases released into the air. If the gases could be contained in a chamber around the candle, you would see that the mass does not change.

The scientist who first performed the careful experiments necessary to prove that mass is conserved was Antoine Lavoisier (AN twan • luh VWAH see ay) in the eighteenth century. It was Lavoisier who recognized that the mass of gases that are given off or taken from the air during chemical changes account for any differences in mass.

Figure 19
The candle looks as if it lost mass when it was burned. However, if you could trap and measure the gases given up during burning you would find that the mass of the candle and the gases is equal to the mass of the original candle.

Use Science Words

Word Origins Tell students that the word *conservation* comes from the Latin prefix *con-*, meaning "with or together," and the Latin verb *servare*, meaning "to keep or guard." Ask how these meanings relate to the law of conservation of mass. Mass is kept or guarded so that it is kept together, or the same. L2 IS **Linguistic**

③ Assess

Reteach

Ask students to look at the illustrations on these pages and describe the physical properties, chemical properties, physical changes, and chemical changes they see. L2 ELL IS **Visual-Spatial**

Challenge

Have students look at objects in the classroom and discuss the physical and chemical changes that took place as they were made. Wood for desks was physically changed from trees; rubber for erasers and plastic for chairs were produced by chemical changes, then physically shaped. L2 IS **Logical-Mathematical**

✔Assessment

Content Have students list five indications that a chemical change may have taken place. changes in color, odor, and energy, the production of gases or solids, and the fact that a change is difficult to reverse Use **Performance Assessment in the Science Classroom,** p. 91.

Section ② Assessment

1. What happens during a physical change?

2. List five physical changes you can observe in your home. Explain how you decided that each change is physical.

3. What kind of change occurs on the surface of bread when it is toasted—physical or chemical? Explain.

4. What does it mean to say that mass is conserved during a chemical change?

5. **Think Critically** A log is reduced to a small pile of ash when it burns. The law of conservation of mass states that the total mass of matter is the same before and after a chemical change. Explain the difference in mass between the log and the ash.

Skill Builder Activities

6. **Classifying** Classify the following changes as physical or chemical: baking a cake, folding towels, burning gasoline, melting snow, grinding beef into a hamburger, pouring milk into a glass, making cookies, and cutting a sheet of paper into paper dolls. **For more help, refer to the** Science Skill Handbook.

7. **Solving One-Step Equations** Magnesium and oxygen undergo a chemical change to form magnesium oxide. How many grams of magnesium oxide will be produced when 0.486 g of oxygen completely react with 0.738 g of magnesium? **For more help, refer to the** Math Skill Handbook.

Answers to Section Assessment

1. Matter is changed in appearance but not in composition.

2. Examples include cutting paper, pouring milk on cereal, mowing the lawn, and melting ice. These are physical changes because the matter does not change composition.

3. Chemical; the bread changes in color and odor, absorbs heat energy, becomes dark, and cannot be returned to its original form.

4. The particles within the matter are rearranged, but the total mass of the matter remains the same.

5. The difference in mass is a result of the mass of gas that was formed in the reaction and escaped.

6. physical: folding towels, melting snow, grinding beef, pouring milk, cutting paper; chemical: baking a cake, burning gasoline, making cookies

7. 1.22 g

Recognize the Problem

Purpose
Students will infer the effectiveness of different brands of toothpaste in preventing tooth decay. L2 **Kinesthetic**

Process Skills
designing an experiment, forming a hypothesis, recording and analyzing data, comparing, inferring, predicting

Time Required
One 45-minute period and daily observations for a week

Alternate Materials
You might want to include a tube of toothpaste that does not contain sodium fluoride in its ingredients list.

Form a Hypothesis

Possible Hypothesis
Most student hypotheses will reflect that toothpastes containing sodium fluoride will prevent the eggshells from reacting with the acid.

Test Your Hypothesis

Possible Procedures
Brush a different brand of toothpaste over each eggshell. Leave two eggshells without toothpaste. Place half the treated eggs in lemon juice and the other half in apple juice. Place one untreated egg in each juice. Observe the eggs each day for one week for signs of a chemical reaction.

Teaching Strategies
It is not necessary that all groups use the same brands of toothpaste.

Activity — *Design Your Own Experiment*

Battle of the Toothpastes

Your teeth are made of a compound called hydroxyapatite (hi DRAHK see A puh tite). The sodium fluoride in toothpaste undergoes a chemical reaction with hydroxyapatite to form a new compound on the surface of your teeth. This compound resists food acids that cause tooth decay, another chemical change. In this activity, you will design an experiment to test the effectiveness of different toothpaste brands. The compound found in your teeth is similar to the mineral compound found in eggshells. Treating hard-boiled eggs with toothpaste is similar to brushing your teeth with toothpaste. Soaking the eggs in food acids such as vinegar for several days will produce similar conditions as eating foods, which contain acids that will produce a chemical change in your teeth, for several months.

Recognize the Problem

Which brands of toothpaste provide the greatest protection against tooth decay?

Form a Hypothesis

Form a hypothesis about the effectiveness of different brands of toothpaste.

Goals
- **Observe** how toothpaste helps prevent tooth decay.
- **Design** an experiment to test the effectiveness of various toothpaste brands.

Safety Precautions

Possible Materials
2 or 3 different brands of toothpaste
drinking glasses or bowls
hard boiled eggs
concentrated lemon juice
apple juice
water
artist's paint brush

Resource Manager

Chapter Resources Booklet
  Activity Worksheet, pp. 7–8
Science Inquiry Labs, p. 51
Lab Management and Safety, p. 67

Egg	Day 1	Day 2	Day 3
Toothpaste 1			
Toothpaste 2			
No Toothpaste			

Test Your Hypothesis

Plan

1. **Describe** how you will use the materials to test the toothpaste.
2. **List** the steps you will follow to test your hypothesis.
3. **Decide** on the length of time that you will conduct your experiment.
4. **Identify** the control and variables you will use in your experiment.
5. **Create** a data table in your Science Journal to record your observations, measurements, and results.

6. **Describe** how you will measure the amount of protection each toothpaste brand provides.

Do

1. Make sure your teacher approves your plan before you start.
2. **Conduct** your experiment as planned. Be sure to follow all proper safety precautions.
3. **Record** your observations in your data table.

Analyze Your Data

1. **Compare** the untreated eggshells with the shells you treated with toothpaste.
2. **Compare** the condition of the eggshells you treated with different brands of toothpaste.

3. **Compare** the condition of the eggshells soaked in lemon juice and in apple juice.
4. **Identify** unintended variables you discovered in your experiment that might have influenced the results.

Draw Conclusions

1. Did the results support your hypothesis? **Identify** strengths and weaknesses of your hypothesis.
2. **Explain** why the eggs treated with toothpaste were better protected than the untreated eggshells.
3. **Identify** which brands of toothpaste, if any best protected the eggshells from decay.
4. **Evaluate** the scientific explanation for why adding fluoride to toothpaste and drinking water prevents tooth decay.

5. **Predict** what would happen to your protected eggs if you left them in the food acids for several weeks.
6. **Infer** why it is a good idea to brush with fluoride toothpaste.

Compare your results with the results of your classmates. **Create** a poster advertising the benefits of fluoride toothpaste.

✓ Assessment

Performance Have students make labeled posters of their experimental designs to share with the class. Encourage them to include their posters in their portfolios. Use **Performance Assessment in the Science Classroom,** p. 145.

Encourage students to use a computer graphics program to prepare their posters.

Troubleshooting

Students should be sure to coat all parts of the eggs with toothpaste. Any unprotected parts will react with the acid.

Expected Outcome

Eggshells coated with a sodium fluoride toothpaste should show little or no reaction with the acid. The control eggshell should show evidence of being eaten away and softening after several days.

Analyze Your Data

1. The untreated eggshell shows evidence of a chemical reaction, while the treated eggshells do not.
2. Answers will depend on the brands of toothpaste tested.
3. The eggshell in lemon juice should show more evidence of a reaction.
4. Answers will vary.

Error Analysis

Have students compare their results and their hypotheses and explain why any differences occurred.

Draw Conclusions

1. Answers will be determined by student hypotheses.
2. The sodium fluoride in the toothpaste prevented the eggshells from chemically reacting with the food acid.
3. Answers will vary.
4. Evidence indicates that fluoride prevents a compound similar to that in teeth from reacting with food acids.
5. The protection would lose its effectiveness and the eggshells would react with the acids.
6. Regular brushing with fluoride toothpaste prevents chemicals in teeth from reacting with food acids.

Science Stats

Content Background

One advantage of hydrogen peroxide over other bleaches is that, as it oxidizes, it breaks down into oxygen and water. Other bleaches might contain materials such as chlorine that can harm the environment if they are present in large quantities.

Discussion

Contact a local packing store for samples of packing peanuts made from corn and those made from traditional plastic. Show students how the corn-based packing decomposes when placed in water but the plastic packing material does not. **How would using such a biodegradable packing material benefit the environment?** The material would decompose into an environmentally safe material when it got wet in a landfill.

Activity

Have students keep track of how many soft drink cans they empty in a week. Have them research how much energy is saved when they recycle these cans. Recycling takes only 5% of the energy needed to refine aluminum from ore. Have groups of students prepare posters to place around the school promoting recycling. If possible, obtain permission from the school administration to establish a recycling program in the school.

Science Stats

Strange Changes

Did you know...

...A hair colorist is also a chemist!

Colorists use hydrogen peroxide and ammonia to swell and open the cuticle-like shafts on your hair. Once these are open, the chemicals in hair dye can get into your natural pigment molecules and chemically change your hair color. The first safe commercial hair color was created in 1909 in France.

...Americans consume about 175 million kg of sauerkraut each year.

During the production of sauerkraut, bacteria produce lactic acid. The acid chemically breaks down the material in the cabbage, making it translucent and tangy.

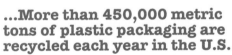

...More than 450,000 metric tons of plastic packaging are recycled each year in the U.S.

Discarded plastics undergo physical changes including melting and shredding. They are then converted into flakes or pellets, which are used to make new products. Recycled plastic is used to make clothes, furniture, carpets, and even lumber.

SCIENCE Online
Internet Addresses

_____

_____

_____

Explore the Glencoe Science Web site at **science.glencoe.com** to find out more about topics in this feature.

...The U.S. population consumes about 1.36 billion L of gasoline each day.
When ignited in an enclosed space, such as in an internal combustion engine, gasoline undergoes many chemical changes to deliver the energy needed for an automobile to move.

Projected Recycling Rates by Material, 2000

Material	1995 Recycling	Proj. Recycling
Paper/Paperboard	40.0%	43 to 46%
Glass	24.5%	27 to 36%
Ferrous Metal	36.5%	42 to 55%
Aluminum	34.6%	46 to 48%
Plastics	5.3%	7 to 10%
Yard Waste	30.3%	40 to 50%
Total Materials	27.0%	30 to 35%

...It is possible to change corn into plastic! Normally plastics are made from petroleum, but chemists have discovered how to chemically convert corn and other plants into plastic. A factory in Nebraska is scheduled to produce about 140,000 metric tons of the corn-based plastic by 2002.

Do the Math

1. There are 275 million people in the United States. Calculate the average amount of sauerkraut consumed by each person in the United States in one year.
2. How many liters of gasoline does the U.S. population consume during a leap year?
3. If chemists can produce 136 kg of plastic from 27 kg of corn, how much corn is needed to make 816 kg of plastic?

Go Further

Every time you cook, you make physical and chemical changes to food. Go to the Glencoe Science Web site at **science.glencoe.com** or to your local or school library to find out what chemical or physical changes take place when cooking ingredients are heated or cooled.

Do the Math

Teaching Strategies
- Have interested students investigate the recycling symbols on many plastic items. These symbols consist of a number contained in a triangle made from three arrows.
- Have students research what each recycling symbol means and which types of plastics are recycled in their locale.
- Show students a diagram of how an internal combustion engine operates. Emphasize to them that the proper proportion of gasoline and oxygen is necessary for efficient use of fuel.

Answers
1. 0.636 kg/person
2. about 498 billion L
3. 162 kg of corn

Go Further

Physical changes include change in state, such as melting. Before investigating chemical changes, ask students, as a class, to brainstorm signs that indicate a chemical change has occurred. Such indications include: energy release or absorption and color or odor change.

Visual Learning

Projected Recycling Rates by Material, 2000 By what percent will the recycling rate increase from 1995 to 2000 for glass and paper? 2.5 to 11.5%; 3.0 to 6.0%, respectively Have students use a dictionary to find out what *ferrous* means. A ferrous metal is any metal that is primarily iron, such as steel. **If 259 kg of aluminum products were used by** a family, what mass of that aluminum was likely to be recycled in 1995? 89.6 kg **The recycling rate is over 60% for aluminum cans. Why doesn't this percent match those in the table?** Aluminum is used in many other products that are not as likely to be recycled. Such products include foil, bicycle parts, and window screen.

Chapter ③
Study Guide

Reviewing Main Ideas

Preview

Students can answer the questions in their Science Journals. Discuss the answers as you go through the chapter. **LS Linguistic**

Review

Students can write their answers, then compare them with those of other students. **LS Interpersonal**

Reteach

Students can look at the illustrations and describe details that support the main ideas of the chapter. **LS Visual-Spatial**

Answers to Chapter Review

SECTION 1
3. 1,500 cm³
5. ability to burn

SECTION 2
4. a change in color

Chapter ③ Study Guide

Reviewing Main Ideas

Section 1 Physical and Chemical Properties

1. Matter can be described by its characteristics, or properties.

2. A physical property is a characteristic that can be observed without altering the composition of the sample.

3. Physical properties include color, shape, smell, taste, and texture, as well as measurable quantities such as mass, volume, density, melting point, and boiling point. *What is the volume of this box?*

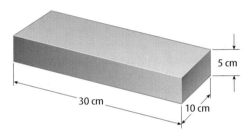

4. Matter can exist in different states—solid, liquid, or gas. The state of matter is a physical property.

5. A chemical property is a characteristic that cannot be observed without changing what the sample is made of. *What chemical property is being shown here?*

Section 2 Physical and Chemical Changes

1. During a physical change, the composition of matter stays the same but the appearance changes in some way.

2. Physical changes occur when matter is ripped, cut, torn, or bent, or when matter changes from one state to another.

3. A chemical change occurs when the composition of matter changes.

4. Signs of chemical change include changes in energy, color, odor, or the production of gases or solids. *What evidence from this photo indicates a chemical change?*

5. According to the law of conservation of mass, mass cannot be created or destroyed. As a result, the mass of the substances that were present before a physical or chemical change is equal to the mass of the substances that are present after the change.

FOLDABLES
Reading & Study
Skills

After You Read

To help you review matter's physical and chemical properties and changes, use the information on your Foldable.

FOLDABLES
Reading & Study
Skills

After You Read

After students have read the chapter and completed the Foldable described in Before You Read, have them do the activity on the student page.

Dinah Zike

Visualizing Main Ideas

Complete the following concept map on matter.

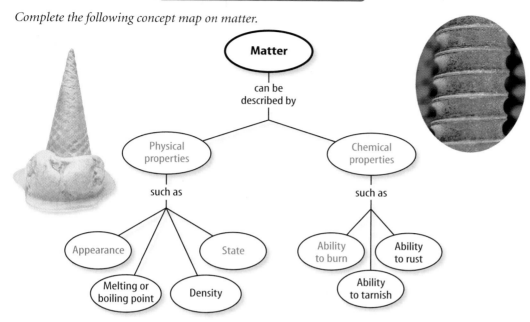

Matter

can be described by

Physical properties → such as → Appearance, Melting or boiling point, Density, State

Chemical properties → such as → Ability to burn, Ability to tarnish, Ability to rust

Vocabulary Review

Vocabulary Words

a. chemical change
b. chemical property
c. physical change
d. physical property
e. law of conservation of mass

Study Tip

Study the material you *don't* understand first. It's easy to review the material you know but it's harder to force yourself to learn the difficult concepts. Reread any topics that you find confusing. You should take notes as you read.

Using Vocabulary

Use what you know about the vocabulary words to answer the following questions. Use complete sentences.

1. Why is color a physical property?
2. What is a physical property that does not change with the amount of matter?
3. What happens during a physical change?
4. What type of change is a change of state?
5. What happens during a chemical change?
6. What are three clues that a chemical change has occurred?
7. What is an example of a chemical change?
8. What is the law of conservation of mass?

Visualizing Main Ideas

See student page.

Vocabulary Review

Using Vocabulary

1. Color can be observed without changing the object.
2. Melting point, boiling point, and density do not change with the amount of matter.
3. The appearance of matter changes but the composition does not change.
4. A change of state is a physical change.
5. During a chemical change, substances are changed into different substances.
6. Clues that a chemical change has occurred include change in color, loss or gain of energy, change of smell, and production of a gas or solid.
7. Accept all reasonable answers. One example of a chemical change is burning wood.
8. The law of conservation of mass states that the total mass of matter is the same before and after a physical or chemical change.

Checking Concepts

1. C
2. C
3. C
4. A
5. D
6. C
7. B
8. C
9. B
10. C

Thinking Critically

11. Beautiful is an opinion; it cannot be measured.

12. Divide the mass of each sample by its volume, and compare the densities. Sample A: $96.5 \div 5 = 19.3$; Sample B: $38.6 \div 4 = 9.65$; Sample A is more likely to be gold.

13. Bending is a physical change because it does not change the composition of the gold.

14. No; some physical changes, such as changing from a liquid to a solid, involve the release of energy, and some chemical changes, such as burning wood, involve the release of energy.

15. During a change of matter, either the form or composition of the matter changes. However, the particles within the matter are not destroyed nor are new particles created. As a result, the total mass of the matter is the same before and after a physical or chemical change.

Checking Concepts

Choose the word or phrase that best answers the question.

1. What changes when the mass of an object increases while volume stays the same?
   - **A)** color
   - **B)** length
   - **C)** density
   - **D)** height

2. What is the volume of a brick that is 20 cm long, 10 cm wide, and 3 cm high?
   - **A)** 33 cm³
   - **B)** 90 cm³
   - **C)** 600 cm³
   - **D)** 1,200 cm³

3. What is the density of an object with a mass of 50 g and a volume of 5 cm³?
   - **A)** 45 g/cm³
   - **B)** 55 g/cm³
   - **C)** 10 g/cm³
   - **D)** 250 g/cm³

4. What word best describes the type of materials that attract iron?
   - **A)** magnetic
   - **B)** chemical
   - **C)** mass
   - **D)** physical

5. Which is an example of a chemical property?
   - **A)** color
   - **B)** mass
   - **C)** density
   - **D)** ability to burn

6. Which is an example of a physical change?
   - **A)** metal rusting
   - **B)** silver tarnishing
   - **C)** water boiling
   - **D)** paper burning

7. What characteristic best describes what happens during a physical change?
   - **A)** composition changes
   - **B)** composition stays the same
   - **C)** form stays the same
   - **D)** mass is lost

8. Which is an example of a chemical change?
   - **A)** water freezes
   - **B)** wood is carved
   - **C)** bread is baked
   - **D)** wire is bent

9. Which is NOT a clue that could indicate a chemical change?
   - **A)** change in color
   - **B)** change in shape
   - **C)** change in energy
   - **D)** change in odor

10. What property stays the same during physical and chemical changes?
    - **A)** density
    - **B)** shape
    - **C)** mass
    - **D)** arrangement of particles

Thinking Critically

11. When asked to give the physical properties of a painting, your friend says the painting is beautiful. Why isn't this description a true scientific property?

12. The density of gold is 19.3 g/cm³. How might you use the properties of matter to figure out which of these two samples is gold?

Mineral Samples		
Sample	Mass	Volume
A	96.5 g	5 cm³
B	38.6 g	4 cm³

13. A jeweler bends gold into a beautiful ring. What type of change is this? Explain.

14. You are told that a sample of matter gives off energy as it changes. Can you conclude which type of change occurred? Why or why not?

15. What happens to mass during chemical and physical changes? Explain.

Developing Skills

16. **Classifying** Decide whether the following properties are physical or chemical.
    - **a.** Sugar can change into alcohol.
    - **b.** Iron can rust.
    - **c.** Alcohol can vaporize.
    - **d.** Paper can burn.
    - **e.** Sugar can dissolve.

Chapter ✓*Assessment* Planner

Portfolio Encourage students to place in their portfolios one or two items of what they consider to be their best work. Examples include:
- Assessment, p. 70
- Assessment, p. 81

Performance Additional performance assessments, Performance Task Assessment Lists, and rubrics for evaluating these activities can be found in Glencoe's **Performance Assessment in the Science Classroom.**

17. Classifying Decide whether the following changes are physical or chemical.
a. Milk spoils.
b. Dynamite explodes.
c. Eggs and milk are stirred together.
d. Ice cream freezes.

18. Comparing and Contrasting Relate such human characteristics as hair and eye color and height and weight to physical properties of matter. Relate human behavior to chemical properties. Think about how you observe these properties.

19. Interpreting Scientific Illustrations Describe the changes shown below and explain why they are different.

Performance Assessment

20. Write a Story Write a story describing an event that you have experienced. Then go back through the story and circle any physical or chemical properties you mentioned. Underline any physical or chemical changes you included.

TECHNOLOGY

 Go to the Glencoe Science Web site at **science.glencoe.com** or use the **Glencoe Science CD-ROM** for additional chapter assessment.

 Test Practice

Unknown matter can be identified by taking a sample of it and comparing its physical properties to those of already identified substances.

Physical Properties		
Substance	Flash Point (°C)	Density (g/cm³)
Gasoline	−45.6	0.720
Palmitic Acid	206.0	0.852
Aluminum	645.0	2.702
Methane	−187.7	0.466

Study the table and answer the following questions.

1. A scientist has a sample of a substance with a density greater than 1 g/cm³. According to the table, which substance might it be?
A) Gasoline   **C)** Aluminum
B) Palmitic acid   **D)** Methane

2. Some substances are very combustible and ignite by themselves if they are warm enough. The flashpoint of a substance is the lowest temperature at which it can catch fire spontaneously. If all the substances in the table have to be stored together, at which of the following temperatures should they be stored?
F) 100°C   **H)** −100°C
G) 0°C   **J)** −200°C

 Test Practice

The Test-Taking Tip was written by The Princeton Review, the nation's leader in test preparation.
1. C
2. J

Developing Skills

16. a. chemical, b. chemical, c. physical, d. chemical, e. physical
17. a. chemical, b. chemical, c. physical, d. physical
18. Human characteristics are like physical properties because they can be observed without interacting with a person. For example, you can observe hair and eye color from a distance. Human behaviors are like chemical properties because they can be observed only by observing that person's interactions.
19. Cutting cake involved only a physical change since only the cake's appearance changed whereas burning a candle involved a definite chemical change.

Performance Assessment

20. Use **Performance Assessment in the Science Classroom**, p. 155.

✓Assessment Resources

📁 **Reproducible Masters**
Chapter Resources Booklet
Chapter Review, pp. 35–36
Chapter Tests, pp. 37–40
Assessment Transparency Activity, p. 47

Glencoe Science Web site
Interactive Tutor
Chapter Quizzes

Glencoe Technology
🖌 Assessment Transparency
💿 Interactive CD-ROM Chapter Quizzes
💿 ExamView Pro Test Bank
💿 Vocabulary PuzzleMaker Software
📼 MindJogger Videoquiz DVD/VHS

CHAPTER 4 THE PERIODIC TABLE

Section/Objectives	Standards		Activities/Features
	National	State/Local	
Chapter Opener	See p. 7T for a Key to Standards.		**Explore Activity:** Make a model of a periodic pattern, p. 97 **Before You Read,** p. 97
Section 1 Introduction to the Periodic Table 🕐 2 sessions 📦 1 block 1. **Describe** the history of the Periodic Table. 2. **Interpret** an element key. 3. **Explain** how the periodic table is organized.	National Content Standards: UCP1, A1, B1, G1, G2		**MiniLAB:** Designing a Periodic Table, p. 99 **Science Online,** p. 102 **Problem-Solving Activity,** p. 103
Section 2 Representative Elements 🕐 3 sessions 📦 1.5 blocks 1. **Recognize** the properties of representative elements. 2. **Identify** uses for the representative elements.	National Content Standards: UCP2, B1, F5		**Life Science Integration,** p. 109
Section 3 Transition Elements 🕐 4 sessions 📦 2 blocks 1. **Identify** properties of some transition elements. 2. **Distinguish** lanthanides from actinides.	National Content Standards: UCP3, A1, B1, G1		**Physics Integration,** p. 114 **Visualizing Synthetic Elements,** p. 115 **Science Online,** p. 116 **Activity:** Preparing a Mixture, p. 117 **Activity:** Health Risks from Heavy Metals, pp. 118–119 **Science and Language Arts:** Anansi Tries to Steal All the Wisdom in the World, pp. 120–121

Activity Materials	Reproducible Resources	Section Assessment	Technology
Explore Activity: sheet of paper, pencil, set of precut shapes (4 of each shape in 4 different colors for each group)	**Chapter Resources Booklet** Foldables Worksheet, p. 13 Directed Reading Overview, p. 15 Note-taking Worksheets, pp. 29–30	**GLENCOE'S ASSESSMENT ADVANTAGE**	
MiniLAB: pens, pencils	**Chapter Resources Booklet** Transparency Activity, p. 40 MiniLAB, p. 3 Enrichment, p. 26 Reinforcement, p. 23 Directed Reading, p. 16 Lab Activity, pp. 9–10, 11–12 Transparency Activity, pp. 43–44 **Home and Community Involvement,** p. 25	**Portfolio** Science Journal, p. 102 **Performance** MiniLAB, p. 99 Skill Builder Activities, p. 104 **Content** Section Assessment, p. 104	⚱ Section Focus Transparency ⚱ Teaching Transparency ◉ Interactive CD-ROM ⌒ Guided Reading Audio Program
Need materials? Contact Science Kit at 1-800-828-7777 or www.sciencekit.com on the Internet.	**Chapter Resources Booklet** Transparency Activity, p. 41 Enrichment, p. 27 Reinforcement, p. 24 Directed Reading, p. 17 **Cultural Diversity,** p. 37 **Physical Science Critical Thinking/Problem Solving,** p. 9	**Portfolio** Assessment, p. 111 **Performance** Skill Builder Activities, p. 111 **Content** Section Assessment, p. 111	⚱ Section Focus Transparency ◉ Interactive CD-ROM ⌒ Guided Reading Audio Program
Activity: copper penny, 30-mesh zinc, hot plate, dilute nitric acid, dilute sodium hydroxide, 2 evaporating dishes, tongs, beakers of cold tap water, teaspoon **Activity:** no materials needed	**Chapter Resources Booklet** Transparency Activity, p. 42 Enrichment, p. 28 Reinforcement, p. 25 Directed Reading, pp. 17, 18 Activity Worksheet, pp. 5–6, 7–8 **Lab Management and Safety,** p. 50 **Physical Science Critical Thinking/Problem Solving,** p. 13	**Portfolio** Activity, p. 114 Assessment, p. 119 **Performance** Skill Builder Activities, p. 116 **Content** Section Assessment, p. 116	⚱ Section Focus Transparency ◉ Interactive CD-ROM ⌒ Guided Reading Audio Program

End of Chapter Assessment

GLENCOE'S ASSESSMENT ADVANTAGE

Blackline Masters	Technology	Professional Series
Chapter Resources Booklet Chapter Review, pp. 33–34 Chapter Tests, pp. 35–38 **Standardized Test Practice by The Princeton Review,** pp. 23–26	📺 MindJogger Videoquiz ◉ Interactive CD-ROM ◉ Vocabulary PuzzleMakers ◉ ExamView Pro Test Bank ◉ Interactive Lesson Planner ◉ Interactive Teacher Edition	Performance Assessment in the Science Classroom (PASC)

Transparencies

Section Focus

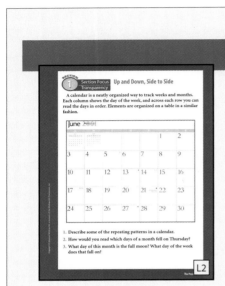

Section Focus Transparency 1 — Up and Down, Side to Side

A calendar is a neatly organized way to track weeks and months. Each column shows the day of the week, and across each row you can read the days in order. Elements are organized on a table in a similar fashion.

1. Describe some of the repeating patterns in a calendar.
2. How would you read which days of a month fell on Thursday?
3. What day of this month is the full moon? What day of the week does that fall on?

L2

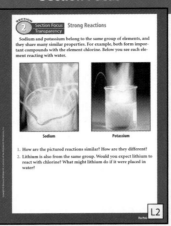

Section Focus Transparency 2 — Strong Reactions

Sodium and potassium belong to the same group of elements, and they share many similar properties. For example, both form important compounds with the element chlorine. Below you see each element reacting with water.

Sodium   Potassium

1. How are the pictured reactions similar? How are they different?
2. Lithium is also from the same group. Would you expect lithium to react with chlorine? What might lithium do if it were placed in water?

L2

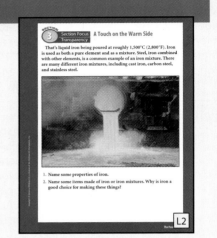

Section Focus Transparency 3 — A Touch on the Warm Side

That's liquid iron being poured at roughly 1,500°C (2,800°F). Iron is used as both a pure element and as a mixture. Steel, iron combined with other elements, is a common example of an iron mixture. There are many different iron mixtures, including cast iron, carbon steel, and stainless steel.

1. Name some properties of iron.
2. Name some items made of iron or iron mixtures. Why is iron a good choice for making these things?

L2

This is a representation of key blackline masters available in the Teacher Classroom Resources. See Resource Manager boxes within the chapter for additional information.

Key to Teaching Strategies

The following designations will help you decide which activities are appropriate for your students.

- **L1** Level 1 activities should be appropriate for students with learning difficulties.
- **L2** Level 2 activities should be within the ability range of all students.
- **L3** Level 3 activities are designed for above-average students.
- **ELL** ELL activities should be within the ability range of English Language Learners.
- **COOP LEARN** Cooperative Learning activities are designed for small group work.
- **LS** Multiple Learning Styles logos are used throughout to indicate strategies that address different learning styles.
- **P** These strategies represent student products that can be placed into a best-work portfolio.

Assessment

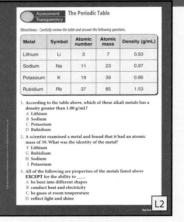

Assessment Transparency — The Periodic Table

Directions: Carefully review the table and answer the following questions.

Metal	Symbol	Atomic number	Atomic mass	Density (g/mL)
Lithium	Li	3	7	0.53
Sodium	Na	11	23	0.97
Potassium	K	19	39	0.86
Rubidium	Rb	37	85	1.53

1. According to the table above, which of these alkali metals has a density greater than 1.00 g/mL?
   A Lithium
   B Sodium
   C Potassium
   D Rubidium
2. A scientist examined a metal and found that it had an atomic mass of 39. What was the identity of the metal?
   F Lithium
   G Rubidium
   H Sodium
   J Potassium
3. All of the following are properties of the metals listed above EXCEPT for the ability to ___.
   A be bent into different shapes
   B conduct heat and electricity
   C be gases at room temperature
   D reflect light and shine

L2

Teaching

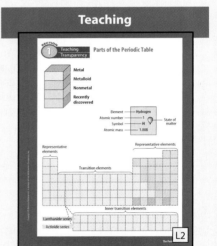

Teaching Transparency 1 — Parts of the Periodic Table

Metal
Metalloid
Nonmetal
Recently discovered

Element — Hydrogen
Atomic number — 1
Symbol — H
Atomic mass — 1.008
State of matter

Representative elements
Representative elements
Transition elements
Inner transition elements
Lanthanide series
Actinide series

L2

Hands-on Activities

Activity Worksheets

Name   Date   Class

Activity — Preparing a Mixture

Lab Preview
Directions: Answer these questions before you begin the Activity.
1. In this activity, you will be treating metals with heat and acids. Explain the safety precautions related to this experiment.

2. Why do you use tongs to hold the penny?

Many of the most important materials in the world are mixtures of elements.

What You'll Investigate
How can two metals form an alloy?

Materials
copper penny   dilute nitric acid   tongs
*copper wire   dilute sodium hydroxide   beaker of cold tap water
30-mesh zinc   evaporating dishes (2)   teaspoon
hot plate   *250-mL beakers (2)   *Alternate materials

Goals
- **Observe** the changes that occur during the preparation of an alloy.
- **Compare** the plating of a metal to the formation of an alloy.

Safety Precautions
CAUTION: Nitric acid and sodium hydroxide can cause burns. Wear eye protection and lab apron while in the lab. Thoroughly wash any spilled material.

Procedure
1. Carefully pour dilute nitric acid into one evaporating dish until the dish is half full. Using tongs, hold the penny in the nitric acid for about 20 s.
2. Still using the tongs, remove the penny from the acid. Rinse it in the beaker of cold water.
3. Place one teaspoonful of 30-mesh zinc in the second evaporating dish.
4. Slowly pour dilute sodium hydroxide into the dish to a depth of about 2 cm above the zinc.
5. Using tongs, gently place the penny on top of the zinc. Rinse the tongs in cold water.
6. Gently heat the contents of the evaporating dish on a hot plate until the penny turns a silver color.
7. Set the control on the hot plate to medium high. Using tongs, remove the penny from the dish and rinse it in the cold tap water.
8. Dry the penny and place it directly on the hot plate until the penny turns a golden color.
9. Your teacher will dispose of the contents of the two evaporating dishes.

L2

Laboratory Activities

Name   Date   Class

Laboratory Activity 1 — Relationships Among Elements

The periodic table is a wonderful source of information about all of the elements scientists have discovered. In this activity, you will investigate the relationship among the elements' atomic numbers, radii, and positions in the periodic table.

An atom's atomic radius is the distance from the center of the nucleus to the edge of the atom. The radii for elements with atomic numbers from 3 through 38 are given in Table 1. The radii are so small that a very small metric unit called a picometer (pm) is used. A picometer (pm) is one trillionth of a meter.

Strategy
You will plot the atomic radii of elements with atomic numbers 3 through 38.
You will examine the graph for repeated patterns.

Materials
copy of the periodic table   graph paper   pencil

Table 1

Name and symbol	Atomic number	Atomic radius (picometers)	Name and symbol	Atomic number	Atomic radius (picometers)
Aluminum Al	13	143	Magnesium Mg	12	160
Argon Ar	18	191	Manganese Mn	25	127
Arsenic As	33	121	Neon Ne	10	131
Beryllium Be	4	112	Nickel Ni	28	124
Boron B	5	85	Nitrogen N	7	71
Bromine Br	35	117	Oxygen O	8	60
Calcium Ca	20	197	Phosphorus P	15	109
Carbon C	6	77	Potassium K	19	231
Chlorine Cl	17	91	Rubidium Rb	37	248
Chromium Cr	24	128	Scandium Sc	21	162
Cobalt Co	27	125	Selenium Se	34	119
Copper Cu	29	128	Silicon Si	14	118
Fluorine F	9	69	Sodium Na	11	186
Gallium Ga	31	134	Strontium Sr	38	215
Germanium Ge	32	123	Sulfur S	16	103
Iron Fe	26	126	Titanium Ti	22	147
Krypton Kr	36	201	Vanadium V	23	134
Lithium Li	3	156	Zinc Zn	30	134

L2

Meeting Different Ability Levels

Content Outline

Note-taking Worksheet — The Periodic Table

L2

Reinforcement

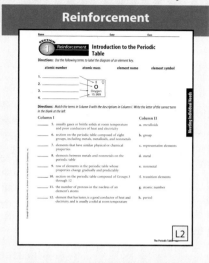

Reinforcement — Introduction to the Periodic Table

L2

Directed Reading

Directed Reading for Content Mastery — Overview The Periodic Table

L1

Assessment

Chapter Tests

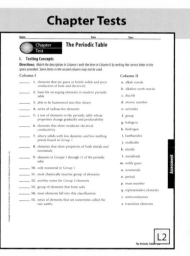

Chapter Test — The Periodic Table

L2

Enrichment

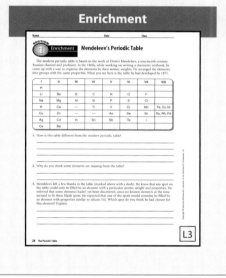

Enrichment — Mendeleev's Periodic Table

L3

Spanish Directed Reading

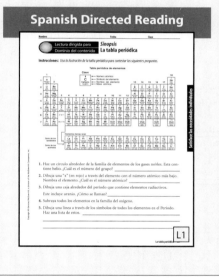

Lectura dirigida para Dominio del contenido — Sinopsis La tabla periódica

L1

Test Practice Workbook

Standardized Test Practice
Teacher Edition

Glencoe Science

The Nature of Matter

L2

Chapter Review

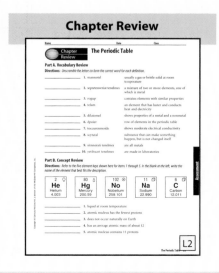

Chapter Review — The Periodic Table

L2

Science Content Background

SECTION 1

Introduction to the Periodic Table

Development of the Periodic Table

As the science of chemistry grew during the nineteenth century, scientists amassed a great deal of information about known elements and their chemistry. Such information helped in the search for an organizing principle for the elements. In 1817, the German chemist Johann Dobereiner found that he could arrange many elements into groups that he called triads. For example, he noticed that lithium, sodium, and potassium all react vigorously with water. When these elements are arranged in order of atomic mass, the mass of the middle element, sodium, is almost the same as the average of the lightest and heaviest elements. Similar regularities were uncovered for calcium, strontium, and barium, and for fluorine, chlorine, and bromine.

Dobereiner's early work laid the groundwork for other chemists in the search for an organizing principle based upon the similarities in chemical properties and trends in atomic

Fun Fact

In his final version of the periodic table in 1871, Mendeleev left gaps, foretelling they would be filled by elements not yet known to scientists. He correctly predicted the properties of three of those elements.

1 H 1.01																	**2** He 4.00
3 Li 6.94	**4** Be 9.01											**5** B 10.8	**6** C 12.0	**7** N 14.0	**8** O 16.0	**9** F 19.0	**10** Ne 20.2
11 Na 23.0	**12** Mg 24.3											**13** Al 27.0	**14** Si 28.1	**15** P 31.0	**16** S 32.1	**17** Cl 35.5	**18** Ar 40.0
19 K 39.1	**20** Ca 40.1	**21** Sc 45.0	**22** Ti 47.9	**23** V 50.9	**24** Cr 52.0	**25** Mn 54.9	**26** Fe 55.8	**27** Co 58.9	**28** Ni 58.7	**29** Cu 63.5	**30** Zn 65.4	**31** Ga 69.7	**32** Ge 72.6	**33** As 74.9	**34** Se 79.0	**35** Br 79.9	**36** Kr 83.8
37 Rb 85.5	**38** Sr 87.6	**39** Y 88.9	**40** Zr 91.2	**41** Nb 92.9	**42** Mo 95.9	**43** Tc 98	**44** Ru 101	**45** Rh 103	**46** Pd 106	**47** Ag 108	**48** Cd 112	**49** In 115	**50** Sn 119	**51** Sb 122	**52** Te 128	**53** I 127	**54** Xe 131
55 Cs 133	**56** Ba 137	**57** La 139	**72** Hf 178	**73** Ta 181	**74** W 184	**75** Re 186	**76** Os 190	**77** Ir 192	**78** Pt 195	**79** Au 197	**80** Hg 201	**81** Tl 204	**82** Pb 207	**83** Bi 209	**84** Po 210	**85** At 210	**86** Rn 222
87 Fr 223	**88** Ra 226	**89** Ac 227	**104** Rf 227	**105** Db 262	**106** Sg 263	**107** Bh 264	**108** Hs 265	**109** Mt 268	**110** Uun 269	**111** Uuu 269	**112** Uub 277	**113**	**114** Uuq 289	**115**	**116** Uun 289	**117**	**118**

58 Ce 140	**59** Pr 141	**60** Nd 144	**61** Pm 147	**62** Sm 150	**63** Eu 152	**64** Gd 157	**65** Tb 159	**66** Dy 163	**67** Ho 165	**68** Er 167	**69** Tm 169	**70** Yb 173	**71** Lu 175
90 Th 232	**91** Pa 231	**92** U 238	**93** Np 237	**94** Pu 244	**95** Am 243	**96** Cm 247	**97** Bk 247	**98** Cf 251	**99** Es 254	**100** Fm 257	**101** Md 258	**102** No 255	**103** Lr 256

color code = light metals -brittle metals -ductile metals -low melting metals -non-metals -noble gases -lanthanides -actinides

mass. In 1864 English chemist John Newlands proposed that when the known elements were arranged according to atomic mass, similarities in chemical properties occurred with every eighth element. He called this regularity the law of octaves.

Russian chemist Dmitri Ivanovich Mendeleev created the first periodic table of elements in 1869. The modern periodic table didn't come into being until a Dutch physicist, Anton van den Broek, proposed that the elements should be arranged according to nuclear charge rather than atomic mass. Henry Moseley confirmed this hypothesis through studies of the X-ray spectra of a series of elements that had consecutive positions on the table. The change to ordering by atomic number resulted in the reversal of the positions of some elements.

SECTION 2

Representative Elements

Sections of the Periodic Table

The periodic table divides into sections of representative elements, transition elements, and inner transition elements. The sections of the table reflect the electron configurations of the elements and the sublevels occupied by the electrons. It is the electron configuration of the atom that determines its chemical reactivity. For every principle quantum number (period or horizontal row), there are sublevels designated by letters, such as s, p, d, and f.

In the sublevels, electrons pairs are found in orbitals. There is one s orbital, three p orbitals, five d orbitals, and seven f orbitals within their respective sublevels. As you move across any period of the table, Groups 1 and 2 are filling s orbitals with two electrons. Groups 13–18 are filling p orbitals with six electrons. In periods 4 through 7, the transition elements, Groups 3–12, are filling five d orbitals with ten electrons. The inner transition elements, located below the periodic table, are filling the $4f$ and $5f$ orbitals with 14 electrons.

SECTION 3

Transition Elements

From Metals to Nonmetals

The alkali metals have one electron in an outer s orbital. This single electron is in a higher energy level than any inner level of electrons, and the inner electrons shield it from the full attractive force of the nucleus. As a result, relatively little energy is needed to remove the outer electron, and thus ionize the atom to a 1+ state. As you move down the alkali metal group, the outermost s electron is farther and farther from the nucleus and ionization becomes successively easier. As a result, the reactivity of the alkali metals increases down the family.

The alkaline earth metals have two electrons in an outer s orbital. The energy needed to remove both of these electrons is low enough to make this group of elements almost as active as the alkali metals. Their chemistry is the chemistry of the 2+ ion. The trend in reactivity for the oxygen group and the halogens is opposite that of Groups 1 and 2. Fluorine is the most active of the halogens, and activity decreases down the group.

Fun Fact

Molecules containing transition elements are important to the life processes of many organisms. Perhaps the most familiar example of this is found in the iron-containing heme complex of hemoglobin, which is responsible for oxygen transport in the blood of all vertebrates and some invertebrates.

SCIENCE *Online*

For additional content background on this topic, go to the Glencoe Science Web site at science.glencoe.com.

CHAPTER 4

The Periodic Table

Chapter Vocabulary

period, p. 99
group, p. 99
representative element, p. 99
transition element, p. 99
metal, p. 102
nonmetal, p. 102
metalloid, p. 102
semiconductor, p. 107
catalyst, p. 110
synthetic elements, p. 111

What do you think?

Science Journal The photograph shows drops of liquid mercury. Mercury is the only metal that occurs as a liquid at room temperature. Thus it would be an inappropriate choice as a material from which to make coins.

CHAPTER 4

The Periodic Table

Many cities have distinctive skylines and the Dallas skyline is no exception. What is truly amazing is that everything in this photograph is made from 90 naturally occurring elements. The buildings, plants, lights, people, and air surrounding it all are composed of elements. These elements, neatly organized on a periodic table, are the building blocks of matter. In this chapter, you will learn more about the elements and the chart that organizes them.

What do you think?

Science Journal Look at the picture below with a classmate. Discuss what this might be. Here's a hint: *This metallic element is similar to gold, silver, and copper, but it could never be made into a coin.* Write your answer or best guess in your Science Journal.

Theme Connection

Stability and Change Many characteristics of an element can be known from its position in the periodic table. Among these are the element's stability and the ways in which it combines with other elements.

EXPLORE
ACTIVITY

E very 29.5 days, the Moon begins to cycle through its phases from full moon to new moon and back again to full moon. Events that follow a predictable pattern are called periodic events. What other periodic events can you think of?

Make a model of a periodic pattern

1. On a blank sheet of paper, make a grid like the one shown in the photograph to the right.

2. Your teacher will give you 16 pieces of paper with different shapes and colors. Identify properties you can use to distinguish one piece of paper from another.

3. Place a piece of paper in each square on your grid. Arrange the pieces on the grid so that each column contains pieces that are similar.

4. Within each column, arrange the pieces to show a gradual change in their appearance.

Observe

In your Science Journal, describe how the properties change in the rows across the grid and in the columns down the grid.

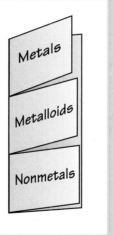

Before You Read

FOLDABLES
Reading & Study
Skills

Making an Organizational Study Fold **Make the following Foldable to help you organize your thoughts into clear categories about types of elements in the periodic table.**

1. Place a sheet of paper in front of you so the short side is at the top. Fold the paper in half from the left side to the right side.

2. Fold in the top and the bottom. Unfold the paper so three sections show.

3. Through the top thickness of paper, cut along each of the fold lines to the left fold, forming three tabs. Label the tabs *Metals, Metalloids,* and *Nonmetals.*

4. As you read the chapter, write information about the three types of elements under the tabs.

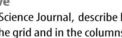

Metals

Metalloids

Nonmetals

Purpose Use the Explore Activity to help students classify items according to properties. [L2] [ELL] [IS] **Visual-Spatial**

Preparation Cut four circles of different diameters from each of four colors of paper. Leave the circles of one color whole. Remove a wedge-shaped quarter of each circle of another color. Cut another color of circles in half. For the last color, cut circles into quarters.

Materials sheet of paper, set of precut shapes (4 of each shape in 4 different colors for each group)

Teaching Strategy Allow students to arrange the pieces in any patterns they can justify.

Observe

Answers will vary depending on student patterns. Check to see that descriptions and grids match.

✓ Assessment

Process Ask students to find another reasonable arrangement of the pieces of paper. Use **Performance Assessment in the Science Classroom,** p. 121.

Before You Read

FOLDABLES
Reading & Study
Skills

Dinah Zike Study Fold

Purpose Have students make and use a Foldable to review the periodic table of elements, organize information they know, and record information they learn about metals, metalloids, and nonmetals.

For additional help, see Foldables Worksheet, p. 13 in **Chapter Resources Booklet,** or go to the Glencoe Science Web site at **science.glencoe.com.** See After You Read in the Study Guide at the end of this chapter.

Introduction to the Periodic Table

1 Motivate

Bellringer Transparency

Display the Section Focus Transparency for Section 1. Use the accompanying Transparency Activity Master. L2

ELL

Tie to Prior Knowledge

Display for the class a periodic table of the elements. If you do not have one large enough to display, have students turn to the one in this chapter. Ask students to find elements they know, and have volunteers tell what they know about the element and describe its location on the periodic table.

As You Read

What You'll Learn
- **Describe** the history of the periodic table.
- **Interpret** an element key.
- **Explain** how the periodic table is organized.

Vocabulary
period   metalloid
group   representative element
metal   transition element
nonmetal

Why It's Important
The periodic table makes it easier for you to find information that you need about the elements.

Development of the Periodic Table

Early civilizations were familiar with a few of the substances now called elements. They made coins and jewelry from gold and silver. They also made tools and weapons from copper, tin, and iron. In the nineteenth century, chemists began to search for new elements. By 1830, they had isolated and named 55 different elements. The list continues to grow today.

Mendeleev's Table of Elements A Russian chemist, Dmitri Mendeleev (men duh LAY uhf), published the first version of his periodic table in the *Journal of the Russian Chemical Society* in 1869. His table is shown in **Figure 1.** When Mendeleev arranged the elements in order of increasing atomic mass, he began to see a pattern. Elements with similar properties fell into groups on the table. At that time, not all the elements were known. To make his table work, Mendeleev had to leave three gaps for missing elements. Based on the groupings in his table, he predicted the properties for the missing elements. Mendeleev's predictions spurred other chemists to look for the missing elements. Within 15 years, all three elements—gallium, scandium, and germanium—were discovered.

Figure 1
Mendeleev published his first periodic table in 1869. This postage stamp, with his table and photo, was issued in 1969 to commemorate the event. Notice the question marks that he used to mark his prediction of yet-undiscovered elements.

Section ✓Assessment Planner

PORTFOLIO
Science Journal, p. 102
PERFORMANCE ASSESSMENT
MiniLAB, p. 99
Skill Builder Activities, p. 104
See page 124 for more options.

CONTENT ASSESSMENT
Section, p. 104
Challenge, p. 104
Chapter, pp. 124–125

Moseley's Contribution Although Mendeleev's table correctly organized most of the elements, a few elements seemed out of place. In the early twentieth century, the English physicist Henry Moseley, before age 27, realized that Mendeleev's table could be improved by arranging the elements according to atomic number rather than atomic mass. Moseley revised the periodic table by arranging the elements in order of increasing number of protons in the nucleus. With Moseley's table, it was clear how many elements still were undiscovered.

Today's Periodic Table

In the modern periodic table on the next page, the elements still are organized by increasing atomic number. The rows or periods are labeled 1–7. A **period** is a row of elements in the periodic table whose properties change gradually and predictably. The periodic table has 18 columns of elements. Each column contains a group, or family, of elements. A **group** contains elements that have similar physical or chemical properties.

Zones on the Periodic Table The periodic table can be divided into sections, as you can see in **Figure 2.** One section consists of the first two groups, Groups 1 and 2, and the elements in Groups 13–18. These eight groups are called the **representative elements.** They include metals, metalloids, and nonmetals. The elements in Groups 3–12 are called **transition elements.** They are all metals. Some transition elements, called the inner transition elements, are placed below the main table. These elements are called the lanthanide and actinide series because one series follows the element lanthanum, element 57, and the other series follows actinium, element 89.

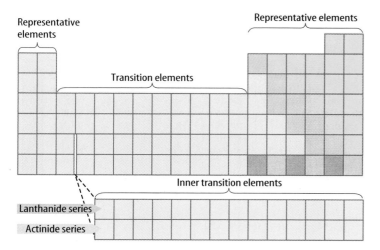

Figure 2
The periodic table is divided into sections. Traditionally, the lanthanides and actinides are placed below the table so that the table will not be as wide. These elements have similar properties.

Development of the Periodic Table

Mini LAB

Designing a Periodic Table

Procedure
1. Collect **pens** and **pencils** from everyone in your class.
2. Decide which properties of the pens and pencils you will use to organize them into a periodic table. Consider properties such as color, mass, or length. Then create your table.

Analysis
1. Explain how your periodic table is similar to the periodic table of the elements.
2. If your classmates brought different pens or pencils to class tomorrow, how would you organize them on your periodic table?

Mini LAB

Purpose Students arrange pens and pencil into a model of the periodic table. L2 ELL COOP LEARN **Kinesthetic**

Materials students' pens and pencils

Teaching Strategy Ask students to bring to school extra pens or pencils.

Analysis
1. Student tables could show that the writing utensils in a column have similar properties, such as color, length, and shape. The properties in a row change gradually.
2. Student answers will vary based on their tables but could include that items would be placed in a column with similar utensils and in a row in which their properties were intermediate between the utensils to the right and left.

✓ Assessment

Performance Have each student make a calendar for the present month and write on it any events he or she has scheduled, such as soccer practice or music lessons. Have them look for periodic events. Use **PASC,** p. 165.

Resource Manager

Chapter Resources Booklet
Transparency Activity, p. 40
MiniLAB, p. 3
Home and Community Involvement, p. 25

Inclusion Strategies

Visually Impaired The MiniLAB can be revised to use a collection of small hardware pieces of various sizes, such as screws, nuts, washers, and bolts, that can be sorted by touch instead of sight. Make sure you do not use sharp pieces, which might puncture skin.

Today's Periodic Table

Discussion

As you move from one element to the next across the periods in the periodic table, atomic number increases by one. What else, therefore, also increases by one? the number of electrons in a neutral atom of each element

Extension

As you move from left to right across the groups of representative elements in the periodic table, the number of electrons in each atom's outer energy level increases by one. Thus, the elements in Group 1 each have one electron in the outer energy level, the elements in Group 2 have two electrons in the outer energy level, elements in Group 13 have three, and so on. Most complete outer energy levels hold eight electrons. Have students find out what effect this has on the elements' behavior. When atoms react with one another, they try to complete their outer energy levels. The elements on the left side of the table (Groups 1, 2, and 13) generally complete their outer energy levels by losing electrons. Elements in Group 14 can either gain or lose electrons. Elements in Groups 15, 16, and 17 generally gain electrons, while elements in Group 18 have full outer electron energy levels, which is why they are so unreactive. L3

IS Logical-Mathematical

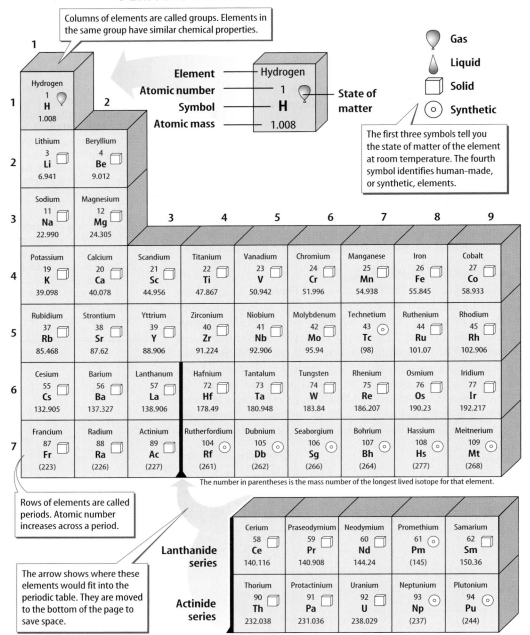

PERIODIC TABLE OF THE ELEMENTS

Columns of elements are called groups. Elements in the same group have similar chemical properties.

Element — Hydrogen
Atomic number — 1
Symbol — H
Atomic mass — 1.008
State of matter

Gas
Liquid
Solid
Synthetic

The first three symbols tell you the state of matter of the element at room temperature. The fourth symbol identifies human-made, or synthetic, elements.

The number in parentheses is the mass number of the longest lived isotope for that element.

Rows of elements are called periods. Atomic number increases across a period.

The arrow shows where these elements would fit into the periodic table. They are moved to the bottom of the page to save space.

Lanthanide series

| Cerium 58 Ce 140.116 | Praseodymium 59 Pr 140.908 | Neodymium 60 Nd 144.24 | Promethium 61 Pm (145) | Samarium 62 Sm 150.36 |

Actinide series

| Thorium 90 Th 232.038 | Protactinium 91 Pa 231.036 | Uranium 92 U 238.029 | Neptunium 93 Np (237) | Plutonium 94 Pu (244) |

Teacher FYI

Different isotopes of an element have different atomic masses. The atomic mass given for an element in the periodic table is calculated by taking the relative abundance of each isotope, multiplying it by the mass of that isotope, and then adding these numbers together.

Curriculum Connection

History The German scientist Lothar Meyer published a periodic table that was almost identical to Mendeleev's table. Have students find out why Meyer was not given equal credit for the periodic table. Because of a delay in the submission of Meyer's article, Mendeleev's work was published one-year earlier.

Metal

Metalloid

Nonmetal

Recently discovered

The color of an element's block tells you if the element is a metal, nonmetal, metalloid, or has been discovered so recently that more study is needed.

SCIENCE *Online*
Visit the Glencoe Science Web site at **science.glencoe.com** for updates to the periodic table.

					18
					Helium 2 **He** 4.003

13	**14**	**15**	**16**	**17**	
Boron 5 **B** 10.811	Carbon 6 **C** 12.011	Nitrogen 7 **N** 14.007	Oxygen 8 **O** 15.999	Fluorine 9 **F** 18.998	Neon 10 **Ne** 20.180
Aluminum 13 **Al** 26.982	Silicon 14 **Si** 28.086	Phosphorus 15 **P** 30.974	Sulfur 16 **S** 32.065	Chlorine 17 **Cl** 35.453	Argon 18 **Ar** 39.948

10	**11**	**12**						
Nickel 28 **Ni** 58.693	Copper 29 **Cu** 63.546	Zinc 30 **Zn** 65.39	Gallium 31 **Ga** 69.723	Germanium 32 **Ge** 72.64	Arsenic 33 **As** 74.922	Selenium 34 **Se** 78.96	Bromine 35 **Br** 79.904	Krypton 36 **Kr** 83.80
Palladium 46 **Pd** 106.42	Silver 47 **Ag** 107.868	Cadmium 48 **Cd** 112.411	Indium 49 **In** 114.818	Tin 50 **Sn** 118.710	Antimony 51 **Sb** 121.760	Tellurium 52 **Te** 127.60	Iodine 53 **I** 126.904	Xenon 54 **Xe** 131.293
Platinum 78 **Pt** 195.078	Gold 79 **Au** 196.967	Mercury 80 **Hg** 200.59	Thallium 81 **Tl** 204.383	Lead 82 **Pb** 207.2	Bismuth 83 **Bi** 208.980	Polonium 84 **Po** (209)	Astatine 85 **At** (210)	Radon 86 **Rn** (222)
Ununnilium * 110 **Uun** (281)	Unununium * 111 **Uuu** (272)	Ununbium * 112 **Uub** (285)		Ununquadium * 114 **Uuq** (289)		Ununhexium * 116 **Uuh** (289)		Ununoctium * 118 **Uuo** (293)

* Names not officially assigned. Discovery of elements 114, 116, and 118 recently reported. Further information not yet available.

Europium 63 **Eu** 151.964	Gadolinium 64 **Gd** 157.25	Terbium 65 **Tb** 158.925	Dysprosium 66 **Dy** 162.50	Holmium 67 **Ho** 164.930	Erbium 68 **Er** 167.259	Thulium 69 **Tm** 168.934	Ytterbium 70 **Yb** 173.04	Lutetium 71 **Lu** 174.967
Americium 95 **Am** (243)	Curium 96 **Cm** (247)	Berkelium 97 **Bk** (247)	Californium 98 **Cf** (251)	Einsteinium 99 **Es** (252)	Fermium 100 **Fm** (257)	Mendelevium 101 **Md** (258)	Nobelium 102 **No** (259)	Lawrencium 103 **Lr** (262)

Use Science Words

Word Usage Have students explain why using *period* and *family* to describe parts of the periodic table corresponds to common usage of these terms. Period refers to something occurring in a repeating pattern; properties repeat in a pattern on the periodic table. Family refers to individuals with similar characteristics; elements in a family have similar properties. L2 **Linguistic**

Use an Analogy

Ask students to brainstorm similar characteristics of human family members. Include those characteristics that can be seen, such as hair color and ear shape, and those that can't be seen, such as artistic talent or disposition. Have them suggest ways in which groups of elements might also have similar properties that can and cannot be observed with the eyes. For example, chlorine and bromine exist in different states at room temperature, but their chemical properties are similar. L2 **Intrapersonal**

Activity

To help students appreciate the different properties of the elements, allow them to handle as many samples of safe-to-handle elements (metals and nonmetals) as you have available. If possible, give them metals in the form of wire or sheets, such as aluminum foil. L1 ELL **Kinesthetic**

Science **Journal**

Periodic Table Call attention to the color-coding of metals, nonmetals, and metalloids. Ask students to locate elements they already know about and classify them in their Science Journals. Have them locate the liquid elements and list all the gaseous elements that they already know. L2 **Visual-Spatial**

Resource Manager

Chapter Resources Booklet
Enrichment, p. 26
Lab Activity, pp. 9–10, 11–12
Note-taking Worksheets, pp. 29–30

Text Question Answer
Answers might include door knobs, wire, automobile engines and bodies, toasters, and so on.

SCIENCE *Online*

Internet Addresses

_____

_____

_____

_____

Explore the Glencoe Science Web site at **science.glencoe.com** to find out more about topics in this section.

✔ **Reading Check**

Answer seventeen elements

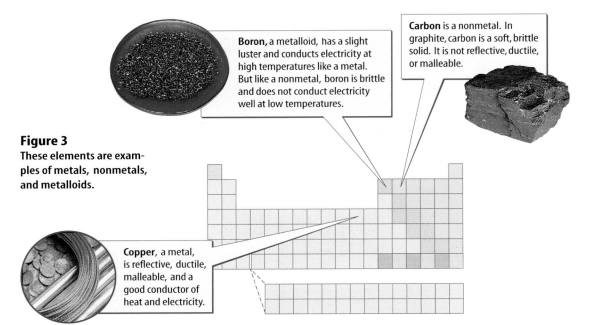

Boron, a metalloid, has a slight luster and conducts electricity at high temperatures like a metal. But like a nonmetal, boron is brittle and does not conduct electricity well at low temperatures.

Carbon is a nonmetal. In graphite, carbon is a soft, brittle solid. It is not reflective, ductile, or malleable.

Figure 3
These elements are examples of metals, nonmetals, and metalloids.

Copper, a metal, is reflective, ductile, malleable, and a good conductor of heat and electricity.

SCIENCE *Online*

Research Visit the Glencoe Science Web site at **science.glencoe.com** for historical information on how the periodic table was developed. Communicate to your class what you learn.

Metals If you look at the periodic table, you will notice it is color coded. The colors represent elements that are metals, nonmetals, or metalloids. Examples of a metal, a nonmental, and a metalloid are illustrated in **Figure 3.** With the exception of mercury, all the metals are solids, most with high melting points. A **metal** is an element that has luster, is a good conductor of heat and electricity, is malleable, and is ductile. The ability to reflect light is a property of metals called luster. Many metals can be pressed or pounded into thin sheets or shaped into objects because they are malleable (MAL ee yuh bul). Metals are also ductile (DUK tul), which means that they can be drawn out into wires. Can you think of any items that are made of metals?

Nonmetals and Metalloids **Nonmetals** are usually gases or brittle solids at room temperature and poor conductors of heat and electricity. There are only 17 nonmetals, but they include many elements that are essential for life—carbon, sulfur, nitrogen, oxygen, phosphorus, and iodine.

The elements between metals and nonmetals on the periodic table are called metalloids (MET ul oydz). As you might expect from the name, a **metalloid** is an element that shares some properties with metals and some with nonmetals. These elements also are called semimetals.

✔ **Reading Check** *How many elements are nonmetals?*

Science Journal

Metalloids Ask each student to choose one of the metalloids and to find out how it is similar to a metal and how it is similar to a nonmetal. Have students write their findings in their Science Journals. Metalloids include boron, silicon, germanium, arsenic, antimony, tellurium, polonium, and astatine. ⃞L3 ⃞IN **Linguistic** ⃞P

Resource Manager

Chapter Resources Booklet
Transparency Activity, pp. 43–44
Directed Reading for Content Mastery, pp. 15, 16
Reinforcement, p. 23

The Element Keys Each element is represented on the periodic table by a box called the element key. An enlarged key for hydrogen is shown in **Figure 4.** An element key shows you the name of the element, its atomic number, its symbol, and its average atomic mass. Element keys for elements that occur naturally on Earth include a logo that tells you whether the element is a solid, a liquid, or a gas at room temperature. All the gases except hydrogen are located on the right side of the table. They are marked with a balloon logo. Most of the other elements are solids at room temperature and are marked with a cube. Locate the two elements on the periodic table that are liquids at room temperature. Their logo is a drop. Elements that do not occur naturally on Earth are marked with a bull's-eye logo. These are synthetic elements.

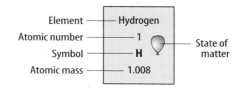

Figure 4
As you can see from the element key, a lot of information about an element is given on the periodic table.

Problem-Solving Activity

What does *periodic* mean in the Periodic Table?

Elements often combine with oxygen to form oxides and chlorine to form chlorides. For example, two hydrogen atoms combine with one oxygen atom to form water, H_2O. One sodium atom combines with one chlorine atom to form sodium chloride, NaCl or table salt. The location of an element on the periodic table is an indication of how it combines with other elements.

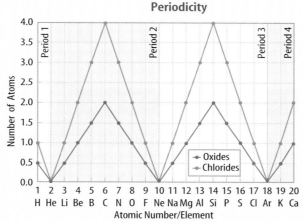

Identifying the Problem
The graph shows the number of oxygen atoms (red) and chlorine atoms (green) that will combine with the first 20 elements. What pattern do you see?

Solving the Problem
1. Find all of the elements in Group 1 on the graph. Do the same with the elements in Groups 14 and 18. What do you notice about their positions on the graph?

2. This relationship demonstrates one of the properties of a group of elements. Follow the elements in order on the periodic table and on the graph. Write a statement using the word *periodic* that describes what occurs with the elements and their properties.

SECTION 1 Introduction to the Periodic Table **K ◆ 103**

Teaching Strategy
Walk students having trouble with Question 2 through the graph and periodic table at the same time.

Answers to Questions
1. Group I elements are all in the same position on the graph. The same is true for Groups 14 and 18.
2. The properties of the elements periodically repeat themselves. Every time a new period begins, the elements repeat their properties. This is the meaning of periodic.

Activity
Have students find symbols that don't match the English names of the elements and find their origins. Possible answers: Ag (silver) from Latin *argentum*, Na (sodium) from Latin *natrium*, K (potassium) from Latin *kalium*, Fe (iron) from Latin *ferrum*, Cu (copper) from Latin *cuprum*, Sn (tin) from Latin *stannum*, Sb (antimony) from Latin *stibium*, W (tungsten) from German *wolfram* L3 IS **Linguistic**

LAB DEMONSTRATION

Assessment

Purpose to help students visualize the properties of nonmetals, using carbon
Materials charcoal, cloth, hammer, conductivity tester
Procedure Show students a piece of charcoal. Have them note its appearance. Cover the charcoal with a cloth, and use a hammer to break off some pieces. Test a piece of the charcoal with the conductivity tester.
Expected Outcome Carbon is dull in appearance, brittle, and charcoal is a nonconductor.

Why aren't nonmetals used for wiring? They are brittle and would break, and they are nonconductors. **Why wouldn't a nonmetal be used to make jewelry?** Nonmetals are too brittle and dull.

Reteach

Give each student a copy of a blank periodic table. Ask students to identify the areas of the table occupied by the representative elements, the transition elements, and the inner transition elements. Ask them to color code the metals, nonmetals, and metalloids. Ask them to label the 18 groups and the 7 periods. L1 LS **Visual-Spatial**

Challenge

Give each student a copy of a blank periodic table. Ask students to write the names of as many elements as they can in the correct spaces. L3 LS **Visual-Spatial**

✓ Assessment

Content Have students make up written questions about the periodic table and give them to you. Sort the questions, and use them to give a rapid-fire oral quiz. Use **PASC,** p. 91.

Table 3 Chemical Symbols and Their Origins

Name	Symbol	Origin of Name
Mendelevium	Md	For Dmitri Mendeleev.
Lead	Pb	The Latin name for lead is plumbum.
Thorium	Th	The Norse god of thunder is Thor.
Polonium	Po	For Poland, where Marie Curie, a famous scientist, was born.
Hydrogen	H	From Greek words meaning "water former."
Mercury	Hg	Hydrargyrum means "liquid silver" in Greek.
Gold	Au	Aurum means "shining dawn" in Latin.
Ununnillium	Uun	Named using the IUPAC naming system.

Symbols for the Elements

The symbols for the elements are either one- or two-letter abbreviations, often based on the element name. For example, V is the symbol for vanadium, and Sc is the symbol for scandium. Sometimes the symbols don't match the names. Examples are Ag for silver and Na for sodium. In those cases, the symbol might come from Greek or Latin names for the elements. Some elements are named for scientists such as Lise Meitner (meitnerium, Mt). Some are named for geographic locations such as France (francium, Fr).

Newly synthesized elements are given a temporary name and 3-letter symbol that is related to the element's atomic number. The International Union of Pure and Applied Chemistry (IUPAC) adopted this system in 1978. Once the discovery of the element is verified, the discoverers can choose a permanent name. **Table 3** shows the origin of some element names and symbols.

Section ① Assessment

1. Use the elements in period 4 to show how the physical state of the elements changes as the atomic number increases.
2. Describe the history of the periodic table.
3. Where are the metals, nonmetals, and metalloids located in the periodic table?
4. What does an element key contain?
5. **Think Critically** How would the modern periodic table be different if elements still were arranged by average atomic mass instead of atomic number?

Skill Builder Activities

6. **Classifying** Classify each of the following elements as a metal, nonmetal, or metalloid: *Fe, Li, B, Cl, Si, Na, Br, Po, Cs, Al, He,* and *Ni.* **For more help, refer to the** Science Skill Handbook.
7. **Calculating Ratios** Prepare a circle graph of the most abundant elements by weight in Earth's crust: *oxygen, 46.6%; silicon, 27.7%; aluminum, 8.1%; iron, 5.0%; calcium, 3.6%; sodium, 2.8%; potassium, 2.6%; magnesium, 2.1%;* and *other, 1.5%.* **For more help, refer to the** Math Skill Handbook.

Answers to Section Assessment

1. Elements are solid through Group 16, liquid in Group 17, and gaseous in Group 18.
2. Mendeleev published the first periodic table, which classified elements according to atomic mass and properties. Moseley arranged this periodic table according to atomic number instead of atomic mass.
3. Metals are on the left side; nonmetals are on the right side; metalloids are on a slanting line between metals and nonmetals.
4. the name of the element, its atomic number, its symbol, its average atomic mass, its state at room temperature, whether it occurs naturally
5. Some pairs of elements, such as K and Ar and Ni and Co, would exchange places and elements that have similar properties would no longer appear in the correct group.
6. metal: Fe, Li, Na, Cs, Al, Ni; nonmetal: Cl, Br, He; metalloid: B, Si, Po
7. The angles used to make the slices of the circle should be the decimal equivalent of the data multiplied by 360° (O, 168°; Si 100°; Al, 29°; Fe, 18°; Ca, 13°; Na, 10°; K, 9°; Mg, 8°; other, 5°).

Representative Elements

Groups 1 and 2

Groups 1 and 2 are always found in nature combined with other elements. They're called active metals because of their readiness to form new substances with other elements. They are all metals except hydrogen, the first element in Group 1. Although hydrogen is placed in Group 1, it shares properties with the elements in Group 1 and Group 17.

Alkali Metals The Group 1 elements have a specific family name—alkali metals. All the alkali metals are silvery solids with low densities and low melting points. These elements increase in their reactivity, or tendency to combine with other substances, as you move from top to bottom on the periodic table. Some uses of the alkali metals are shown in **Figure 5.**

Alkali metals are found in many items. Lithium batteries are used in cameras. Sodium chloride is common table salt. Sodium and potassium, dietary requirements, are found in small quantities in potatoes and bananas.

As You Read

What You'll Learn
- **Recognize** the properties of representative elements.
- **Identify** uses for the representative elements.

Vocabulary
semiconductor

Why It's Important
Many representative elements play key roles in your body, your environment, and in the things you use every day.

Figure 5
These items contain alkali metals.

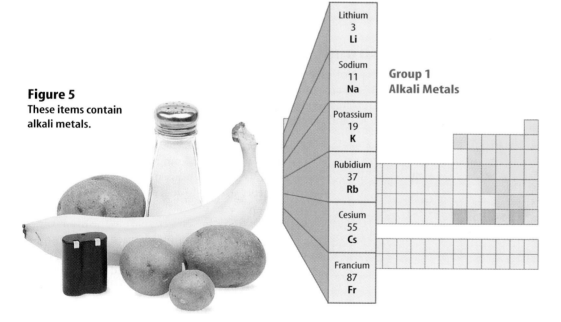

Lithium
3
Li

Sodium
11
Na

Potassium
19
K

Rubidium
37
Rb

Cesium
55
Cs

Francium
87
Fr

Group 1
Alkali Metals

Section ✓*Assessment* Planner

PORTFOLIO
Assessment, p. 111
PERFORMANCE ASSESSMENT
Skill Builder Activities, p. 111
See page 124 for more options.

CONTENT ASSESSMENT
Section, p. 111
Challenge, p. 111
Chapter, pp. 124–125

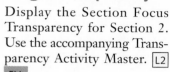 Motivate

Bellringer Transparency
Display the Section Focus Transparency for Section 2. Use the accompanying Transparency Activity Master. L2
ELL

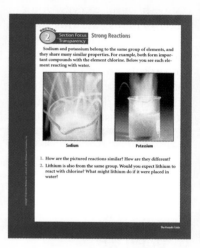

Tie to Prior Knowledge

Have students look at the eight groups of representative elements on the periodic table. Ask volunteers to name any of the elements they are familiar with from these groups and explain what they know about them. On the board, keep a list of student responses organized according to group.

Resource Manager

Chapter Resources Booklet
Transparency Activity, p. 41
Directed Reading for Content Mastery, p. 17

Groups 1 and 2

Discussion

Tell students that alkali metals are stored under mineral oil or kerosene. **Why?** because they react so readily with both oxygen and water vapor in the air L2

LS Logical-Mathematical

Quick Demo

Magnesium burns readily with an intense, white light. Fireworks displays make use of this property. Although looking directly at burning magnesium can be harmful to eyes, you can safely demonstrate this intense energy by darkening the room and burning a strip of magnesium inside an empty can. Students will observe the reflected light. L2 ELL **LS** Visual-Spatial

✔ Reading Check

Answer beryllium, magnesium, calcium, strontium, barium, radium

Groups 13 through 18

Teacher FYI

Elemental boron has two forms, an amorphous black or brown powder and a brittle, black or silver crystalline form with the high luster of metals. Because the bonds in crystalline boron are not the same as those of metals, it is not malleable or ductile. Boron carbide is one of the hardest substances known and is used to make bulletproof armor.

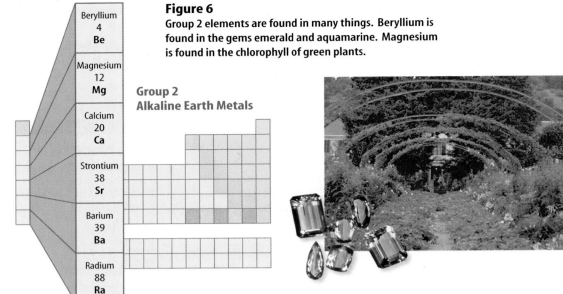

Figure 6
Group 2 elements are found in many things. Beryllium is found in the gems emerald and aquamarine. Magnesium is found in the chlorophyll of green plants.

Group 2 Alkaline Earth Metals

Alkaline Earth Metals Next door to the alkali metals' family are their Group 2 neighbors, the alkaline earth metals. Each alkaline earth metal is denser and harder and has a higher melting point than the alkali metal in the same period. Alkaline earth metals are active, but not as active as the alkali metals. Some uses of the alkaline earth elements are shown in **Figure 6.**

✔ Reading Check
What are the names of the elements that are alkaline earth metals?

Groups 13 through 18

Notice on the periodic table that the elements in Groups 13–18 are not all solid metals like the elements of Groups 1 and 2. In fact, a single group can contain metals, nonmetals, and metalloids and have members that are solids, liquids, and gases.

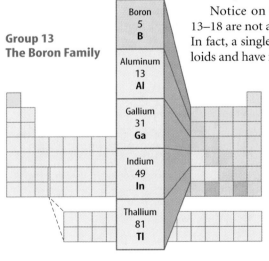

Group 13 The Boron Family

Group 13—The Boron Family The elements in Group 13 are all metals except boron, which is a brittle, black metalloid. This family of elements is used to make a variety of products. Cookware made with boron can be moved directly from the refrigerator into the oven without cracking. Aluminum is used to make soft-drink cans, cookware, siding for homes, and baseball bats. Gallium is a solid metal, but its melting point is so low that it will melt in your hand. It is used to make computer chips.

106 ◆ K CHAPTER 4 The Periodic Table

Science Journal

Calcium Have students research how the alkaline earth metal calcium is found in Earth's crust and write their findings in their Science Journals. Most calcium is found as calcium carbonate in marble and limestone rocks. Most limestone was formed from the skeletons of marine invertebrates, who take calcium from the sea and use it to make their shells. When the animals die, their shells fall to the sea floor, where the shells are compressed into the sedimentary rock limestone. When limestone is subjected to heat and pressure, it becomes the metamorphic rock marble. L2 **LS** Linguistic

Group 14—The Carbon Group If you look at Group 14, you can see that carbon is a nonmetal, silicon and germanium are metalloids, and tin and lead are metals. The non-metal carbon exists as an element in several forms. You're familiar with two of them—diamond and graphite. Carbon also is found in all living things. Carbon is followed by the metalloid silicon, an abundant element contained in sand. Sand contains ground-up particles of minerals such as quartz, which is composed of silicon and oxygen. Glass is an important product made from sand.

Silicon and its Group 14 neighbor, germanium, are metalloids. They are used in electronics as semiconductors. A **semiconductor** doesn't conduct electricity as well as a metal, but does conduct electricity better than a nonmetal. Silicon, and small amounts of other elements, are used for computer chips as shown in **Figure 7.**

Tin and lead are the two heaviest elements in Group 14. Lead is used in the apron, shown in **Figure 7,** to protect your torso during dental X-rays. It also is used in car batteries, low-melting alloys, protective shielding around nuclear reactors, particle accelerators, X-ray equipment, and containers used for storing and transporting radioactive materials. Tin is used in pewter, toothpaste, and the coating on steel cans used for food.

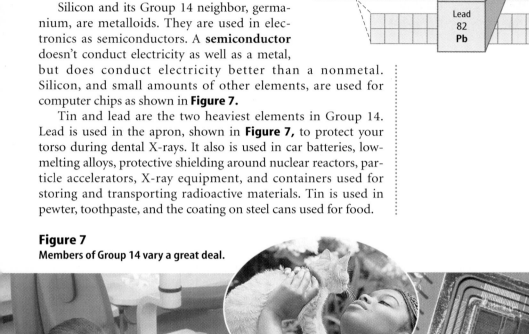

Group 14
The Carbon Family

| Carbon |
| 6 |
| C |

| Silicon |
| 14 |
| Si |

| Germanium |
| 32 |
| Ge |

| Tin |
| 50 |
| Sn |

| Lead |
| 82 |
| Pb |

Figure 7
Members of Group 14 vary a great deal.

B All living things contain carbon compounds.

A Lead is used to shield your body from unwanted X-ray exposure.

C Silicon crystals are used to make computer chips.

Make a Model

Have students use a model kit or toothpicks and gumdrops to model how carbon atoms are connected to each other in diamond and graphite. In diamond, each carbon atom bonds with four other carbon atoms in a rigid, tetrahedral, three-dimensional array. In graphite, the carbon atoms form planar sheets of connecting hexagons. The sheets are not connected by carbon-to-carbon bonds, so one sheet can slide easily past another. This property makes graphite a good lubricant for the moving parts of machinery and explains the use of graphite in pencils. L3 🟦 **Kinesthetic**

IDENTIFYING
Misconceptions

Not all metalloids are semiconductors, and not all semiconductors are metalloids. Some semiconductors, such as gallium arsenide, indium antimonide, and aluminum phosphide, are compounds. Gray tin has also been used as a semiconductor.

Cultural Diversity

Women and Semiconductors Today women from all over the world make contributions to our knowledge of the behavior of matter. A few of the women making contributions to the field of semiconductors are Dr. Tineke Thio, Dr. Gertrude Neumark, Prof. Jingyu Lin, Dr. Hilda Kanber, Dr. Shirley A. Jackson, and Dr. Elsa Garmire. Have students report on the contributions of at least two of these women to their fields.

Resource Manager

Chapter Resources Booklet
　Enrichment, p. 27
Cultural Diversity, p. 37

Groups 13 through 18 continued

Quick Demo

Dampen a cloth with some household cleaning solution containing ammonia, and let students smell the sharp odor as it diffuses through the air. **CAUTION:** *Do not let students smell the ammonia directly.* Tell them that smelling salts containing ammonia and a compound made from ammonia have often been used to arouse a person who has fainted. L2

LS Kinesthetic

Activity

Allow students to feel a piece of nylon cloth and a piece of silk. Discuss with them the similarities and differences between the two fabrics. L1

LS Kinesthetic

Extension

In addition to red phosphorus and white phosphorus, a third form of elemental phosphorus, called black phosphorus, exists. Have students find out the differences in the structures of these three types of phosphorus.
White phosphorus exists as tetrahedral P_4 molecules. In black phosphorus, the P_4 molecules form layers. Red phosphorus consists of P_4 molecules bonded in an amorphous structure that some believe to be polymeric. L3 **LS Linguistic**

Fun Fact

Nitrogen is relatively unreactive. Sometimes it is used inside a sealed case to protect valuable documents that might react with oxygen or other gases in air.

Figure 8
Ammonia is used to make nylon, a tough, light fiber capable of replacing silk in many applications, including parachutes.

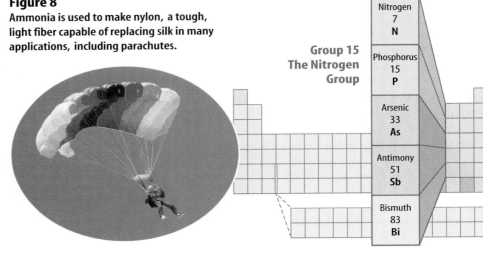

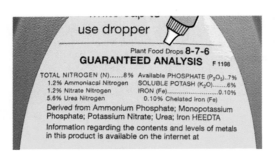

Figure 9
Nitrogen and phosphorus are required for healthy green plants. This synthetic fertilizer label shows the nitrogen and phosphorous compounds that provide these.

Group 15—The Nitrogen Group At the top of Group 15 are the two nonmetals—nitrogen and phosphorus. Nitrogen and phosphorus are required by living things and are used to manufacture various items. These elements also are parts of the biological materials that store genetic information and energy in living organisms. Although almost 80 percent of the air you breathe is nitrogen, you can't get the nitrogen your body needs by breathing nitrogen gas. Bacteria in the soil must first change nitrogen gas into substances that can be absorbed through the roots of plants. Then, by eating the plants, nitrogen becomes available to your body.

Ammonia is a gas that contains nitrogen and hydrogen. When ammonia is dissolved in water, it can be used as a cleaner and disinfectant. Liquid ammonia is sometimes applied directly to soil as a fertilizer. Ammonia also can be converted into solid fertilizers. It also is used to freeze-dry food and as a refrigerant.

The element phosphorus comes in two forms—white and red. White phosphorus is so active it can't be exposed to oxygen in the air or it will burst into flames. The heads of matches contain the less active red phosphorus, which ignites from the heat produced by friction when the match is struck. Phosphorous compounds are essential ingredients for healthy teeth and bones. Plants also need phosphorus, so it is one of the nutrients in most fertilizers. The fertilizer label in **Figure 9** shows the compounds of nitrogen and phosphorus that are used to give plants a synthetic supply of these elements.

Curriculum Connection

History The age of polymers and plastics began with the synthesis of celluloid in 1869. Ask students to find more about the first synthetic plastic material and the other new polymers that followed. John Wesley Hyatt, an American, made celluloid from cellulose nitrate and camphor. Celluloid was soon replaced by Bakelite, a registered trademark of Union Carbide. Many new synthetic materials were available after WW II.

Resource Manager

Physical Science Critical Thinking/ Problem Solving, p. 9

Earth Science Critical Thinking/ Problem Solving, p. 13

Group 16—The Oxygen Family The first two members of Group 16, oxygen and sulfur, are essential for life. The heavier members of the group, tellurium and polonium, are both metalloids.

About 20 percent of Earth's atmosphere is the oxygen you breathe. Your body needs oxygen to release the energy from the foods you eat. Oxygen is abundant in Earth's rocks and minerals because it readily combines with other elements. Oxygen also is required for combustion to occur. Foam is used in fire fighting to keep oxygen away from the burning item, as shown in **Figure 10.** Ozone, a less common form of oxygen, is formed in the upper atmosphere through the action of electricity during thunderstorms. The presence of ozone is important because it shields living organisms from some harmful radiation from the Sun.

Sulfur is a solid, yellow nonmetal. Large amounts of sulfur are used to manufacture sulfuric acid, one of the most commonly used chemicals in the world. Sulfuric acid is a combination of sulfur, hydrogen, and oxygen. It is used in the manufacture of paints, fertilizers, detergents, synthetic fibers, and rubber.

Selenium conducts electricity when exposed to light, so it is used in solar cells, light meters, and photographic materials. Its most important use is as the light-sensitive component in photocopy machines. Traces of selenium are also necessary for good health.

**Group 16
The Oxygen
Family**

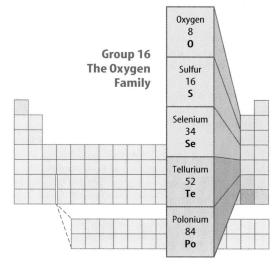

| Oxygen 8 **O** |
| Sulfur 16 **S** |
| Selenium 34 **Se** |
| Tellurium 52 **Te** |
| Polonium 84 **Po** |

Figure 10
The foam used in aircraft fires forms a film of water over the burning fuel which suffocates the fire.

**Life Science
INTEGRATION**

Arsenic disrupts the normal function of an organism by disrupting cellular metabolism. Because arsenic builds up in hair, forensic scientists can test hair samples to confirm or disprove a case of arsenic poisoning. Tests of Napoleon's hair suggest that he was poisoned with arsenic. Use reference books to find out who Napoleon I was and why someone might have wanted to poison him.

**Life Science
INTEGRATION**

Sulfur is a part of almost all enzymes, catalysts in the body that carry out cell functions. Replacement of sulfur in the enzyme by arsenic can seriously affect the healthy functioning of cells and can lead to death. Napoleon I (1769–1821) led the French in wars against Italy, Austria, England, Russia, Germany, and the Ottoman Empire. He ruled France as a dictator from 1799 to 1814, and was finally defeated at the Battle of Waterloo in 1815.

Extension

The Frasch process is a method of removing sulfur from deposits below Earth's surface. Have students research this mining method and write descriptions of the process that include diagrams. The Frasch process uses three tubes nested inside one another. Hot water is forced through the outer tube into the deposit, where it melts the sulfur. Air is then forced into the deposit through the inner tube and pushes the liquid sulfur to the surface through the middle tube. L2 L3
Visual-Spatial

Fun Fact

About 46 percent of Earth's crust is oxygen, nearly all of it in the form of silicates, oxides, or water.

✔ Active Reading

Jigsaw In this collaborative learning technique, individuals become experts on a portion of a text and share their expertise with a small group, called their home group. Everyone shares responsibility for learning the assigned reading. Assign each person in each home group an expert number (1 through 5, for example). Have students gather into the expert groups that correspond to the number they were assigned. Have them read, discuss, and master chapter concepts and determine how best to teach them to their home groups. Have students return to their home groups and share the content they learned in their expert groups. Have students use the Jigsaw strategy with the groups of elements in the periodic table discussed in this section.

Quick Demo

Bring to class a bottle of household chlorine bleach. Without telling students what it is, open it and give them the opportunity to smell it. Be sure they use the waft method rather than directly sniffing the bleach. Ask whether they can identify the odor. L2 ELL LS **Kinesthetic**

Extension

Most toothpaste manufacturers use fluorine compounds in their toothpastes. Have students write letters to toothpaste manufacturers asking for a copy of the results of studies that support the use of fluorine compounds as a decay-fighting additive in toothpaste. Have them share their letters and the responses with the class. L2 LS **Linguistic** P

✔ Reading Check

Answer salts

Visual Learning

Figure 12A What properties of helium make it desirable for use in this balloon? Helium is relatively unreactive and has a lower density than air, allowing it to float upward in the air.

Figure 11
The halogens are a group of elements that are important to us in a variety of ways.

A Chlorine is added to drinking water to kill harmful, disease-causing bacteria.

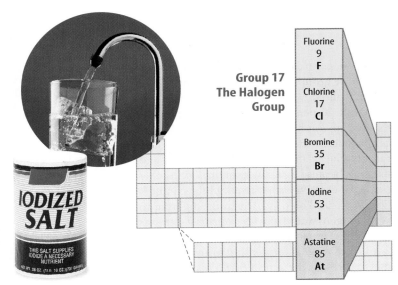

B Small amounts of iodine are needed by many systems in your body.

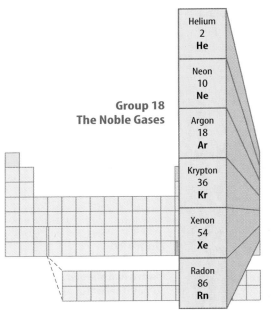

Group 17
The Halogen Group

Fluorine 9 **F**	
Chlorine 17 **Cl**	
Bromine 35 **Br**	
Iodine 53 **I**	
Astatine 85 **At**	

Group 17—The Halogen Group All the elements in Group 17 are nonmetals except for astatine, which is a radioactive metalloid. These elements are called halogens, which means "salt-former." Table salt, sodium chloride, is a substance made from sodium and chlorine. All of the halogens form similar salts with sodium and with the other alkali metals.

The halogen fluorine is the most active of the halogens in combining with other elements. Chlorine is less active than fluorine, and bromine is less active than chlorine. Iodine is the least active of the four nonmetals. **Figure 11** shows some uses of halogens.

✔ Reading Check

What do halogens form with the alkali metals?

Group 18
The Noble Gases

Helium 2 **He**	
Neon 10 **Ne**	
Argon 18 **Ar**	
Krypton 36 **Kr**	
Xenon 54 **Xe**	
Radon 86 **Rn**	

Group 18—The Noble Gases The Group 18 elements are called the noble gases. This is because they rarely combine with other elements and are found only as uncombined elements in nature.

Helium is less dense than air, so it's great for all kinds of balloons, from party balloons to blimps that carry television cameras high above sporting events. Helium balloons, such as the one in **Figure 12A,** lift instruments into the upper atmosphere to measure atmospheric conditions. Even though hydrogen is lighter than helium, helium is preferred for these purposes because helium will not burn.

110 ◆ K CHAPTER 4 The Periodic Table

Resource Manager

Chapter Resources Booklet
  Reinforcement, p. 24
Life Science Critical Thinking/Problem Solving, p. 15

Inclusion Strategies

Gifted Have students use dictionaries to find the origins of the names of the halogens and the noble gases and explain why the names are appropriate. (all Greek except F) Cl, *chloros*, greenish yellow; F, Latin, *fluere*, flow; Br, *bromos*, bad smell; I, *ioeides*, violet-colored; As, *astatos*, unsteady; Ar, *argos*, lazy; Ne, *neos*, new; Kr, *kryptos*, hidden; Xe, *xenos*, stranger; He, *helios*, god of the Sun L3 LS **Linguistic**

Uses for the Noble Gases The "neon" lights you see in advertising signs, like the one in **Figure 12B,** can contain any of the noble gases, not just neon. Electricity is passed through the glass tubes that make up the sign. These tubes contain the noble gas, and the electricity causes the gas to glow. Each noble gas produces a unique color. Helium glows yellow, neon glows red-orange, and argon produces a bluish-violet color.

Argon, the most abundant of the noble gases on Earth, was first found in 1894. Krypton is used with nitrogen in ordinary lightbulbs because these gases keep the glowing filament from burning out. When a mixture of argon, krypton, and xenon is used, a bulb can last longer than bulbs that do not contain this mixture. Krypton lights are used to illuminate landing strips at airports, and xenon is used in strobe lights and was once used in photographic flash cubes.

At the bottom of the group is radon, a radioactive gas produced naturally as uranium decays in rocks and soil. If radon seeps into a home, the gas can be harmful because it continues to emit radiation. When people breathe the gas over a period of time, it can cause lung cancer.

Figure 12
Noble gases are used in many applications.

A Scientists use balloons filled with helium to measure atmospheric conditions.

B Each noble gas glows a different color when an electric current is passed through it.

 Reading Check *Why are noble gases used in lights?*

Section 2 Assessment

1. What do the elements in Group 1 have in common with the elements in Group 17?

2. List two uses for a member of each representative group.

3. Which group of elements does not readily combine with other elements?

4. **Think Critically** Francium is a rare radioactive alkali metal at the bottom of Group 1. Its properties have not been studied carefully. Would you predict that francium would combine with water more or less readily than cesium?

Skill Builder Activities

5. **Predicting** Predict how readily astatine would form a salt compared to the other elements in Group 17. Is there a trend for reactivity in this group? **For more help, refer to the** Science Skill Handbook.

6. **Using a Database**)ose an element from the periodic table. Use an online or electronic database to find a recent news article that talks about that element. Why was the element in the news? **For more help, refer to the** Technology Skill Handbook.

SECTION 2 Representative Elements **K ◆ 111**

Answers to Section Assessment

1. They combine readily with other elements.
2. Answers will vary.
3. Group 18
4. more readily because the activity of alkali metals increases down Group 1

5. It would combine less readily than other halogens because activity decreases down Group 17.
6. Students' results will vary.

Teacher FYI

Radon is formed from the radioactive decay of uranium and radium. Small amounts of uranium and radium exist in most rocks and soil but are most often found in granite, shale, and phosphate. The half-life of radon is about three days.

✔ **Reading Check**

Answer They glow in bright colors and they are relatively unreactive.

③ Assess

Reteach

Give students a blank periodic table, and have them fill in the symbols and group numbers for the elements studied in this section. Have them identify by color or shading the metals, nonmetals, and metalloids. L1
LS **Visual-Spatial**

Challenge

Have teams of students make charts on the board with a column for each family of the representative elements. Challenge the groups to list in each column as many of the uses of the elements in that family as they know. L2 COOP LEARN
LS **Interpersonal**

✔ Assessment

Content Have groups of students make posters of photos and drawings that illustrate the importance of carbon, oxygen, and nitrogen in their lives. Use **PASC,** p. 145. P

1 Motivate

Bellringer Transparency

Display the Section Focus Transparency for Section 3. Use the accompanying Transparency Activity Master. L2 ELL

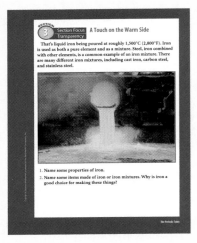

Tie to Prior Knowledge

Ask students why we don't often see elements from the alkali metal and alkaline earth metal groups in the form of uncombined metals. These elements are almost always found combined with other elements because they are too reactive to exist as separate metals. Tell students that in this section they will study some elements they see every day as metals.

Caption Answer

Figure 13 strength, durability, and malleability

✔ Reading Check

Answer iron, cobalt, nickel

Transition Elements

As You Read

What You'll Learn
- **Identify** properties of some transition elements.
- **Distinguish** lanthanides from actinides.

Vocabulary
catalyst
synthetic elements

Why It's Important
Transition elements provide the materials for many things including electricity in your home and steel for construction.

Figure 13
These buildings and bridges have steel in their structure. *Why do you think steel is used in their construction?*

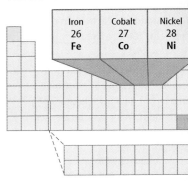

The Iron Triad

| Iron 26 Fe | Cobalt 27 Co | Nickel 28 Ni |

The Metals in the Middle

Groups 3-12 are called the transition elements and all of them are metals. Across any period from Group 3 through 12, the properties of the elements change less noticeably than they do across a period of representative elements.

Most transition elements are found combined with other elements in ores. A few transition elements such as gold and silver are found as pure elements.

The Iron Triad Three elements in period 4—iron, cobalt, and nickel—have such similar properties that they are known as the iron triad. These elements, among others, have magnetic properties. Industrial magnets are made from an alloy of nickel, cobalt, and aluminum. Nickel is used in batteries along with cadmium. Iron is a necessary part of hemoglobin, the substance that transports oxygen in the blood.

Iron also is mixed with other metals and with carbon to create a variety of steels with different properties. Structures such as bridges and skyscrapers, shown in **Figure 13,** depend upon steel for their strength.

✔ **Reading Check** *Which metals make up the iron triad?*

Section ✔ Assessment Planner

PORTFOLIO
Activity, p. 114
Assessment, p. 119
PERFORMANCE ASSESSMENT
Skill Builder Activities, p. 116
See page 124 for more options.

CONTENT ASSESSMENT
Section, p. 116
Challenge, p. 116
Chapter, pp. 124–125

Transition Metals Most transition metals have higher melting points than the representative elements. The filaments of lightbulbs like the one in **Figure 14** are made of tungsten, element 74. Tungsten has the highest melting point of any metal (3,410°C) and will not melt with the heat of the bulb.

Mercury, which has the lowest melting point of any metal (-39°C), is used in thermometers and in barometers. Mercury is the only metal that is a liquid at room temperatures. Like many of the heavy metals, mercury is poisonous to living beings. Therefore, mercury must be handled with care.

Chromium's name comes from the Greek word for color, *chroma,* and the element lives up to its name. Two substances containing chromium are shown in **Figure 15A.** Many other transition elements combine to form substances with equally brilliant colors.

Ruthenium, rhodium, palladium, osmium, iridium, and platinum are sometimes called the platinum group because they have similar properties. They do not combine easily with other elements. As a result, they can be used as catalysts. A **catalyst** is a substance that can make something happen faster but is not changed itself. Industrial smokestacks, like the one shown in **Figure 15B,** use catalysts to change pollutants into harmless substances before they are released into the air.

Figure 14
The transition metal tungsten is used in lightbulbs because of its high melting point.

Figure 15
Transition metals are used in a variety of products.

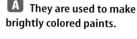

A They are used to make brightly colored paints.

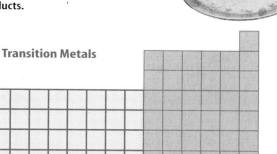

Transition Metals

 B Catalysts in smoke stacks change pollutants into harmless substances.

Visual Learning

Figure 14 Point out the tungsten filament. **Describe what happens in the tungsten when the light is turned on.** Electricity flows through the tungsten. The tungsten has enough resistance to the electricity that it heats up and glows as the electricity passes through it. L2
IS Visual-Spatial

Discussion

Why are mercury thermometers not recommended for school laboratory work? Mercury liquid and vapors are poisonous. If a thermometer breaks, the mercury is difficult to pick up. Some of it might be absorbed through the skin or remain in the classroom and contaminate the air with its vapors. L2
IS Logical-Mathematical

Teacher FYI

In the transition elements, as you move from left to right along a period of the periodic table, the electrons that are added fill the next-to-outer energy level, the *d* energy level, of the atom. The outer energy level, the *s* energy level is already filled. The differences between the energies of the *d* energy level electrons and the energies of the electrons of the outer *s* energy level are very small. Therefore, each of these elements is capable of forming several different oxidation states.

Resource Manager

Chapter Resources Booklet
   Transparency Activity, p. 42
   Directed Reading for Content Mastery,
      pp. 17, 18

Earth Science Critical Thinking/ Problem Solving, p. 2

Science Journal

Surface Catalysis Finely divided platinum can act as a surface catalyst. Ask students how surface catalysis works and give an example of its use. In surface catalysis, the reactants are absorbed onto the surface of the finely divided metal where the reaction occurs. For example, the reaction of H with O to form water is speeded up by the presence of powdered Pt. L3
IS Linguistic

Inner Transition Elements

Physics
INTEGRATION

A color television picture tube uses three electron guns to produce each of three primary colors. These electron guns stimulate color phosphor dots on the color monitor. More than 1 million tiny dots are arranged in clusters. Each cluster contains a red, green, and blue phosphor. The stream of electrons from each gun falls only on its appropriate color phosphor.

✔ Reading Check

Answer rare earths

Activity

Ask each student to choose one of the synthetic actinides and prepare a poster illustrating its structure, telling when and where it was first synthesized, and giving the half-life of its most stable isotope. Example: Neptunium was first synthesized in 1940 at the University of California at Berkeley. It has 93 protons and electrons, and its most stable isotope, neptunium-237, has 144 neutrons and a half-life of about 2 million years.
[L3] **IS** **Visual-Spatial** [P]

✔ Reading Check

Answer They are all radioactive.

Physics
INTEGRATION

Yttrium oxide(Y_2O_3) and europium oxide (Eu_2O_3) are used in color television screens to give a bright, natural color red. This blend of lanthanide elements will give off a red light when it's hit with a beam of electrons. Other compounds are used to make the additional colors required for a natural-looking picture.

Figure 16
The flint in this lighter is called misch metal, which is about 50% cerium, 25% lanthanum, 15% neodymium, and 10% other rare earth metals and iron.

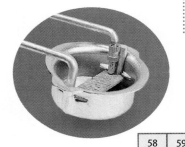

Lanthanide Series

Actinide Series

Inner Transition Elements

There are two series of inner transition elements. The first series, from cerium to lutetium, is called the lanthanides. The lanthanides also are called the rare earths because at one time they were thought to be scarce. The lanthanides are usually found combined with oxygen in Earth's crust. The second series of elements, from thorium to lawrencium, is called the actinides.

✔ Reading Check
What other name is used to refer to the lanthanides?

The Lanthanides The lanthanides are soft metals that can be cut with a knife. The elements are so similar that they are hard to separate when they occur in the same ore, which they often do. Despite the name rare earth, the lanthanides are not as rare as originally thought. Earth's crust contains more cerium than lead. Cerium makes up 50 percent of an alloy called misch (MIHSH) metal. Flints in lighters, like the one in **Figure 16,** are made from misch metal. The other ingredients in flint are lanthanum, neodymium, and iron.

The Actinides All the actinides are radioactive. The nuclei of atoms of radioactive elements are unstable and decay to form other elements. Thorium, protactinium, and uranium are the only actinides that now are found naturally on Earth. Uranium is found in Earth's crust because its half-life is long—4.5 billion years. All the others are synthetic elements. **Synthetic elements** are made in laboratories and nuclear reactors. **Figure 17** shows how synthetic elements are made. The synthetic elements have many uses. Plutonium is used as a fuel in nuclear power plants. Americium is used in some home smoke detectors. Californium-252 is used to kill cancer cells.

✔ Reading Check
What property do all actinides share?

					Inner Transition Elements								
58 Ce	59 Pr	60 Nd	61 Pm	62 Sm	63 Eu	64 Gd	65 Tb	66 Dy	67 Ho	68 Er	69 Tm	70 Yb	71 Lu
90 Th	91 Pa	92 U	93 Np	94 Pu	95 Am	96 Cm	97 Bk	98 Cf	99 Es	100 Fm	101 Md	102 No	103 Lr

Curriculum Connection

History The term *misch metal* comes from the German word *mischen*, which means "to mix." Have students find out more about misch metal. Misch metal was developed by the Austrian chemist Carl Auer von Welsbach, who lived from 1858 to 1929. Misch metal is also used in miners' lamps and in carbon arc lamps, and to remove sulfur, gases, and oxides from other alloys.
[L3] **IS** **Linguistic**

Teacher **FYI**

Like that of the transition metals, the outer energy level of the inner transition elements is filled, and as you move from left to right across each period, the added electrons fill the next-to-last energy level. Unlike the transition metals, the inner transition elements mostly form +3 oxidation states.

Figure 17

No element heavier than uranium, with 92 protons and 146 neutrons, is typically found in nature. But by using a device called a particle accelerator, scientists can make synthetic elements with atomic numbers greater than that of uranium. Within the accelerator, atomic nuclei are made to collide at high speeds in the hope that some will fuse together to form new, heavier elements. These "heavy" synthetic elements are radioactive isotopes, some of which are so unstable that they survive only a fraction of a second before emitting radioactive particles and decaying into other, lighter elements.

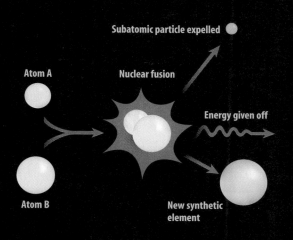

Subatomic particle expelled

Atom A

Nuclear fusion

Energy given off

Atom B

New synthetic element

▲ When atoms collide in an accelerator, their nuclei may undergo a fusion reaction to form a new—and often short-lived—synthetic element. Energy and one or more subatomic particles typically are given off in the process.

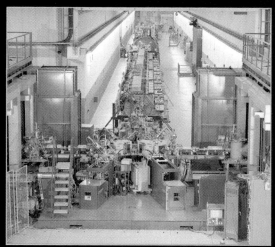

▲ Inside the airless vacuum chamber of a particle accelerator, such as this one in Hesse, Germany, streams of atoms move at incredibly high speeds.

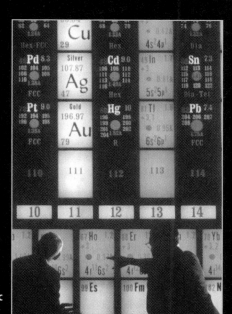

▶ At the Lawrence Berkeley National Laboratory in California, right, researchers recently succeeded in creating three atoms of element 118 by bombarding lead atoms with krypton atoms in a particle accelerator. The new element decayed almost instantly to element 116, which itself was short-lived. A few heavy synthetic elements remain elusive, including 113, 115, and 117.

SECTION 3 Transition Elements   **K ◆ 115**

Visualizing Synthetic Elements

Have students examine the pictures and read the captions. Then ask the following questions.

Why do you think that elements above atomic number 92 are not typically found in nature? because they are structurally unstable and decay quickly into less complex particles

Why do you think it is important for the particle accelerator to have an airless vacuum chamber? Answers may vary, but may be similar to the following. Scientists are interested in fusing two specific nuclei together in the chamber. If the chamber contains air, there is a multitude of molecules inside the chamber, in addition to the ones that the scientists are interested in. This would create too many variables for the scientists to try to control.

Activity

Challenge the students to research uses for the elements above atomic number 92. Students should report the information that they find to the class. L2 IS **Linguistic**

Extension

Have each student choose a synthetic element and research how it was made. Students should prepare a poster detailing the reaction sequence that took place. Subatomic particle information should be included whenever possible, throughout the reaction sequence. L3 IS **Visual-Spatial**

Resource Manager

Chapter Resources Booklet

Reinforcement, p. 25
Enrichment, p. 28
Activity Worksheet, pp. 5–6

Reading Check

Answer The new materials are strong, chemically resistant to body fluids, can be tinted, and contain no mercury.

SCIENCE Online
Internet Addresses
_____
_____
_____

Explore the Glencoe Science Web site at **science.glencoe.com** to find out more about topics in this section.

3 Assess

Reteach

Name transition metals and inner transition elements one at a time, and record what students tell you about each element. Then have students check this information against the text. L1
IS Interpersonal

Challenge

Ask students to name the elements in Group 11 and explain why the name *coinage metals* is appropriate. Copper, silver, and gold have been used for coins since ancient times because they are malleable, hard, and relatively unreactive. L3
IS Logical-Mathematical

✔Assessment

Content Have each student make a large sign with the name of an element on it. Have students work together to form a living periodic table. Use **PASC,** p. 135. L2 COOP LEARN
IS Interpersonal

Resource Manager

Chapter Resources Booklet
Activity Worksheet, pp. 5–6

Research Visit the Glencoe Science Web site at **science.glencoe.com** for information about the health risks due to mercury. Communicate to your class what you learn.

Dentistry and Dental Materials

Dentists have been using amalgam for over 150 years to fill cavities in decayed teeth. Amalgam, a mixture of silver, copper, tin, and mercury, is the familiar "silver filling." Because amalgam contains mercury, some people are concerned that the use of this type of filling may unnecessarily expose a person to mercury vapor. Today dentists have alternatives to amalgam. New composites, resins, and porcelains are being used to repair decayed, broken, or missing teeth. These new materials are strong, chemically resistant to body fluids, and can be altered to have the natural color of the tooth. Some of the new resins also contain fluoride that will protect the tooth from further decay. Many of these new materials would be useless without the development of new bonding agents. The new "glues" or bonding agents adhere the new materials to the natural tooth. These bonding agents must be strong and chemically resistant to body fluids.

✔ Reading Check *Why are these new dental materials desirable for repairing teeth?*

Orthodontists are using new nickel and titanium alloys for the wires on braces. These wires have shape memory. The wires undergo a special heat treatment process to lock in their shapes. If the wires are forced out of their heat-treated shape, the wires will try to return to their original shape. Orthodontists have found these wires useful in straightening crooked teeth. How do you think these wires help to straighten crooked teeth?

Section 3 Assessment

1. How do the elements in the iron triad differ from other transition metals?
2. What is the major difference between the lanthanides and actinides? Explain.
3. What is mercury used for?
4. Describe in your own words how synthetic elements are made.
5. **Think Critically** Of the elements iridium and cadmium, predict which is likely to be toxic and which could act as a catalyst. Explain.

Skill Builder Activities

6. **Forming Hypotheses** How does the appearance of a burned-out lightbulb compare to a new lightbulb? What could explain the difference? **For more help, refer to the** Science Skill Handbook.
7. **Communicating** In your Science Journal, discuss the term valuable as it relates to elements. How do relative abundance, number of uses, and durability contribute to value? **For more help, refer to the** Science Skill Handbook.

Answers to Section Assessment

1. They have magnetic properties.
2. All of the actinides are radioactive while the lanthanides are not. Also, many of the actinides are synthetic elements not found naturally on Earth.
3. thermometers, barometers, dental materials

4. Answers will vary. Synthetic elements are made by fusing two smaller nuclei together in a particle accelerator.
5. Cadmium is likely to be toxic because it is in the same group as mercury. Iridium is likely to be a catalyst because it is part of the platinum group.

6. A burned-out lightbulb is darker than a new lightbulb from deposits of tungsten caused by the constant heating of the metal.
7. Gold and silver are valuable because they are rare and beautiful. Metals such as iron and aluminum are valuable because their properties make them useful.

Activity

Preparing a Mixture

Many of the most important materials in the world are mixtures of elements.

What You'll Investigate
How can two metals form a metal mixture?

Materials
copper penny
*copper wire
30-mesh zinc
hot plate
dilute nitric acid
dilute sodium hydroxide

evaporating dishes (2)
*250-mL beakers (2)
tongs
beaker of cold tap water
teaspoon
*Alternate materials

Goals
- **Observe** the changes that occur during the preparation of a metal mixture.
- **Compare** the plating of a metal to the formation of a metal mixture.

Safety Precautions

WARNING: *Nitric acid and sodium hydroxide can cause burns and damage eyes. Wear your eye protection and lab apron at all times in the lab. Thoroughly wash any spilled material.*

Procedure

1. Carefully pour dilute nitric acid into one evaporating dish until the dish is half full. Using tongs, hold the penny in the nitric acid for about 20 s.
2. Still using the tongs, remove the penny from the acid. Rinse it in the beaker of cold water.
3. Place one teaspoonful of 30-mesh zinc in the second evaporating dish.
4. Slowly pour dilute sodium hydroxide into the dish to a depth of about 2 cm above the zinc.

5. Using tongs, gently place the penny on top of the zinc. Rinse the tongs in cold water.
6. Gently heat the contents of the evaporating dish on a hot plate until the penny turns a silver color.
7. Set the control on the hot plate to medium high. Using tongs, remove the penny from the dish and rinse it in the cold tap water.
8. Dry the penny and place it directly on the hot plate until the penny turns a golden color.
9. Your teacher will dispose of the contents of the two evaporating dishes.

Conclude and Apply

1. Why did the appearance of the penny change when it was placed in the nitric acid?
2. What two metals formed the golden color on the penny? What is this mixture called?

Communicating
Your Data

Compare your results with those of other students in the classroom. **For more help, refer to the** Science Skill Handbook.

Activity

BENCH TESTED

Purpose Students make an alloy and distinguish between an alloy and a plated metal. L2 ELL COOP LEARN IS **Visual-Spatial**

Process Skills observing, comparing, inferring

Time Required 40 minutes

Materials To prepare dilute nitric acid, add 15 mL of concentrated acid to 85 mL of distilled water while constantly stirring the mixture. To prepare $2M$ NaOH solution, dissolve 80 g NaOH in enough distilled water to make 1 L of solution. This solution becomes hot; allow time for it to cool.

Safety Precautions Emphasize the need for caution in using HNO_3 and NaOH.

Teaching Strategy After the lab, collect all materials that are in the evaporating dishes. Filter out and discard any remaining zinc. Check the pH of the solution. If the pH is below 6, add a base until the pH is 6 to 8. If it is above 8, add an acid until the pH is 6 to 8. Then, pour the solution down the drain with plenty of water.

Answers to Questions

1. Nitric acid removed dirt and substances formed when copper combines with substances in the air.
2. Copper and Zinc mix to form brass.

✓*Assessment*

Process Ask students to draw an atomic-level diagram of the process of mixing copper and zinc to form brass. Have them use two different colors to represent atoms of copper and zinc. Use **Performance Assessment in the Science Classroom,** p. 127.

Communicating
Your Data

Students should discuss why their results did or did not agree. Causes of error can include heating at too low a temperature or for too short a time.

Activity

BENCH TESTED

Recognize the Problem

Internet Students will gather data from the Internet that can be accessed through the Glencoe Science Web site at **science.glencoe.com.** Students can post their findings and acquire information from other schools around the country.

Non-Internet Sources Contact libraries, and gather data from newspapers and local television news broadcasts. Possible references:

- Kusinitz, Mark. *Poisons and Toxins (Encyclopedia of Health, Medical Disorders and Their Treatment).* Chelsea House Pub., 1992
- W. Salomons, U. Forstner, P. Mader. *Heavy Metals: Problems and Solutions.* Springer Verlag, 1995

Time Required

one to two weeks

Preparation

Internet Access the Glencoe Science Web site at **science. glencoe.com** to run through the steps that students will follow.

Non-Internet Sources Scan the local newspaper for articles that connect health to chemical use.

Form a Hypothesis

Possible Hypothesis

Student hypotheses should involve chemicals or heavy metals that are current or potential problems in your area.

Activity  Use the Internet

Health Risks from Heavy Metals

For years the lead recycling plant operated in a nearby neighborhood. The plant recycled lead from old batteries and other materials. The smokestack above the plant sprayed the surrounding areas with fine particles of lead and arsenic. Unsuspecting children played in the playgrounds where the soil was contaminated. The hazards from heavy metals are not unique to this neighborhood. One way to reduce the threat is to know as much as possible about the effects of chemicals on you and the environment.

Recognize the Problem

Do heavy metals and other chemicals pose a threat to the health of humans?

Form a Hypothesis

Could health problems be caused by exposure to heavy metals such as lead, or a radioactive chemical element, such as radon? Is the incidence of these problems higher in one area than another? Form a hypothesis as to the potential health risk of a chemical in your area.

Goals
- **Organize** and synthesize information on a chemical or heavy metal thought to cause health problems in the area where you live.
- **Communicate** your findings to others in your class.

Data Source
SCIENCE*Online* Go to the Glencoe Science Web site at **science. glencoe.com** for more information about health risks from heavy metals, hints on health risks, and data from other students.

Health Risk Data Table				
Location	Chemical or Heavy Metal	How People Come in Contact with Chemical	Potential Health Problem	Who Is Affected
Austin	lead	paint, eaten	causes brain damage	small children

Resource Manager

Chapter Resources Booklet
  Activity Worksheet, pp. 7–8

Physical Science Critical Thinking/Problem Solving, p. 13

Lab Management and Safety, p. 50

SCIENCE *Online*

Internet Addresses

_____

_____

_____

Explore the Glencoe Science Web site at **science.glencoe.com** to find out more about topics in this activity.

Test Your Hypothesis

Plan

1. Read general information concerning heavy metals and other potentially hazardous chemicals.

2. Use the sites listed on the Glencoe Science Web site to research possible health problems in your area caused by exposure to chemicals or heavy metals. Do you see a pattern in the type of health risks that you found in your research?

3. Check the Glencoe Science Web site to see what others have learned.

Do

1. Make sure your teacher approves your plan before you start.

2. Search for resources that can help you find out about health risks in your area.

3. Organize your information in a data table like the one shown.

4. Write a report in your Science Journal using the results of your research on heavy metals.

5. Post your data in the table provided on the Glencoe Science Web site.

Analyze Your Data

1. Did all your sources agree on the health risk of the chemical or heavy metal?

2. Analyze all your sources for possible bias. Are some sources more reliable than others?

3. How did the health risk differ for adults and children?

4. What were the sources of the heavy metals in your area? Are the heavy metals still being deposited in your area?

Draw Conclusions

1. Were the same substances found to be health risks in other parts of the country? From the data on the Glencoe Science Web site, try to predict what chemicals or heavy metals are health risks in different parts of the country.

2. From your report, what information do you think is the most important for the public to be aware of?

3. What could be done to decrease the risk of the health problems you identified?

*C*ommunicating
Your Data

SCIENCE*Online* Find this *Use the Internet* activity on the Glencoe Science Web site at **science.glencoe.com**. **Post** your data in the table provided. **Compare** your data to those of other students. **Analyze** and look for patterns in the data.

ACTIVITY   K ◆ 119

Test Your Hypothesis

Teaching Strategies

• Motivate students to start their investigations by brainstorming ways that chemicals benefit society. Then, present a few examples of severe health or environmental problems that have resulted from lack of information about chemicals such as dioxin, DDT, or CFCs.

• Present examples of initial research questions, such as: Are heavy metals present in fertilizer? How harmful is antimony to humans? Where in the human body does mercury accumulate?

• Go over some of the unfamiliar words that students may encounter, such as *carcinogenic*, *soluble*, and *toxic*.

Analyze Your Data

Answers will be subjective and based on the students' individual research.

Draw Conclusions

Answers will be individualized and often based on the students' own opinion of their research. Look for depth and quality of research performed.

✓*Assessment*

Portfolio Have students design and produce an informational pamphlet. The pamphlet should be geared to the general population and should include information found by all of the students in the class. It could provide facts and figures that explain the potential health risks posed by chemicals for the local environment and/or population. Use **PASC,** p. 129. P

*C*ommunicating
Your Data

Students might choose different criteria for patterns. For example, students might choose to make generalizations based on location. They might find that certain types of chemicals and heavy metals are found in urban areas only.

Pre-Reading Activity

Ask each student to think back to a favorite childhood fable or fairytale featuring an animal that possesses human characteristics. Students should make two lists of traits the animal displays: one of positive traits and a second of negative traits. Then have them do a quickwrite explaining which of these characteristics they admire and which they do not.

Respond to the Reading

Active Reading Strategies

Predict Can you tell from the title whether Anansi, the main character, will be a hero or a villain?

Evaluate As you read, take time to wonder what will happen next as Anansi takes his journey. Follow Anansi's thoughts throughout the selection. Ask yourself why Anansi interacts with the people in the town and with his son as he does. **Can you guess how Anansi feels about his son by his interactions with him?**

Answers to Questions.

1. Students' answers may vary, but should indicate that Anansi was not as clever as his youngest son.

1. because all the wisdom in the world did not help him solve a simple problem

Science and Language Arts

Anansi Tries to Steal All the Wisdom in the World
A folktale, adapted by Matt Evans

Respond to the Reading

1. Is Anansi a clever spider?

2. Why did Anansi scatter the wisdom he had collected?

The following African folktale about a spider named Anansi (or Anancy) is from the Ashanti people in Western Africa.

Anansi the spider knew that he was not wise… Then one day he had a clever thought. "I know," he said to no one in particular, "if I can get all of the wisdom in the village and put it in a hollow gourd… I would be the wisest of all!" So he set out to find a suitable gourd and then began his journey to collect the village's wisdom… Soon Anansi's gourd was overflowing with wisdom and he could hold no more. He now needed to find a place to store it… He looked around and spotted a tall, tall tree. "Ah," he said to himself, "if I could hide my wisdom high in that tree, I would never have to worry about someone stealing it from me!" So Anansi set out to climb the towering tree. He first took a cloth band and tied it around his waist. Then he tied the heavy gourd to the front of his belly where it would be safe. As he began to climb, however, the gourd full of wisdom kept getting in the way. He tried and tried, but he could not make progress around it.

Soon Anansi's youngest son walked by… "But Father," said the son, "wouldn't it be much easier if you tied the gourd behind you instead of in front?"… The son skipped down the path and when he had disappeared, Anansi moved the gourd so that it was behind him and proceeded up the tree with no problems at all. When he had reached the top, he cried out, "I walked all over and collected so much wisdom I am the wisest person ever, but still my baby son is wiser than me. Take back your wisdom!" He lifted the gourd high over his head and spilled its contents into the wind. The wisdom blew far and wide and settled across the land. And this is how wisdom came to the world.

120 ◆ K   CHAPTER 4 The Periodic Table

Reading Further

Other sources on this topic include:

A Dictionary of African Mythology: The Mythmaker as Storyteller, by Harold Scheub, Oxford University Press, 2000.

The Hero with an African Face: Mythic Wisdom of Traditional Africa, by Clyde W. Ford, Bantam Books, 1999.

The Center for Folklife and Cultural Heritage, 750 Ninth Street NW, Suite 4100, Smithsonian Institution, Washington, D.C. 20560-0953, (202) 275-1150.

Understanding Literature

Folktales: The Trickster The tale you have just read is an African folk tale called an animal-trickster tale. Trickster tales come from Africa, the Caribbean, and Latin American countries. Trickster tales portray a wily and cunning animal or human who at times bewilders the more powerful and at other times becomes a victim of his or her own schemes, as in the tale you just read. Other kinds of folktales include nursery tales, humorous tales, fairy tales, and tall tales.

Science Connection Elements are classified in relation to one another in a Periodic Table. They also are classified in groups of elements that share similar characteristics. Thus, there is a group of elements known as the alkali metals, another called the halogens, and so on. This way of classifying elements is similar to the way in which folktales are classified. Trickster tales have similar characteristics such as a character that has certain traits, such as cleverness, wit, cunning, and an ability to survive. Fairy tales are usually set in fantasy lands, while tall tales generally portray historical characters who perform superhuman deeds.

Linking Science and Writing

Create a Folktale Write your own folktale featuring a trickster character. The trickster can be any animal or living thing. You might use as a guide a cartoon character or other television personality. Describe the qualities that your trickster has. Write about an incident in which the trickster uses his or her wits to get by.

Career Connection

Farmer

John Reifsteck grows corn and soybeans on a 160-acre farm in Illinois. He must pay careful attention to the quality of the soil on his farm. In order to grow, plants draw nutrients from the soil. Once the plants are harvested, the soil may not have enough nutrients to support a new crop. Every year, Reifsteck tests his soil to make sure it is rich in nutrients. The results of his tests help him decide how much nitrogen, phosphorus, and potassium to add to different parts of his fields. By keeping his soil rich, he increases his chances of having a good crop.

SCIENCE*Online* To learn more about careers in farming, visit the Glencoe Science Web site at **science.glencoe.com.**

Career Connection

The best background for becoming a farmer is growing up or working on a farm. Participating in 4-H clubs and Future Farmers of America provides valuable preparation. A two- or four-year college degree in dairy science, crop science, agricultural economics, horticulture, or animal science is advised. Today's farmers are business people who need managerial and computer skills.

SCIENCE *Online*
Internet Addresses
_____
_____
_____
_____

Explore the Glencoe Science Web site at **science.glencoe.com** to find out more about topics in this feature.

Understanding Literature

Science Connection

Dmitri Ivanovich Mendeleev, a nineteenth century Russian chemist, drew up the first satisfactory periodic table. He found that certain natural patterns reveal an underlying regularity in the variation of properties among the elements. This happens because the electrons in atoms are arranged in energy levels, and each energy level holds a certain number of electrons. All the elements with the same number of electrons in the outermost energy level act in similar ways.

The table of elements is arranged in order of increasing proton number to show similarities in chemical behavior between elements. Horizontal rows of elements are called periods. Across a period there is a general trend from metallic to non-metallic behavior. Vertical columns of related elements are called groups. There is an increase in atomic size and in electro-positive behavior down a group.

Linking Science and Writing

Teaching Strategy

Students should write in their Science Journals about an animal that seems wise or clever. They should describe what behavior they have observed that makes this animal seem smart. They can then use this animal as the basis for their trickster character.

Chapter 4 Study Guide

Reviewing Main Ideas

Preview

Students can answer the questions in their Science Journals. Discuss the answers as you go through the chapter. **Linguistic**

Review

Students can write their answers, then compare them with those of other students. **Interpersonal**

Reteach

Students can look at the illustrations and describe details that support the main ideas of the chapter. **Visual-Spatial**

Answers to Chapter Review

SECTION 1

1. Group 1, the alkali metals

SECTION 2

1. Group 2, the alkaline earth metals

SECTION 3

2. They would not react with other substances in the environment, and they could be shaped into coins easily.

Chapter 4 Study Guide

Reviewing Main Ideas

Section 1 Introduction to the Periodic Table

1. When organized according to atomic number in a table, elements with similar properties occupy the same column and are called a group or family. *Which group is highlighted in the drawing below?*

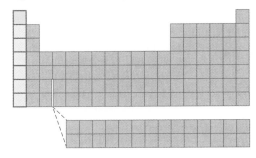

2. On the periodic table, the properties of the elements change gradually across a horizontal row called a period.

3. The periodic table can be divided into representative elements and transition elements.

Section 2 Representative Elements

1. The groups on the periodic table are known also by other names. For instance Group 17 is known as halogens. *What are the two names used to refer to the group highlighted below?*

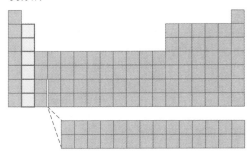

2. Atoms of elements in Groups 1 and 2 readily combine with atoms of other elements.

3. Each element in Group 2 combines less readily than its neighbor in Group 1. Each alkaline earth metal is denser and has a higher melting point than the alkali metal in its period.

4. Sodium, potassium, magnesium, and calcium have important biological roles.

Section 3 Transition Elements

1. The metals in the iron triad are found in a variety of places. Iron is found in blood and in the structure of skyscrapers.

2. Copper, silver, and gold are fairly unreactive, malleable elements. *Why would these properties make these elements a good choice for making coins?*

3. The lanthanides are naturally occurring elements with similar properties.

4. The actinides are radioactive elements. All actinides except thorium, proactinium, and uranium are synthetic.

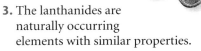

FOLDABLES Reading & Study Skills **After You Read**

Use the information in your Foldable to explain how metalloids have properties between those of metals and nonmetals.

FOLDABLES Reading & Study Skills **After You Read**

After students have read the chapter and completed the Foldable described in Before You Read, have them do the activity on the student page.

Dinah Zike

Visualizing Main Ideas

Complete the following concept map on the periodic table.

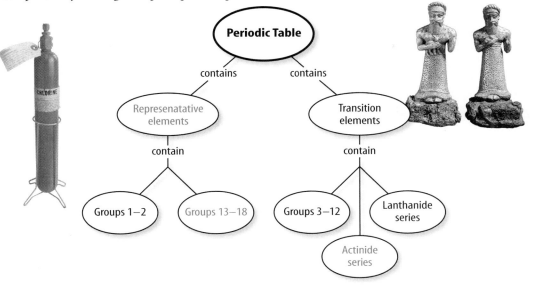

Periodic Table

contains → contains

Represenatative elements

Transition elements

contain

Groups 1–2

Groups 13–18

contain

Groups 3–12

Lanthanide series

Actinide series

Vocabulary Review

Vocabulary Words

a. catalyst
b. group
c. metal
d. metalloid
e. nonmetal
f. period

g. representative element
h. semiconductor
i. synthetic elements
j. transition elements

THE PRINCETON REVIEW **Study Tip**

Make a study schedule for yourself. If you have a planner, write down exactly which hours you plan to spend studying and stick to it. If you plan your schedule carefully, you will be prepared for tests and major projects without a lot of stress.

Using Vocabulary

Answer the following questions using complete sentences.

1. What is the difference between a group and a period?

2. What is the connection between a metalloid and a semiconductor?

3. What is a catalyst?

4. Arrange the terms *nonmetal*, *metal*, and *metalloid* according to increasing heat and electrical conductivity.

5. How is a metalloid like a metal? How is it different from a metal?

6. What are synthetic elements?

7. How are transition elements alike?

Visualizing Main Ideas

See student page.

Vocabulary Review

Using Vocabulary

1. A group is a column on the periodic table, and a period is a row on the periodic table.

2. Metalloids are elements that share properties with both metals and nonmetals. Semiconductors are materials that conduct electricity better than nonmetals but not as well as metals. Some semiconductors are metalloids.

3. A catalyst is a substance that can make something happen faster but is not changed itself.

4. The terms nonmetal, metalloid, and metal are in order of increasing ability to conduct heat and electricity.

5. Both conduct electricity, but a metal conducts better. A metalloid has some other properties of metals.

6. Synthetic elements are elements that don't occur in nature but that have been made by scientists.

7. In general, transition elements are metals that are malleable, ductile, and lustrous; conduct heat and electricity; and have high boiling points.

Chapter 4 Assessment

Checking Concepts

1. C
2. B
3. B
4. D
5. A
6. A
7. D
8. C
9. D
10. D

Thinking Critically

11. Mercury is poisonous and can kill organisms that live in waterways.
12. Yes, fluorine is the most reactive nonmetal.
13. Hydrogen can burn while helium cannot.
14. The foam keeps oxygen away from the fire, causing the fire to go out.
15. They would be shorter.

Checking Concepts

Choose the word or phrase that best answers the question.

1. Which of the following groups from the periodic table combines most readily with other elements to form compounds?
   - **A)** transition metals
   - **B)** alkaline earth metals
   - **C)** alkali metals
   - **D)** iron triad

2. Which element is located in Group 6, period 4?
   - **A)** tungsten
   - **B)** chromium
   - **C)** titanium
   - **D)** hafnium

3. Which element below is NOT a transition element?
   - **A)** gold
   - **B)** calcium
   - **C)** silver
   - **D)** copper

4. Several groups contain only metals. Which group contains only nonmetals?
   - **A)** Group 1
   - **B)** Group 12
   - **C)** Group 2
   - **D)** Group 18

5. Which of the following elements is likely to be contained in a substance with a brilliant yellow color?
   - **A)** chromium
   - **B)** carbon
   - **C)** iron
   - **D)** tin

6. Which halogen is radioactive?
   - **A)** astatine
   - **B)** chlorine
   - **C)** bromine
   - **D)** iodine

7. Which of the following is unlikely to happen to zinc?
   - **A)** It is rolled into sheets.
   - **B)** It is used to coat a steel hull.
   - **C)** It is used in a battery.
   - **D)** It is used as an insulator.

8. Which of the following describes the element tellurium?
   - **A)** alkali metal
   - **B)** transition metal
   - **C)** metalloid
   - **D)** lanthanide

9. Which element has the highest melting point of all the elements?
   - **A)** bromine
   - **B)** iodine
   - **C)** mercury
   - **D)** tungsten

10. A brittle, non-conducting, solid might belong to which of the following groups?
    - **A)** alkali metals
    - **B)** alkaline earth metals
    - **C)** actinide series
    - **D)** oxygen group

Thinking Critically

11. Why is it important that mercury be kept out of streams and waterways?

12. If you were going to try to get the noble gas argon to combine with another element, would fluorine be a good choice for the other element? Explain.

13. Hydrogen, which is lighter than helium, used to be used in blimps that carried passengers. Why is using helium a better choice?

14. Why is foam a good choice for putting out some fires?

15. It is theorized that some of the actinides beyond uranium were once present in Earth's crust. If this theory is true, how would their half-lives compare with the half-life of uranium, which is 4.5 billion years?

Developing Skills

16. **Recognizing Cause and Effect** Why do photographers work in low light when they work with materials containing selenium?

Chapter ✓Assessment Planner

Portfolio Encourage students to place in their portfolios one or two items of what they consider to be their best work. Examples include:
- Science Journal, p. 102
- Assessment, p. 111
- Activity, p. 114
- Assessment, p. 119

Performance Additional performance assessments, Performance Task Assessment Lists, and rubrics for evaluating these activities can be found in Glencoe's **Performance Assessment in the Science Classroom.**

17. Predicting How would life on Earth be different if the atmosphere were 80 percent oxygen and 20 percent nitrogen instead of the other way around?

18. Making and Using Graphs Make a bar graph of the representative elements that shows how many of the elements are solids, liquids, and gases at room temperature.

19. Making and Using Tables The periodic table below shows the locations of a few elements. For each element shown, give the element's period and group number; whether the element is a metal or a nonmetal; and whether it is a solid, liquid, or gas at room temperature.

(periodic table diagram with H, Li, N, F, Co, Ag, Hg, I marked)

Performance Assessment

20. Asking Questions Research the contribution that Henry G. J. Moseley made to the development of the modern periodic table. Research the background and work of this scientist and write your findings in the form of an interview.

TECHNOLOGY

Go to the Glencoe Science Web site at **science.glencoe.com** or use the **Glencoe Science CD-ROM** for additional chapter assessment.

Test Practice

The box below shows the formulas of four different chemical substances. These substances are carbon dioxide (CO_2), calcium carbonate ($CaCO_3$), propane (C_3H_8), and acetic acid ($HC_2H_3O_2$).

$$CO_2 \quad CaCO_3 \quad C_3H_8 \quad HC_2H_3O_2$$

Study the formulas above and answer the following questions.

1. All of the substances listed above contain _____ .
A) carbon   **C)** nitrogen
B) hydrogen   **D)** oxygen

2. Each of the four substances shown contains a _____ .
F) metal
G) metalloid
H) nonmetal
J) transition metal

3. Which of the four compounds shown above contains a metal?
A) $HC_2H_3O_2$
B) $CaCO_3$
C) C_3H_8
D) CO_2

4. Which of the following shows the compounds in order of decreasing ratio of carbon to oxygen?
F) $HC_2H_3O_2$, $CaCO_3$, CO_2
G) CO_2, $CaCO_3$, $HC_2H_3O_2$
H) $CaCO_3$, $HC_2H_3O_2$, CO_2
J) $HC_2H_3O_2$, CO_2, $CaCO_3$

Test Practice

The Test-Taking Tip was written by The Princeton Review, the nation's leader in test preparation.
1. A
2. F
3. B
4. J

Developing Skills

16. Selenium is light-sensitive. Too much light might interfere with imaging.
17. Answers should include recognition of oxygen's ability to react with other elements while nitrogen won't.
18. Graphs should show that 32 are solid, 1 is liquid, and 11 are gaseous.
19. H: 1, 1, nonmetal, gas
Li: 2, 1, metal, solid
Co: 4, 9, metal, solid
Ag: 5, 11, metal, solid
Hg: 6, 12, metal, liquid
N: 2, 15, nonmetal, gas
F: 2, 17, nonmetal, gas
I: 5, 17, nonmetal, solid

Performance Assessment

20. Answers will vary but should include that he discovered a method for determining the number of protons in the nucleus of an atom. Use **PASC**, p. 141.

✓Assessment Resources

 Reproducible Masters

Chapter Resources Booklet
Chapter Review, pp. 33–34
Chapter Tests, pp. 35–38
Assessment Transparency Activity, p. 45

Glencoe Science Web site
Interactive Tutor
Chapter Quizzes

Glencoe Technology
- Assessment Transparency
- Interactive CD-ROM Chapter Quizzes
- ExamView Pro Test Bank
- Vocabulary PuzzleMaker Software
- MindJogger Videoquiz DVD/VHS

Standardized Test Practice

QUESTION 1: C

Students must recall chronology of events from the passage to identify which answer choice occurred first.

- **Choice A** No; this event occurred after Mendeleev made his predictions.
- **Choice B** No; this happened much later, in the 20th century.
- **Choice C** Yes; this event occurred first.
- **Choice D** No; this happened much later, in the 20th century.

Teaching Tip

Suggest students make a timeline to help them answer questions about sequence of events in a passage.

QUESTION 2: F

Students must use clues from the passage such as *made . . . in the laboratory* to identify that the best meaning of the underlined word *artificially* is choice F, *unnaturally*.

THE PRINCETON REVIEW — All questions written and validated by The Princeton Review.

Read the passage. Then read each question that follows the passage. Decide which is the best answer to each question.

Grouping the Elements Using their Properties

By 1860, scientists had discovered a total of 63 chemical elements. Dmitri Mendeleev, a Russian chemist, thought that there had to be some order among the elements.

He made a card for each element. On the card, he listed the physical and chemical properties of the element, such as atomic mass, density, color, and melting point. He also wrote each element's combining power, or its ability to form compounds with other elements.

When he arranged the cards in order of increasing atomic mass, Mendeleev noticed that the elements followed a periodic, or repeating, pattern. After every seven cards, the properties repeated. He placed each group of seven cards in rows, one row under another. He noticed that the columns in his chart formed groups of elements that had similar chemical and physical properties.

In a few places, Mendeleev had to move a card one space to the left or right to maintain the similarities of his groups. This left a few empty spaces. He predicted that they would be filled with elements that were unknown. He even predicted their properties. Fifteen years later, three new elements were discovered and placed in the empty spaces of the periodic table. Their physical and chemical properties agreed with Mendeleev's predictions.

Today there are more than 100 known elements. An extra column has been added for the noble gases, a group of elements that were not yet discovered in Mendeleev's time.

Members of this group almost never combine with other elements. As new elements are discovered or are made <u>artificially</u>, scientists can place them in their proper place on the periodic table thanks to Mendeleev.

Test-Taking Tip To answer questions about a sequence of events, make a time line of what happened in each paragraph of the passage.

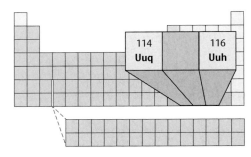

Even the modern periodic table has empty spaces for elements that have not been discovered yet.

1. Which of the following occurred FIRST in the passage?
   A) Three new elements were discovered 15 years after Mendeleev developed the periodic table.
   B) The noble gases were discovered and added to the periodic table.
   C) Mendeleev predicted properties of unknown elements.
   D) New elements were made in the laboratory and added to the periodic table.

2. The word <u>artificially</u> in this passage means _____.
   F) unnaturally
   G) artistically
   H) atomically
   J) radioactively

Reasoning and Skills

Read each question and choose the best answer.

Changes in States of Matter

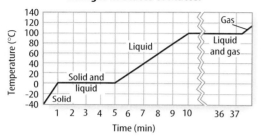

1. The graph shows the change in temperature that occurs as ice changes to water vapor. How much higher than the starting temperature is the boiling point?
   A) 40°C   C) 140°C
   B) 100°C   D) 180°C

Test-Taking Tip Boiling point is the flat section of the graph where liquid changes to gas.

2. What is being measured in the illustration?
   F) boiling point   H) density
   G) melting point   J) flammability

Test-Taking Tip Think about what you would measure with a thermometer in a liquid that you are heating.

Properties of Selected Pure Substances

Substance	Melting Point (°C)	Boiling Point (°C)	Color
Aluminum	660.4	2,519	silver metallic
Argon	-189.2	-185.7	colorless
Mercury	-38.8	356.6	silver metallic
Water	0	100	colorless

3. Room temperature is about 20°C. In the table, which substance is a solid at room temperature?
   A) aluminum
   B) argon
   C) mercury
   D) water

Test-Taking Tip Remember that negative temperatures are below zero.

Read this question carefully before writing your answer on a separate sheet of paper.

4. The density of pure water is 1.00 g/cm³. Ice floats on water. Therefore, the density of ice is *less* than that of water. Design an experiment to determine the density of an ice cube. List all the necessary steps.
   (Volume = Length × Width × Height; Density = Mass / Volume)

Test-Taking Tip Consider all the information provided in the question.

Reasoning and Skills

QUESTION 1: C
Students must interpret the graph to identify the correct answer. Because the starting temperature was –40°C and the boiling point is 100°C, the correct answer is choice C, *140°C*.

QUESTION 2: F
Students must carefully examine the diagram. Because the substance in the beaker is already a liquid and appears to be boiling, the correct answer is choice F, *boiling point*.

QUESTION 3: A
Students must retrieve information from the table to identify the correct answer. Because there is only one substance with a melting point greater than 20°C, the correct answer is choice A, *aluminum*.

Teaching Tip

Review with students how to analyze the chart to determine at what temperature each substance changes from a solid to a liquid.

QUESTION 4: Answers will vary.

Answers should include measuring the length, width, and height of the ice cube with a metric ruler in order to find volume. In addition, the mass of the ice cube should be determined using a triple-beam balance. After these measurements have been determined, students should describe how to calculate volume and density.

Student Resources

CONTENTS

Field GUIDE

About the Field Guide

- A field guide contains a key that enables the user to classify or identify an item or concept.

- In using a field guide, students will apply steps of a scientific method as they observe, investigate, and draw conclusions.

- This field guide applies nationally; local and regional field guides are usually available for more specific local use.

- Encourage students to use the field guide outside the classroom.

Tie to Prior Knowledge

Ask students how they dispose of trash at home. Do they separate out the newspapers, aluminum cans, and plastics from the rest of the "garbage"? Ask them if they recognize recycling containers when they see them. Usually large, red or blue plastic containers. Tell students that identifying and separating the different materials is the first step in the process of recycling. In this field activity, they'll learn more about the different varieties of plastics and how they are recycled.

Field Activity

Caution students to wear rubber gloves, aprons, and safety goggles before handling the discarded materials. Also, encourage students to make a chart to record their findings before they begin. Students should discover more plastics of types 1 and 2. These are the easiest to recycle.

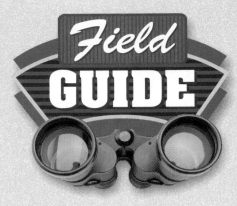

Field GUIDE

Have you ever noticed the arrows, numbers, and letters on the bottom of plastic shampoo bottles, margarine tubs, and milk jugs? These recycling labels identify the type of plastic used in making the container. Plastics are made of repeating chemical units joined end to end, as in a chain. The specific elements in these units and their structure determine each plastic's characteristics. Because most plastics are not biodegradable, or easily broken down, discarded plastics pile up in landfills and can harm the environment. Items that are recycled, however, become new products that are reused.

The recycling process is a cycle. After you discard plastics in the recycling bins, they are collected, melted, shredded, and converted into flakes or pellets that can be used to make new products. The cycle is complete when you purchase products made from recycled plastics.

Types of Plastics

In 1988, the Society of the Plastics Industry, Inc. (SPI) developed a system that identifies the resin, or plastic, content of bottles and other commonly used containers. The seven codes that are used make it easier to sort and recycle plastics.

Recyclable Plastic

Terephthalate Polyethylene (PET)

1

PETE

PET is used to make bottles and videotapes. It is clear, durable, heat-resistant, and water-resistant. PET also is called polyester and many kinds of polyester exist. Although polyesters have similar chemical structures, they are different enough to give each one unique characteristics. For example, one type of polyester produces a soft fiber that is woven into cloth. This fiber can be recycled into clothes, furniture, and carpet.

From 1990 to 1998, the recycling of plastic soft-drink bottles has increased six-fold. Today more than 75 percent of Americans have access to community-based recycling programs for one or more types of plastics.

Field Activity

Using this field guide, identify the type of plastic that is used to make each of the containers in a recycling bin. In your Science Journal, list the number and types of containers made from each type of plastic. Which types were recycled most often?

Resources for Teachers and Students

The McGraw-Hill Recycling Handbook, Herbert Lund, ed., McGraw-Hill, 2000.

Waste and Want: A Social History of Trash, Susan Strasser, Owl Books, 2000.

Recycler's Handbook, Earthworks Press, 1990.

The Plastic Waste Primer/A Handbook for Citizens, Jeffrey Porro, et al., The Lyons Press, 1993.

Field Guides

High-Density Polyethylene (HDPE)

2

HDPE

HDPE is used in plastic grocery bags and in the manufacture of bottles for water, milk, and laundry detergent. Properties of HDPE include strength, rigidity, resistance to moisture and chemicals, permeability to gas, and ease of processing and forming. Because it has a highly ordered structure, HDPE is a dense plastic. This makes it harder and more heat resistant than other types of plastic. HDPE plastic is recycled into floor tile, fencing, drainage pipes, and toys.

You can find many examples of HDPE plastic containers in your refrigerator.

The floorboards of this deck are from recycled PVC plastic.

Polyvinyl Chloride (PVC)

3

V

Shampoo bottles and "bubble" packaging are common uses for PVC. It is used to make medical tubing as well as garden hoses. PVC is tough and resistant to chemicals—it can withstand rough weather conditions. It has a simple chain structure of carbon, hydrogen, and chlorine. When additives called plasticizers are used in its manufacture, PVC remains flexible. Products made from recycled PVC include decking, packaging materials, and paneling.

FIELD GUIDE   K ◆ 131

Quick Demo

Throw packing peanuts into a beaker of acetone. Have students observe how they disintegrate (or melt) almost instantly upon contact. Using a glass stirring rod, pick up a few of the polymer strands that have formed. How can this be the same material that made the peanuts? Possible answer: To make the peanuts, the polymer strands curl up, like a piece of string being made into a ball.

SCIENCE
Online
Internet Addresses

_____
_____
_____
_____

Explore the Glencoe Science Web site at **science.glencoe.com** to find out more about topics in this field guide.

Teacher FYI

The plastic soda bottle you're probably very familiar with was developed by the chemist Nathaniel Wyeth. His brother, Andrew, is a famous American painter. Nathaniel Wyeth has said that he believes one day we'll be able to melt down his plastic bottles, treat them with chemicals, and then make cars out of them. Once these cars have served their purpose, they could again be turned into bottles.

Discussion

For the recycling of plastics to reach its fullest potential, more work than simply gathering and preparing the materials needs to be done. **Can you think of any other aspects necessary for a complete recycling program?** Possible answers: Laws can be created to make recycling mandatory. Marketing campaigns can encourage recycling. People should know if the products they are buying come from recycled plastics; this way, they can choose them over others. Those in charge of plastic recycling programs should know exactly what they can use the recycled plastic for.

Extension

Plastics come from petroleum, the same stuff we burn to get energy. Petroleum works well because it's a good source of carbon, which is needed to construct plastic polymers. But the petroleum supply is running short. Should we save some of the petroleum supply to make plastic polymers or can you think of another way around this dilemma? Have students research possible alternatives. Possible answers: Any material containing carbon is a potential source of plastic. Currently, the possibility of making plastics from wood and biomass is being explored.

Field GUIDE

Low-Density Polyethylene (LDPE)

4 LDPE

LDPE is used to make frozen food bags and bottles that can be squeezed, such as syrup bottles. LDPE is durable, transparent, and moisture resistant. This plastic has a branched chain structure of carbon and hydrogen that makes it flexible and easy to seal. Mailing envelopes, furniture, compost bins, and trash-can liners are some of the recycled products made with LDPE.

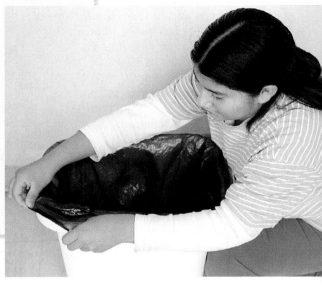

The strength and flexibility of LDPE plastic make it ideal for use in garbage can liners.

Polypropylene often is used to make medicine bottles because it is resistant to chemicals.

Polypropylene (PP)

5 PP

Common uses for PP include ketchup bottles, indoor-outdoor carpeting, and medicine bottles. A chain structure of carbon and hydrogen with short, regular branching gives polypropylene strength; resistance to heat, oil, and chemicals; and moisture-barrier properties. Recycled products manufactured with polypropylene include bike racks, battery cables, and rakes.

132 ◆ K STUDENT RESOURCES

Visual Learning

Have students look at the different plastics illustrated on these pages. **What is similar about these materials?** Possible answers: All can be shaped. All are smooth and apparently water resistant. **What's different about them?** Possible answers: One is thin like paper, another is a foam. **Does this give you any clue as to why plastics are so popular?** Possible answer: Plastics are very versatile, and so useful in many ways.

Polystyrene is a versatile plastic.

Polystyrene (PS)

6

PS

Polystyrene's insulating qualities make it well suited for use in coffee cups, lids, and protective containers. The chain structure of polystyrene is similar to that of polypropylene, but the regular branches are larger and more complex so they produce different characteristics. Polystyrene also can be foam—it is used for a variety of applications because of its versatility. Egg cartons, take-out containers, and foam packaging materials are made with recycled polystyrene.

Other

7

OTHER

When the Other code is used, it means that the package is composed of a type of plastic other than the first six listed here or of a combination of plastics. The properties depend on which plastics were used. Large water bottles and plastic lumber are recycled products that are made from plastics that have this code.

About 8.5 percent of all plastics are identified by SPI *Code 7,* which means "other."

Make a Model

Using chains, yarn, or simply pieces of string, make models of plastic polymers and demonstrate to the class different ways they can pack together. If time permits, you can construct more detailed models of the different plastic polymers. These will show how only a little change in the monomer (a chlorine atom substituted for a hydrogen atom, for example) can give the plastic different properties.

Teacher FYI

In 1996, 25% of all plastic bottles made in the United States were recycled. This translates into 1.3 billion pounds of plastic material that did not go into landfills. Legislation also has been enacted to increase the amount of recycled plastics used in the United States. In California, for example, all HDPE packaging is required to contain at least 25% recycled material.

Curriculum Connection

Social Studies Some historians think that disposable items became so popular because they made it possible for poorer people to enjoy a more clean lifestyle. They also think that disposable products made people feel rich. In their Science Journals, have students write what they think are the greatest benefits of disposable products. Suggest other ways these benefits could be obtained in a society that promotes the reuse of materials.

Organizing Information

As you study science, you will make many observations and conduct investigations and experiments. You will also research information that is available from many sources. These activities will involve organizing and recording data. The quality of the data you collect and the way you organize it will determine how well others can understand and use it. In **Figure 1,** the student is obtaining and recording information using a thermometer.

Putting your observations in writing is an important way of communicating to others the information you have found and the results of your investigations and experiments.

Researching Information

Scientists work to build on and add to human knowledge of the world. Before moving in a new direction, it is important to gather the information that already is known about a subject. You will look for such information in various reference sources. Follow these steps to research information on a scientific subject:

Step 1 Determine exactly what you need to know about the subject. For instance, you might want to find out about one of the elements in the periodic table.

Step 2 Make a list of questions, such as: Who discovered the element? When was it discovered? What makes the element useful or interesting?

Step 3 Use multiple sources such as textbooks, encyclopedias, government documents, professional journals, science magazines, and the Internet.

Step 4 List where you found the sources. Make sure the sources you use are reliable and the most current available.

Figure 1
Making an observation is one way to gather information directly.

Evaluating Print and Nonprint Sources

Not all sources of information are reliable. Evaluate the sources you use for information, and use only those you know to be dependable. For example, suppose you want to find ways to make your home more energy efficient. You might find two Web sites on how to save energy in your home. One Web site contains "Energy-Saving Tips" written by a company that sells a new type of weatherproofing material you put around your door frames. The other is a Web page on "Conserving Energy in Your Home" written by the U.S. Department of Energy. You would choose the second Web site as the more reliable source of information.

In science, information can change rapidly. Always consult the most current sources. A 1985 source about saving energy would not reflect the most recent research and findings.

Interpreting Scientific Illustrations

As you research a science topic, you will see drawings, diagrams, and photographs. Illustrations help you understand what you read. Some illustrations are included to help you understand an idea that you can't see easily by yourself. For instance, you can't see the tiny particles in an atom, but you can look at a diagram of an atom as labeled in **Figure 2** that helps you understand something about it. Visualizing a drawing helps many people remember details more easily. Illustrations also provide examples that clarify difficult concepts or give additional information about the topic you are studying.

Most illustrations have a label or caption. A label or caption identifies the illustration or provides additional information to better explain it. Can you find the caption or labels in **Figure 2?**

Figure 2
This drawing shows an atom of carbon with its six protons, six neutrons, and six electrons.

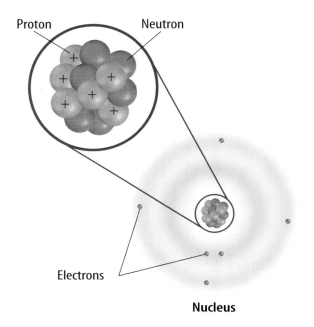

Venn Diagram

Although it is not a concept map, a Venn diagram illustrates how two subjects compare and contrast. In other words, you can see the characteristics that the subjects have in common and those that they do not.

The Venn diagram in **Figure 3** shows the relationship between two different substances made from the element carbon. However, due to the way their atoms are arranged, one substance is the gemstone diamond, and the other is the graphite found in pencils.

Concept Mapping

If you were taking a car trip, you might take some sort of road map. By using a map, you begin to learn where you are in relation to other places on the map.

A concept map is similar to a road map, but a concept map shows relationships among ideas (or concepts) rather than places. It is a diagram that visually shows how concepts are related. Because a concept map shows relationships among ideas, it can make the meanings of ideas and terms clear and help you understand what you are studying.

Overall, concept maps are useful for breaking large concepts down into smaller parts, making learning easier.

Figure 3
A Venn diagram shows how objects or concepts are alike and how they are different.

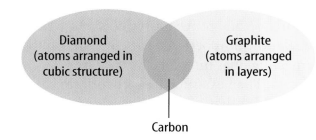

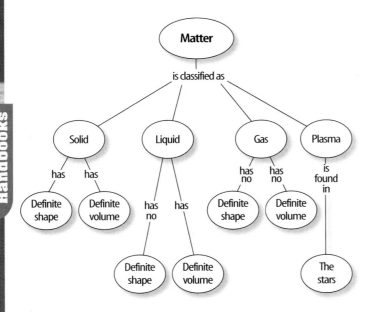

Figure 4
A network tree shows how concepts or objects are related.

Network Tree Look at the network tree in **Figure 4,** that describes the different types of matter. A network tree is a type of concept map. Notice how some words are in ovals while others are written across connecting lines. The words inside the ovals are science terms or concepts. The words written on the connecting lines describe the relationships between the concepts.

When constructing a network tree, write the topic on a note card or piece of paper. Write the major concepts related to that topic on separate note cards or pieces of paper. Then arrange them in order from general to specific. Branch the related concepts from the major concept and describe the relationships on the connecting lines. Continue branching to more specific concepts. If necessary, write the relationships between the concepts on the connecting lines until all concepts are mapped. Then examine the network tree for relationships that cross branches, and add them to the network tree.

Events Chain An events chain is another type of concept map. It models the order, or sequence, of items. In science, an events chain can be used to describe a sequence of events, the steps in a procedure, or the stages of a process.

When making an events chain, first find the one event that starts the chain. This event is called the initiating event. Then, find the next event in the chain and continue until you reach an outcome. Suppose you are asked to describe why and how a sound might make an echo. You might draw an events chain such as the one in **Figure 5.** Notice that connecting words are not necessary in an events chain.

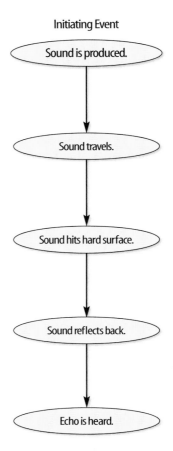

Figure 5
Events chains show the order of steps in a process or event.

Cycle Map A cycle concept map is a specific type of events chain map. In a cycle concept map, the series of events does not produce a final outcome. Instead, the last event in the chain relates back to the beginning event.

You first decide what event will be used as the beginning event. Once that is decided, you list events in order that occur after it. Words are written between events that describe what happens from one event to the next. The last event in a cycle concept map relates back to the beginning event. The number of events in a cycle concept varies, but is usually three or more. Look at the cycle map, as shown in **Figure 6.**

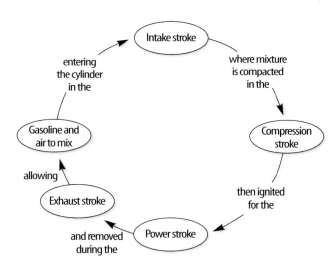

Figure 6
A cycle map shows events that occur in a cycle.

Spider Map A type of concept map that you can use for brainstorming is the spider map. When you have a central idea, you might find you have a jumble of ideas that relate to it but are not necessarily clearly related to each other. The spider map on sound in **Figure 7** shows that if you write these ideas outside the main concept, then you can begin to separate and group un-related terms so they become more useful.

Figure 7
A spider map allows you to list ideas that relate to a central topic but not necessarily to one another.

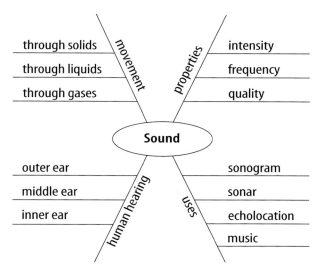

Writing a Paper

You will write papers often when researching science topics or reporting the results of investigations or experiments. Scientists frequently write papers to share their data and conclusions with other scientists and the public. When writing a paper, use these steps.

Step 1 Assemble your data by using graphs, tables, or a concept map. Create an outline.

Step 2 Start with an introduction that contains a clear statement of purpose and what you intend to discuss or prove.

Step 3 Organize the body into paragraphs. Each paragraph should start with a topic sentence, and the remaining sentences in that paragraph should support your point.

Step 4 Position data to help support your points.

Step 5 Summarize the main points and finish with a conclusion statement.

Step 6 Use tables, graphs, charts, and illustrations whenever possible.

Investigating and Experimenting

You might say the work of a scientist is to solve problems. When you decide to find out why your neighbor's hydrangeas produce blue flowers while yours are pink, you are problem solving, too. You might also observe that your neighbor's azaleas are healthier than yours are and decide to see whether differences in the soil explain the differences in these plants.

Scientists use orderly approaches to solve problems. The methods scientists use include identifying a question, making observations, forming a hypothesis, testing a hypothesis, analyzing results, and drawing conclusions.

Scientific investigations involve careful observation under controlled conditions. Such observation of an object or a process can suggest new and interesting questions about it. These questions sometimes lead to the formation of a hypothesis. Scientific investigations are designed to test a hypothesis.

Identifying a Question

The first step in a scientific investigation or experiment is to identify a question to be answered or a problem to be solved. You might be interested in knowing how beams of laser light like the ones in **Figure 8** look the way they do.

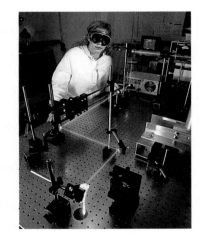

Figure 8
When you see lasers being used for scientific research, you might ask yourself, "Are these lasers different from those that are used for surgery?"

Forming Hypotheses

Hypotheses are based on observations that have been made. A hypothesis is a possible explanation based on previous knowledge and observations.

Perhaps a scientist has observed that certain substances dissolve faster in warm water than in cold. Based on these observations, the scientist can make a statement that he or she can test. The statement is a hypothesis. The hypothesis could be: *A substance dissolves in warm water faster.* A hypothesis has to be something you can test by using an investigation. A testable hypothesis is a valid hypothesis.

Predicting

When you apply a hypothesis to a specific situation, you predict something about that situation. First, you must identify which hypothesis fits the situation you are considering. People use predictions to make everyday decisions. Based on previous observations and experiences, you might form a prediction that if substances dissolve in warm water faster, then heating the water will shorten mixing time for powdered fruit drinks. Someone could use this prediction to save time in preparing a fruit punch for a party.

Testing a Hypothesis

To test a hypothesis, you need a procedure. A procedure is the plan you follow in your experiment. A procedure tells you what materials to use, as well as how and in what order to use them. When you follow a procedure, data are generated that support or do not support the original hypothesis statement.

For example, premium gasoline costs more than regular gasoline. Does premium gasoline increase the efficiency or fuel mileage of your family car? You decide to test the hypothesis: "If premium gasoline is more efficient, then it should increase the fuel mileage of my family's car." Then you write the procedure shown in **Figure 9** for your experiment and generate the data presented in the table below.

Figure 9
A procedure tells you what to do step by step.

> ### Procedure
> 1. Use regular gasoline for two weeks.
> 2. Record the number of kilometers between fill-ups and the amount of gasoline used.
> 3. Switch to premium gasoline for two weeks.
> 4. Record the number of kilometers between fill-ups and the amount of gasoline used.

Gasoline Data			
Type of Gasoline	Kilometers Traveled	Liters Used	Liters per Kilometer
Regular	762	45.34	0.059
Premium	661	42.30	0.064

These data show that premium gasoline is less efficient than regular gasoline in one particular car. It took more gasoline to travel 1 km (0.064) using premium gasoline than it did to travel 1 km using regular gasoline (0.059). This conclusion does not support the hypothesis.

Are all investigations alike? Keep in mind as you perform investigations in science that a hypothesis can be tested in many ways. Not every investigation makes use of all the ways that are described on these pages, and not all hypotheses are tested by investigations. Scientists encounter many variations in the methods that are used when they perform experiments. The skills in this handbook are here for you to use and practice.

Identifying and Manipulating Variables and Controls

In any experiment, it is important to keep everything the same except for the item you are testing. The one factor you change is called the independent variable. The factor that changes as a result of the independent variable is called the dependent variable. Always make sure you have only one independent variable. If you allow more than one, you will not know what causes the changes you observe in the dependent variable. Many experiments also have controls—individual instances or experimental subjects for which the independent variable is not changed. You can then compare the test results to the control results.

For example, in the fuel-mileage experiment, you made everything the same except the type of gasoline that was used. The driver, the type of automobile, and the type of driving were the same throughout. In this way, you could be sure that any mileage differences were caused by the type of fuel—the independent variable. The fuel mileage was the dependent variable.

If you could repeat the experiment using several automobiles of the same type on a standard driving track with the same driver, you could make one automobile a control by using regular gasoline over the four-week period.

Collecting Data

Whether you are carrying out an investigation or a short observational experiment, you will collect data, or information. Scientists collect data accurately as numbers and descriptions and organize it in specific ways.

Observing Scientists observe items and events, then record what they see. When they use only words to describe an observation, it is called qualitative data. For example, a scientist might describe the color, texture, or odor of a substance produced in a chemical reaction. Scientists' observations also can describe how much there is of something. These observations use numbers, as well as words, in the description and are called quantitative data. For example, if a sample of the element gold is described as being "shiny and very dense," the data are clearly qualitative. Quantitative data on this sample of gold might include "a mass of 30 g and a density of 19.3 g/cm^3." Quantitative data often are organized into tables. Then, from information in the table, a graph can be drawn. Graphs can reveal relationships that exist in experimental data.

When you make observations in science, you should examine the entire object or situation first, then look carefully for details. If you're looking at an element sample, for instance, check the general color and pattern of the sample before using a hand lens to examine its surface for any smaller details or characteristics. Remember to record accurately everything you see.

Scientists try to make careful and accurate observations. When possible, they use instruments such as microscopes, metric rulers, graduated cylinders, thermometers, and balances. Measurements provide numerical data that can be repeated and checked.

Sampling When working with large numbers of objects or a large population, scientists usually cannot observe or study every one of them. Instead, they use a sample or a portion of the total number. To *sample* is to take a small, representative portion of the objects or organisms of a population for research. By making careful observations or manipulating variables within a portion of a group, information is discovered and conclusions are drawn that might apply to the whole population.

Estimating Scientific work also involves estimating. To estimate is to make a judgment about the size or the number of something without measuring or counting every object or member of a population. Scientists first measure or count the amount or number in a small sample. A geologist, for example, might remove a 10-g sample from a large rock that is rich in copper ore, as in **Figure 10.** Then a chemist would determine the percentage of copper by mass and multiply that percentage by the total mass of the rock to estimate the total mass of copper in the large rock.

Figure 10
Determining the percentage of copper by mass that is present in a small piece of a large rock, which is rich in copper ore, can help estimate the total mass of copper ore that is present in the rock.

Measuring in SI

The metric system of measurement was developed in 1795. A modern form of the metric system, called the International System, or SI, was adopted in 1960. SI provides standard measurements that all scientists around the world can understand.

The metric system is convenient because unit sizes vary by multiples of 10. When changing from smaller units to larger units, divide by a multiple of 10. When changing from larger units to smaller, multiply by a multiple of 10. To convert millimeters to centimeters, divide the millimeters by 10. To convert 30 mm to centimeters, divide 30 by 10 (30 mm equal 3 cm).

Prefixes are used to name units. Look at the table below for some common metric prefixes and their meanings. Do you see how the prefix *kilo-* attached to the unit *gram* is *kilogram*, or 1,000 g?

Metric Prefixes			
Prefix	Symbol		Meaning
kilo-	k	1,000	thousand
hecto-	h	100	hundred
deka-	da	10	ten
deci-	d	0.1	tenth
centi-	c	0.01	hundredth
milli-	m	0.001	thousandth

Now look at the metric ruler shown in **Figure 11.** The centimeter lines are the long, numbered lines, and the shorter lines are millimeter lines.

When using a metric ruler, line up the 0-cm mark with the end of the object being measured, and read the number of the unit where the object ends. In this instance it would be 4.5 cm.

Figure 11
This metric ruler has centimeter and millimeter divisions.

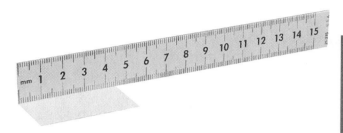

Liquid Volume In some science activities, you will measure liquids. The unit that is used to measure liquids is the liter. A liter has the volume of 1,000 cm³. The prefix *milli-* means "thousandth (0.001)." A milliliter is one thousandth of 1 L, and 1 L has the volume of 1,000 mL. One milliliter of liquid completely fills a cube measuring 1 cm on each side. Therefore, 1 mL equals 1 cm³.

You will use beakers and graduated cylinders to measure liquid volume. A graduated cylinder, as illustrated in **Figure 12,** is marked from bottom to top in milliliters. This one contains 79 mL of a liquid.

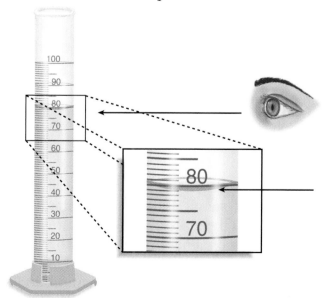

Figure 12
Graduated cylinders measure liquid volume.

Mass Scientists measure mass in grams. You might use a beam balance similar to the one shown in **Figure 13.** The balance has a pan on one side and a set of beams on the other side. Each beam has a rider that slides on the beam.

Before you find the mass of an object, slide all the riders back to the zero point. Check the pointer on the right to make sure it swings an equal distance above and below the zero point. If the swing is unequal, find and turn the adjusting screw until you have an equal swing.

Place an object on the pan. Slide the largest rider along its beam until the pointer drops below zero. Then move it back one notch. Repeat the process on each beam until the pointer swings an equal distance above and below the zero point. Sum the masses on each beam to find the mass of the object. Move all riders back to zero when finished.

Figure 13
A triple beam balance is used to determine the mass of an object.

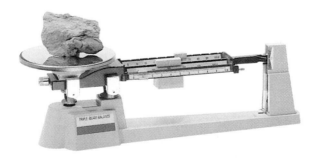

You should never place a hot object on the pan or pour chemicals directly onto the pan. Instead, find the mass of a clean container. Remove the container from the pan, then place the chemicals in the container. Find the mass of the container with the chemicals in it. To find the mass of the chemicals, subtract the mass of the empty container from the mass of the filled container.

Making and Using Tables

Browse through your textbook and you will see tables in the text and in the activities. In a table, data, or information, are arranged so that they are easier to understand. Activity tables help organize the data you collect during an activity so results can be interpreted.

Making Tables To make a table, list the items to be compared in the first column and the characteristics to be compared in the first row. The title should clearly indicate the content of the table, and the column or row heads should tell the reader what information is found in there. The table below lists materials collected for recycling on three weekly pick-up days. The inclusion of kilograms in parentheses also identifies for the reader that the figures are mass units.

Recyclable Materials Collected During Week			
Day of Week	Paper (kg)	Aluminum (kg)	Glass (kg)
Monday	5.0	4.0	12.0
Wednesday	4.0	1.0	10.0
Friday	2.5	2.0	10.0

Using Tables How much paper, in kilograms, is being recycled on Wednesday? Locate the column labeled "Paper (kg)" and the row "Wednesday." The information in the box where the column and row intersect is the answer. Did you answer "4.0"? How much aluminum, in kilograms, is being recycled on Friday? If you answered "2.0," you understand how to read the table. How much glass is collected for recycling each week? Locate the column labeled "Glass (kg)" and add the figures for all three rows. If you answered "32.0," then you know how to locate and use the data provided in the table.

Recording Data

To be useful, the data you collect must be recorded carefully. Accuracy is key. A well-thought-out experiment includes a way to record procedures, observations, and results accurately. Data tables are one way to organize and record results. Set up the tables you will need ahead of time so you can record the data right away.

Record information properly and neatly. Never put unidentified data on scraps of paper. Instead, data should be written in a notebook like the one in **Figure 14.** Write in pencil so information isn't lost if your data get wet. At each point in the experiment, record your information and label it. That way, your data will be accurate and you will not have to determine what the figures mean when you look at your notes later.

Figure 14
Record data neatly and clearly so they are easy to understand.

Recording Observations

It is important to record observations accurately and completely. That is why you always should record observations in your notes immediately as you make them. It is easy to miss details or make mistakes when recording results from memory. Do not include your personal thoughts when you record your data. Record only what you observe to eliminate bias. For example, when you record the time required for five students to climb the same set of stairs, you would note which student took the longest time. However, you would not refer to that student's time as "the worst time of all the students in the group."

Making Models

You can organize the observations and other data you collect and record in many ways. Making models is one way to help you better understand the parts of a structure you have been observing or the way a process for which you have been taking various measurements works.

Models often show things that are too large or too small for normal viewing. For example, you normally won't see the inside of an atom. However, you can understand the structure of the atom better by making a three-dimensional model of an atom. The relative sizes, the positions, and the movements of protons, neutrons, and electrons can be explained in words. An atomic model made of a plastic-ball nucleus and pipe-cleaner electron shells can help you visualize how the parts of the atom relate to each other.

Other models can be devised on a computer. Some models, such as those that illustrate the chemical combinations of different elements, are mathematical and are represented by equations.

Skill Handbooks

Making and Using Graphs

After scientists organize data in tables, they might display the data in a graph that shows the relationship of one variable to another. A graph makes interpretation and analysis of data easier. Three types of graphs are the line graph, the bar graph, and the circle graph.

Line Graphs A line graph like in **Figure 15** is used to show the relationship between two variables. The variables being compared go on two axes of the graph. For data from an experiment, the independent variable always goes on the horizontal axis, called the x-axis. The dependent variable always goes on the vertical axis, called the y-axis. After drawing your axes, label each with a scale. Next, plot the data points.

A data point is the intersection of the recorded value of the dependent variable for each tested value of the independent variable. After all the points are plotted, connect them.

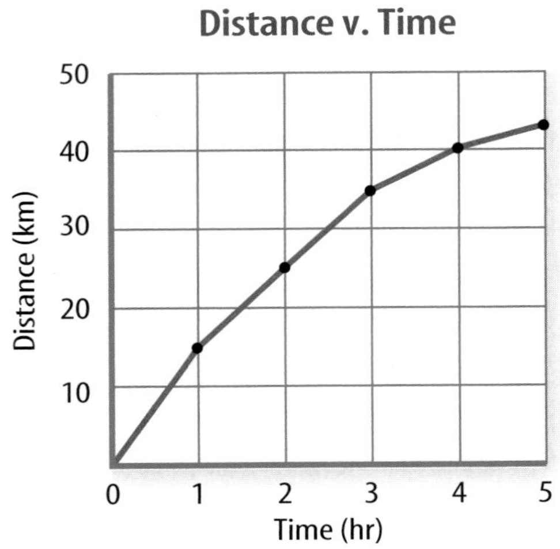

Distance v. Time

Figure 15
This line graph shows the relationship between distance and time during a bicycle ride lasting several hours.

Bar Graphs Bar graphs compare data that do not change continuously. Vertical bars show the relationships among data.

To make a bar graph, set up the y-axis as you did for the line graph. Draw vertical bars of equal size from the x-axis up to the point on the y-axis that represents the value of x.

Figure 16
The amount of aluminum collected for recycling during one week can be shown as a bar graph or circle graph.

Aluminum Collected During Week

Circle Graphs A circle graph uses a circle divided into sections to display data as parts (fractions or percentages) of a whole. The size of each section corresponds to the fraction or percentage of the data that the section represents. So, the entire circle represents 100 percent, one-half represents 50 percent, one-fifth represents 20 percent, and so on.

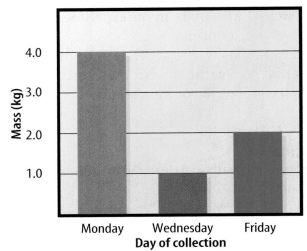

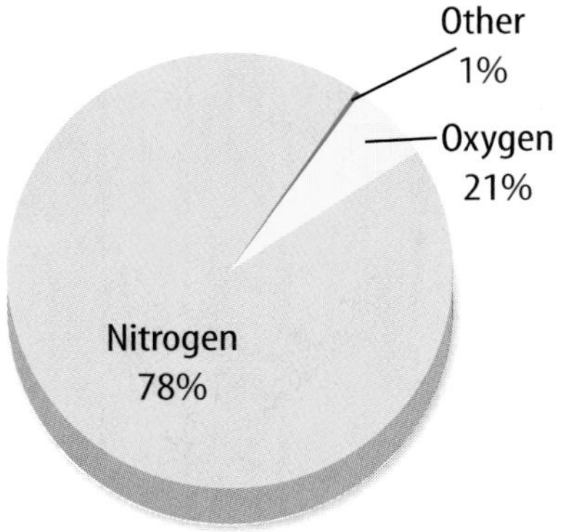

Analyzing Results

To determine the meaning of your observations and investigation results, you will need to look for patterns in the data. You can organize your information in several of the ways that are discussed in this handbook. Then you must think critically to determine what the data mean. Scientists use several approaches when they analyze the data they have collected and recorded. Each approach is useful for identifying specific patterns in the data.

Forming Operational Definitions

An operational definition defines an object by showing how it functions, works, or behaves. Such definitions are written in terms of how an object works or how it can be used; that is, they describe its job or purpose.

For example, a ruler can be defined as a tool that measures the length of an object (how it can be used). A ruler also can be defined as something that contains a series of marks that can be used as a standard when measuring (how it works).

Classifying

Classifying is the process of sorting objects or events into groups based on common features. When classifying, first observe the objects or events to be classified. Then select one feature that is shared by some members in the group but not by all. Place those members that share that feature into a subgroup. You can classify members into smaller and smaller subgroups based on characteristics.

How might you classify a group of chemicals? You might first classify them by state of matter, putting solids, liquids, and gases into separate groups. Within each group, you could then look for another common feature by which to further classify members of the group, such as color or how reactive they are.

Remember that when you classify, you are grouping objects or events for a purpose. For example, classifying chemicals can be the first step in organizing them for storage. Both at home and at school, poisonous or highly reactive chemicals should all be stored in a safe location where they are not easily accessible to small children or animals. Solids, liquids, and gases each have specific storage requirements that may include waterproof, airtight, or pressurized containers. Are the dangerous chemicals in your home stored in the right place? Keep your purpose in mind as you select the features to form groups and subgroups.

Figure 17
Color is one of many characteristics that are used to classify chemicals.

Comparing and Contrasting

Observations can be analyzed by noting the similarities and differences between two or more objects or events that you observe. When you look at objects or events to see how they are similar, you are comparing them. Contrasting is looking for differences in objects or events. The table below compares and contrasts the characteristics of two elements.

Elemental Characteristics		
Element	Aluminum	Gold
Color	silver	gold
Classification	metal	metal
Density (g/cm^3)	2.7	19.3
Melting Point (°C)	660	1064

Recognizing Cause and Effect

Have you ever heard a loud pop right before the power went out and then suggested that an electric transformer probably blew out? If so, you have observed an effect and inferred a cause. The event is the effect, and the reason for the event is the cause.

When scientists are unsure of the cause of a certain event, they design controlled experiments to determine what caused it.

Interpreting Data

The word *interpret* means "to explain the meaning of something." Look at the problem originally being explored in an experiment and figure out what the data show. Identify the control group and the test group so you can see whether or not changes in the independent variable have had an effect. Look for differences in the dependent variable between the control and test groups.

These differences you observe can be qualitative or quantitative. You would be able to describe a qualitative difference using only words, whereas you would measure a quantitative difference and describe it using numbers. If there are differences, the independent variable that is being tested could have had an effect. If no differences are found between the control and test groups, the variable that is being tested apparently had no effect.

For example, suppose that three beakers each contain 100 mL of water. The beakers are placed on hot plates, and two of the hot plates are turned on, but the third is left off for a period of 5 min. Suppose you are then asked to describe any differences in the water in the three beakers. A qualitative difference might be the appearance of bubbles rising to the top in the water that is being heated but no rising bubbles in the unheated water. A quantitative difference might be a difference in the amount of water that is present in the beakers.

Inferring Scientists often make inferences based on their observations. An inference is an attempt to explain, or interpret, observations or to indicate what caused what you observed. An inference is a type of conclusion.

When making an inference, be certain to use accurate data and accurately described observations. Analyze all of the data that you've collected. Then, based on everything you know, explain or interpret what you've observed.

Drawing Conclusions

When scientists have analyzed the data they collected, they proceed to draw conclusions about what the data mean. These conclusions are sometimes stated using words similar to those found in the hypothesis formed earlier in the process.

Skill Handbooks

Conclusions To analyze your data, you must review all of the observations and measurements that you made and recorded. Recheck all data for accuracy. After your data are rechecked and organized, you are almost ready to draw a conclusion such as "salt water boils at a higher temperature than freshwater."

Before you can draw a conclusion, however, you must determine whether the data allow you to come to a conclusion that supports a hypothesis. Sometimes that will be the case, other times it will not.

If your data do not support a hypothesis, it does not mean that the hypothesis is wrong. It means only that the results of the investigation did not support the hypothesis. Maybe the experiment needs to be redesigned, but very likely, some of the initial observations on which the hypothesis was based were incomplete or biased. Perhaps more observation or research is needed to refine the hypothesis.

Avoiding Bias Sometimes drawing a conclusion involves making judgments. When you make a judgment, you form an opinion about what your data mean. It is important to be honest and to avoid reaching a conclusion if no supporting evidence for it exists or if it was based on a small sample. It also is important not to allow any expectations of results to bias your judgments. If possible, it is a good idea to collect additional data. Scientists do this all the time.

For example, the *Hubble Space Telescope* was sent into space in April, 1990, to provide scientists with clearer views of the universe. *Hubble* is the size of a school bus and has a 2.4-m-diameter mirror. *Hubble* helped scientists answer questions about the planet Pluto.

For many years, scientists had only been able to hypothesize about the surface of the planet Pluto. *Hubble* has now provided pictures of Pluto's surface that show a rough texture with light and dark regions on it. This might be the best information about Pluto scientists will have until they are able to send a space probe to it.

Evaluating Others' Data and Conclusions

Sometimes scientists have to use data that they did not collect themselves, or they have to rely on observations and conclusions drawn by other researchers. In cases such as these, the data must be evaluated carefully.

How were the data obtained? How was the investigation done? Was it carried out properly? Has it been duplicated by other researchers? Were they able to follow the exact procedure? Did they come up with the same results? Look at the conclusion, as well. Would you reach the same conclusion from these results? Only when you have confidence in the data of others can you believe it is true and feel comfortable using it.

Communicating

The communication of ideas is an important part of the work of scientists. A discovery that is not reported will not advance the scientific community's understanding or knowledge. Communication among scientists also is important as a way of improving their investigations.

Scientists communicate in many ways, from writing articles in journals and magazines that explain their investigations and experiments, to announcing important discoveries on television and radio, to sharing ideas with colleagues on the Internet or presenting them as lectures.

People who study science rely on computers to record and store data and to analyze results from investigations. Whether you work in a laboratory or just need to write a lab report with tables, good computer skills are a necessity.

Using a Word Processor

Suppose your teacher has assigned a written report. After you've completed your research and decided how you want to write the information, you need to put all that information on paper. The easiest way to do this is with a word processing application on a computer.

A computer application that allows you to type your information, change it as many times as you need to, and then print it out so that it looks neat and clean is called a word processing application. You also can use this type of application to create tables and columns, add bullets or cartoon art to your page, include page numbers, and check your spelling.

Helpful Hints

- If you aren't sure how to do something using your word processing program, look in the help menu. You will find a list of topics there to click on for help. After you locate the help topic you need, just follow the step-by-step instructions you see on your screen.
- Just because you've spell checked your report doesn't mean that the spelling is perfect. The spell check feature can't catch misspelled words that look like other words. If you've accidentally typed *cold* instead of *gold*, the spell checker won't know the difference. Always reread your report to make sure you didn't miss any mistakes.

Figure 18
You can use computer programs to make graphs and tables.

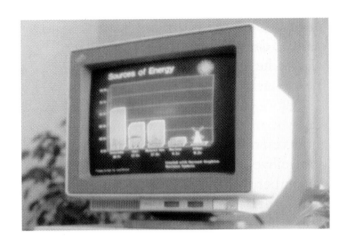

Using a Database

Imagine you're in the middle of a research project, busily gathering facts and information. You soon realize that it's becoming more difficult to organize and keep track of all the information. The tool to use to solve information overload is a database. Just as a file cabinet organizes paper records, a database organizes computer records. However, a database is more powerful than a simple file cabinet because at the click of a mouse, the contents can be reshuffled and reorganized. At computer-quick speeds, databases can sort information by any characteristics and filter data into multiple categories.

Helpful Hints

- Before setting up a database, take some time to learn the features of your database software by practicing with established database software.
- Periodically save your database as you enter data. That way, if something happens such as your computer malfunctions or the power goes off, you won't lose all of your work.

Doing a Database Search

When searching for information in a database, use the following search strategies to get the best results. These are the same search methods used for searching internet databases.

- Place the word *and* between two words in your search if you want the database to look for any entries that have both the words. For example, "gold *and* silver" would give you information that mentions both gold and silver.
- Place the word *or* between two words if you want the database to show entries that have at least one of the words. For example "gold *or* silver" would show you information that mentions either gold or silver.
- Place the word *not* between two words if you want the database to look for entries that have the first word but do not have the second word. For example, "gold *not* jewelry" would show you information that mentions gold but does not mention jewelry.

In summary, databases can be used to store large amounts of information about a particular subject. Databases allow biologists, Earth scientists, and physical scientists to search for information quickly and accurately.

Using an Electronic Spreadsheet

Your science fair experiment has produced lots of numbers. How do you keep track of all the data, and how can you easily work out all the calculations needed? You can use a computer program called a spreadsheet to record data that involve numbers. A spreadsheet is an electronic mathematical worksheet.

Type your data in rows and columns, just as they would look in a data table on a sheet of paper. A spreadsheet uses simple math to do data calculations. For example, you could add, subtract, divide, or multiply any of the values in the spreadsheet by another number. You also could set up a series of math steps you want to apply to the data. If you want to add 12 to all the numbers and then multiply all the numbers by 10, the computer does all the calculations for you in the spreadsheet. Below is an example of a spreadsheet that records test car data.

Helpful Hints

- Before you set up the spreadsheet, identify how you want to organize the data. Include any formulas you will need to use.
- Make sure you have entered the correct data into the correct rows and columns.
- You also can display your results in a graph. Pick the style of graph that best represents the data with which you are working.

Figure 19
A spreadsheet allows you to display large amounts of data and do calculations automatically.

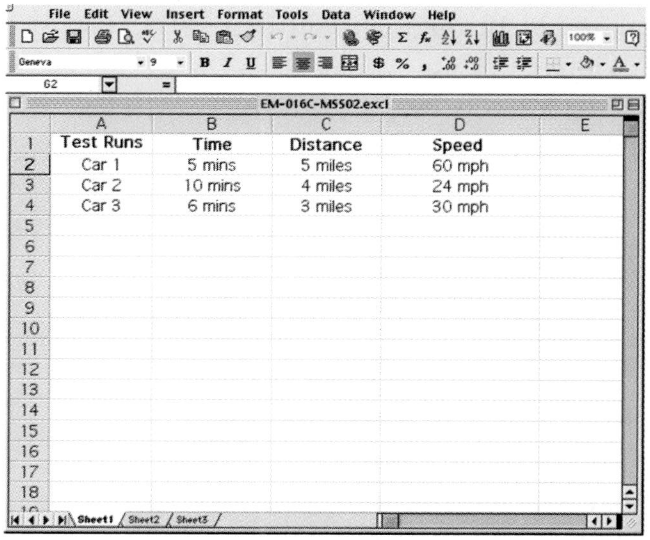

	A	B	C	D	E
1	Test Runs	Time	Distance	Speed	
2	Car 1	5 mins	5 miles	60 mph	
3	Car 2	10 mins	4 miles	24 mph	
4	Car 3	6 mins	3 miles	30 mph	

Skill Handbooks

Using a Computerized Card Catalog

When you have a report or paper to research, you probably go to the library. To find the information you need in the library, you might have to use a computerized card catalog. This type of card catalog allows you to search for information by subject, by title, or by author. The computer then will display all the holdings the library has on the subject, title, or author requested.

A library's holdings can include books, magazines, databases, videos, and audio materials. When you have chosen something from this list, the computer will show whether an item is available and where in the library to find it.

Helpful Hints

- Remember that you can use the computer to search by subject, author, or title. If you know a book's author but not the title, you can search for all the books the library has by that author.
- When searching by subject, it's often most helpful to narrow your search by using specific search terms, such as *and, or,* and *not.* If you don't find enough sources this way, you can broaden your search.
- Pay attention to the type of materials found in your search. If you need a book, you can eliminate any videos or other resources that come up in your search.
- Knowing how your library is arranged can save you a lot of time. If you need help, the librarian will show you where certain types of materials are kept and how to find specific holdings.

Using Graphics Software

Are you having trouble finding that exact piece of art you're looking for? Do you have a picture in your mind of what you want but can't seem to find the right graphic to represent your ideas? To solve these problems, you can use graphics software. Graphics software allows you to create and change images and diagrams in almost unlimited ways. Typical uses for graphics software include arranging clip art, changing scanned images, and constructing pictures from scratch. Most graphics software applications work in similar ways. They use the same basic tools and functions. Once you master one graphics application, you can use other graphics applications.

Figure 20
Graphics software can use your data to draw bar graphs.

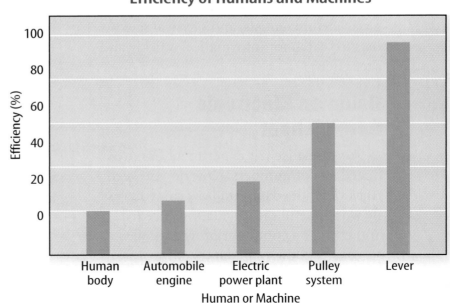

Efficiency of Humans and Machines

Figure 21
Graphics software can use your data to draw circle graphs.

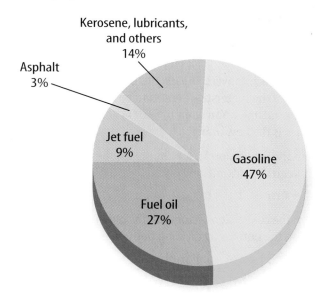

Kerosene, lubricants, and others 14%

Asphalt 3%

Jet fuel 9%

Gasoline 47%

Fuel oil 27%

Helpful Hints

- As with any method of drawing, the more you practice using the graphics software, the better your results will be.
- Start by using the software to manipulate existing drawings. Once you master this, making your own illustrations will be easier.
- Clip art is available on CD-ROMs and the Internet. With these resources, finding a piece of clip art to suit your purposes is simple.
- As you work on a drawing, save it often.

Developing Multimedia Presentations

It's your turn—you have to present your science report to the entire class. How do you do it? You can use many different sources of information to get the class excited about your presentation. Posters, videos, photographs, sound, computers, and the Internet can help show your ideas.

First, determine what important points you want to make in your presentation. Then, write an outline of what materials and types of media would best illustrate those points. Maybe you could start with an outline on an overhead projector, then show a video, followed by something from the Internet or a slide show accompanied by music or recorded voices. You might choose to use a presentation builder computer application that can combine all these elements into one presentation. Make sure the presentation is well constructed to make the most impact on the audience.

Figure 22
Multimedia presentations use many types of print and electronic materials.

Helpful Hints

- Carefully consider what media will best communicate the point you are trying to make.
- Make sure you know how to use any equipment you will be using in your presentation.
- Practice the presentation several times.
- If possible, set up all of the equipment ahead of time. Make sure everything is working correctly.

Skill Handbooks

Use this Math Skill Handbook to help solve problems you are given in this text. You might find it useful to review topics in this Math Skill Handbook first.

Converting Units

In science, quantities such as length, mass, and time sometimes are measured using different units. Suppose you want to know how many miles are in 12.7 km.

Conversion factors are used to change from one unit of measure to another. A conversion factor is a ratio that is equal to one. For example, there are 1,000 mL in 1 L, so 1,000 mL equals 1 L, or:

$$1{,}000 \text{ mL} = 1 \text{ L}$$

If both sides are divided by 1 L, this equation becomes:

$$\frac{1{,}000 \text{ mL}}{1 \text{ L}} = 1$$

The **ratio** on the left side of this equation is equal to 1 and is a conversion factor. You can make another conversion factor by dividing both sides of the top equation by 1,000 mL:

$$1 = \frac{1 \text{ L}}{1{,}000 \text{ mL}}$$

To **convert units,** you multiply by the appropriate conversion factor. For example, how many milliliters are in 1.255 L? To convert 1.255 L to milliliters, multiply 1.255 L by a conversion factor.

Use the **conversion factor** with new units (mL) in the numerator and the old units (L) in the denominator.

$$1.255 \text{ L} \times \frac{1{,}000 \text{ mL}}{1 \text{ L}} = 1{,}255 \text{ mL}$$

The unit L divides in this equation, just as if it were a number.

Example 1 There are 2.54 cm in 1 inch. If a meterstick has a length of 100 cm, how long is the meterstick in inches?

Step 1 Decide which conversion factor to use. You know the length of the meterstick in centimeters, so centimeters are the old units. You want to find the length in inches, so inch is the new unit.

Step 2 Form the conversion factor. Start with the relationship between the old and new units.

$$2.54 \text{ cm} = 1 \text{ inch}$$

Step 3 Form the conversion factor with the old unit (centimeter) on the bottom by dividing both sides by 2.54 cm.

$$1 = \frac{2.54 \text{ cm}}{2.54 \text{ cm}} = \frac{1 \text{ inch}}{2.54 \text{ cm}}$$

Step 4 Multiply the old measurement by the conversion factor.

$$100 \text{ cm} \times \frac{1 \text{ inch}}{2.54 \text{ cm}} = 39.37 \text{ inches}$$

The meterstick is 39.37 inches long.

Example 2 There are 365 days in one year. If a person is 14 years old, what is his or her age in days? (Ignore leap years)

Step 1 Decide which conversion factor to use. You want to convert years to days.

Step 2 Form the conversion factor. Start with the relation between the old and new units.

$$1 \text{ year} = 365 \text{ days}$$

Step 3 Form the conversion factor with the old unit (year) on the bottom by dividing both sides by 1 year.

$$1 = \frac{1 \text{ year}}{1 \text{ year}} = \frac{365 \text{ days}}{1 \text{ year}}$$

Step 4 Multiply the old measurement by the conversion factor:

$$14 \text{ years} \times \frac{365 \text{ days}}{1 \text{ year}} = 5{,}110 \text{ days}$$

The person's age is 5,110 days.

Practice Problem A book has a mass of 2.31 kg. If there are 1,000 g in 1 kg, what is the mass of the book in grams? 2310 g

Using Fractions

A **fraction** is a number that compares a part to the whole. For example, in the fraction $\frac{2}{3}$, the 2 represents the part and the 3 represents the whole. In the fraction $\frac{2}{3}$, the top number, 2, is called the numerator. The bottom number, 3, is called the denominator.

Sometimes fractions are not written in their simplest form. To determine a fraction's **simplest form,** you must find the greatest common factor (GCF) of the numerator and denominator. The greatest common factor is the largest factor that is common to the numerator and denominator.

For example, because the number 3 divides into 12 and 30 evenly, it is a common factor of 12 and 30. However, because the number 6 is the largest number that evenly divides into 12 and 30, it is the **greatest common factor.**

After you find the greatest common factor, you can write a fraction in its simplest form. Divide both the numerator and the denominator by the greatest common factor. The number that results is the fraction in its **simplest form.**

Example Twelve of the 20 chemicals used in the science lab are in powder form. What fraction of the chemicals used in the lab are in powder form?

Step 1 Write the fraction.

$$\frac{\text{part}}{\text{whole}} = \frac{12}{20}$$

Step 2 To find the GCF of the numerator and denominator, list all of the factors of each number.

Factors of 12: 1, 2, 3, 4, 6, 12 (the numbers that divide evenly into 12)

Factors of 20: 1, 2, 4, 5, 10, 20 (the numbers that divide evenly into 20)

Step 3 List the common factors.

1, 2, 4.

Step 4 Choose the greatest factor in the list of common factors.

The GCF of 12 and 20 is 4.

Step 5 Divide the numerator and denominator by the GCF.

$$\frac{12 \div 4}{20 \div 4} = \frac{3}{5}$$

In the lab, $\frac{3}{5}$ of the chemicals are in powder form.

Practice Problem There are 90 rides at an amusement park. Of those rides, 66 have a height restriction. What fraction of the rides has a height restriction? Write the fraction in simplest form. $\frac{11}{15}$

Calculating Ratios

A **ratio** is a comparison of two numbers by division.

Ratios can be written 3 to 5 or 3:5. Ratios also can be written as fractions, such as $\frac{3}{5}$. Ratios, like fractions, can be written in simplest form. Recall that a fraction is in **simplest form** when the greatest common factor (GCF) of the numerator and denominator is 1.

Example A chemical solution contains 40 g of salt and 64 g of baking soda. What is the ratio of salt to baking soda as a fraction in simplest form?

Step 1 Write the ratio as a fraction. $\dfrac{\text{salt}}{\text{baking soda}} = \dfrac{40}{64}$

Step 2 Express the fraction in simplest form. The GCF of 40 and 64 is 8.

$$\frac{40}{64} = \frac{40 \div 8}{64 \div 8} = \frac{5}{8}$$

The ratio of salt to baking soda in the solution is $\frac{5}{8}$.

Practice Problem Two metal rods measure 100 cm and 144 cm in length. What is the ratio of their lengths in simplest fraction form? $\frac{25}{36}$

Using Decimals

A **decimal** is a fraction with a denominator of 10, 100, 1,000, or another power of 10. For example, 0.854 is the same as the fraction $\frac{854}{1,000}$.

In a decimal, the decimal point separates the ones place and the tenths place. For example, 0.27 means twenty-seven hundredths, or $\frac{27}{100}$, where 27 is the **number of units** out of 100 units. Any fraction can be written as a decimal using division.

Example Write $\frac{5}{8}$ as a decimal.

Step 1 Write a division problem with the numerator, 5, as the dividend and the denominator, 8, as the divisor. Write 5 as 5.000.

Step 2 Solve the problem.

```
      0.625
  8)5.000
    48
    ──
    20
    16
    ──
     40
     40
     ──
      0
```

Therefore, $\frac{5}{8} = 0.625$.

Practice Problem Write $\frac{19}{25}$ as a decimal. 0.76

Math Skill Handbook

Using Percentages

The word *percent* means "out of one hundred." A **percent** is a ratio that compares a number to 100. Suppose you read that 77 percent of Earth's surface is covered by water. That is the same as reading that the fraction of Earth's surface covered by water is $\frac{77}{100}$. To express a fraction as a percent, first find an equivalent decimal for the fraction. Then, multiply the decimal by 100 and add the percent symbol. For example, $\frac{1}{2} = 1 \div 2 = 0.5$. Then $0.5 \cdot 100 = 50 = 50\%$.

Example Express $\frac{13}{20}$ as a percent.

Step 1 Find the equivalent decimal for the fraction.

$$\begin{array}{r} 0.65 \\ 20\overline{)13.00} \\ \underline{120} \\ 100 \\ \underline{100} \\ 0 \end{array}$$

Step 2 Rewrite the fraction $\frac{13}{20}$ as 0.65.

Step 3 Multiply 0.65 by 100 and add the % sign.

$0.65 \cdot 100 = 65 = 65\%$

So, $\frac{13}{20} = 65\%$.

Practice Problem In one year, 73 of 365 days were rainy in one city. What percent of the days in that city were rainy? 20%

Using Precision and Significant Digits

When you make a **measurement,** the value you record depends on the precision of the measuring instrument. When adding or subtracting numbers with different precision, the answer is rounded to the smallest number of decimal places of any number in the sum or difference. When multiplying or dividing, the answer is rounded to the smallest number of significant figures of any number being multiplied or divided. When counting the number of **significant figures,** all digits are counted except zeros at the end of a number with no decimal such as 2,500, and zeros at the beginning of a decimal such as 0.03020.

Example The lengths 5.28 and 5.2 are measured in meters. Find the sum of these lengths and report the sum using the least precise measurement.

Step 1 Find the sum.

5.28 m	2 digits after the decimal
+ 5.2 m	1 digit after the decimal
10.48 m	

Step 2 Round to one digit after the decimal because the least number of digits after the decimal of the numbers being added is 1.

The sum is 10.5 m.

Practice Problem Multiply the numbers in the example using the rule for multiplying and dividing. Report the answer with the correct number of significant figures. 27.5 m^2

Skill Handbooks

Solving One-Step Equations

An **equation** is a statement that two things are equal. For example, $A = B$ is an equation that states that A is equal to B.

Sometimes one side of the equation will contain a **variable** whose value is not known. In the equation $3x = 12$, the variable is x.

The equation is solved when the variable is replaced with a value that makes both sides of the equation equal to each other. For example, the solution of the equation $3x = 12$ is $x = 4$. If the x is replaced with 4, then the equation becomes $3 \cdot 4 = 12$, or $12 = 12$.

To solve an equation such as $8x = 40$, divide both sides of the equation by the number that multiplies the variable.

$$8x = 40$$
$$\frac{8x}{8} = \frac{40}{8}$$
$$x = 5$$

You can check your answer by replacing the variable with your solution and seeing if both sides of the equation are the same.

$$8x = 8 \cdot 5 = 40$$

The left and right sides of the equation are the same, so $x = 5$ is the solution.

Sometimes an equation is written in this way: $a = bc$. This also is called a **formula.** The letters can be replaced by numbers, but the numbers must still make both sides of the equation the same.

Example 1 Solve the equation $10x = 35$.

Step 1 Find the solution by dividing each side of the equation by 10.

$$10x = 35 \qquad \frac{10x}{10} = \frac{35}{10} \qquad x = 3.5$$

Step 2 Check the solution.

$$10x = 35 \qquad 10 \times 3.5 = 35 \qquad 35 = 35$$

Both sides of the equation are equal, so $x = 3.5$ is the solution to the equation.

Example 2 In the formula $a = bc$, find the value of c if $a = 20$ and $b = 2$.

Step 1 Rearrange the formula so the unknown value is by itself on one side of the equation by dividing both sides by b.

$$a = bc$$
$$\frac{a}{b} = \frac{bc}{b}$$
$$\frac{a}{b} = c$$

Step 2 Replace the variables a and b with the values that are given.

$$\frac{a}{b} = c$$
$$\frac{20}{2} = c$$
$$10 = c$$

Step 3 Check the solution.

$$a = bc$$
$$20 = 2 \times 10$$
$$20 = 20$$

Both sides of the equation are equal, so $c = 10$ is the solution when $a = 20$ and $b = 2$.

Practice Problem In the formula $h = gd$, find the value of d if $g = 12.3$ and $h = 17.4$. 1.41

A **proportion** is an equation that shows that two ratios are equivalent. The ratios $\frac{2}{4}$ and $\frac{5}{10}$ are equivalent, so they can be written as $\frac{2}{4} = \frac{5}{10}$. This equation is an example of a proportion.

When two ratios form a proportion, the **cross products** are equal. To find the cross products in the proportion $\frac{2}{4} = \frac{5}{10}$, multiply the 2 and the 10, and the 4 and the 5. Therefore $2 \cdot 10 = 4 \cdot 5$, or $20 = 20$.

Because you know that both proportions are equal, you can use cross products to find a missing term in a proportion. This is known as **solving the proportion.** Solving a proportion is similar to solving an equation.

Example The heights of a tree and a pole are proportional to the lengths of their shadows. The tree casts a shadow of 24 m at the same time that a 6-m pole casts a shadow of 4 m. What is the height of the tree?

Step 1 Write a proportion.

$$\frac{\text{height of tree}}{\text{height of pole}} = \frac{\text{length of tree's shadow}}{\text{length of pole's shadow}}$$

Step 2 Substitute the known values into the proportion. Let h represent the unknown value, the height of the tree.

$$\frac{h}{6} = \frac{24}{4}$$

Step 3 Find the cross products.

$$h \cdot 4 = 6 \cdot 24$$

Step 4 Simplify the equation.

$$4h = 144$$

Step 5 Divide each side by 4.

$$\frac{4h}{4} = \frac{144}{4}$$

$$h = 36$$

The height of the tree is 36 m.

Practice Problem The ratios of the weights of two objects on the Moon and on Earth are in proportion. A rock weighing 3 N on the Moon weighs 18 N on Earth. How much would a rock that weighs 5 N on the Moon weigh on Earth? 30 N

Math Skill Handbook

Using Statistics

Statistics is the branch of mathematics that deals with collecting, analyzing, and presenting data. In statistics, there are three common ways to summarize the data with a single number—the mean, the median, and the mode.

The **mean** of a set of data is the arithmetic average. It is found by adding the numbers in the data set and dividing by the number of items in the set.

The **median** is the middle number in a set of data when the data are arranged in numerical order. If there were an even number of data points, the median would be the mean of the two middle numbers.

The **mode** of a set of data is the number or item that appears most often.

Another number that often is used to describe a set of data is the range. The **range** is the difference between the largest number and the smallest number in a set of data.

A **frequency table** shows how many times each piece of data occurs, usually in a survey. The frequency table below shows the results of a student survey on favorite color.

Color	Tally	Frequency
red	||||	4
blue	|||||	5
black	||	2
green	|||	3
purple	||||| ||	7
yellow	|||||		6

Based on the frequency table data, which color is the favorite?

Example The speeds (in m/s) for a race car during five different time trials are 39, 37, 44, 36, and 44.

To find the mean:

Step 1 Find the sum of the numbers.

$$39 + 37 + 44 + 36 + 44 = 200$$

Step 2 Divide the sum by the number of items, which is 5.

$$200 \div 5 = 40$$

The mean measure is 40 m/s.

To find the median:

Step 1 Arrange the measures from least to greatest.

$$36, \ 37, \ \underline{39}, \ 44, \ 44$$

Step 2 Determine the middle measure.

The median measure is 39 m/s.

To find the mode:

Step 1 Group the numbers that are the same together.

$$44, 44, 36, 37, 39$$

Step 2 Determine the number that occurs most in the set.

$$\underline{44, 44}, 36, 37, 39$$

The mode measure is 44 m/s.

To find the range:

Step 1 Arrange the measures from largest to smallest.

$$44, 44, 39, 37, 36$$

Step 2 Determine the largest and smallest measures in the set.

$$\underline{44}, 44, 39, 37, \underline{36}$$

Step 3 Find the difference between the largest and smallest measures.

$$44 - 36 = 8$$

The range is 8 m/s.

Practice Problem Find the mean, median, mode, and range for the data set 8, 4, 12, 8, 11, 14, 16.

mean, 10; media, 11; mode, 8; range, 12

Safety in the Science Classroom

1. Always obtain your teacher's permission to begin an investigation.

2. Study the procedure. If you have questions, ask your teacher. Be sure you understand any safety symbols shown on the page.

3. Use the safety equipment provided for you. Goggles and a safety apron should be worn during most investigations.

4. Always slant test tubes away from yourself and others when heating them or adding substances to them.

5. Never eat or drink in the lab, and never use lab glassware as food or drink containers. Never inhale chemicals. Do not taste any substances or draw any material into a tube with your mouth.

6. Report any spill, accident, or injury, no matter how small, immediately to your teacher, then follow his or her instructions.

7. Know the location and proper use of the fire extinguisher, safety shower, fire blanket, first aid kit, and fire alarm.

8. Keep all materials away from open flames. Tie back long hair and tie down loose clothing.

9. If your clothing should catch fire, smother it with the fire blanket, or get under a safety shower. NEVER RUN.

10. If a fire should occur, turn off the gas then leave the room according to established procedures.

Follow these procedures as you clean up your work area

1. Turn off the water and gas. Disconnect electrical devices.

2. Clean all pieces of equipment and return all materials to their proper places.

3. Dispose of chemicals and other materials as directed by your teacher. Place broken glass and solid substances in the proper containers. Make sure never to discard materials in the sink.

4. Clean your work area. Wash your hands thoroughly after working in the laboratory.

First Aid	
Injury	**Safe Response ALWAYS NOTIFY YOUR TEACHER IMMEDIATELY**
Burns	Apply cold water.
Cuts and Bruises	Stop any bleeding by applying direct pressure. Cover cuts with a clean dressing. Apply ice packs or cold compresses to bruises.
Fainting	Leave the person lying down. Loosen any tight clothing and keep crowds away.
Foreign Matter in Eye	Flush with plenty of water. Use eyewash bottle or fountain.
Poisoning	Note the suspected poisoning agent.
Any Spills on Skin	Flush with large amounts of water or use safety shower.

Reference Handbook

SAFETY SYMBOLS

SAFETY SYMBOLS	HAZARD	EXAMPLES	PRECAUTION	REMEDY
DISPOSAL	Special disposal procedures need to be followed.	certain chemicals, living organisms	Do not dispose of these materials in the sink or trash can.	Dispose of wastes as directed by your teacher.
BIOLOGICAL	Organisms or other biological materials that might be harmful to humans	bacteria, fungi, blood, unpreserved tissues, plant materials	Avoid skin contact with these materials. Wear mask or gloves.	Notify your teacher if you suspect contact with material. Wash hands thoroughly.
EXTREME TEMPERATURE	Objects that can burn skin by being too cold or too hot	boiling liquids, hot plates, dry ice, liquid nitrogen	Use proper protection when handling.	Go to your teacher for first aid.
SHARP OBJECT	Use of tools or glassware that can easily puncture or slice skin	razor blades, pins, scalpels, pointed tools, dissecting probes, broken glass	Practice common-sense behavior and follow guidelines for use of the tool.	Go to your teacher for first aid.
FUME	Possible danger to respiratory tract from fumes	ammonia, acetone, nail polish remover, heated sulfur, moth balls	Make sure there is good ventilation. Never smell fumes directly. Wear a mask.	Leave foul area and notify your teacher immediately.
ELECTRICAL	Possible danger from electrical shock or burn	improper grounding, liquid spills, short circuits, exposed wires	Double-check setup with teacher. Check condition of wires and apparatus.	Do not attempt to fix electrical problems. Notify your teacher immediately.
IRRITANT	Substances that can irritate the skin or mucous membranes of the respiratory tract	pollen, moth balls, steel wool, fiber glass, potassium permanganate	Wear dust mask and gloves. Practice extra care when handling these materials.	Go to your teacher for first aid.
CHEMICAL	Chemicals that can react with and destroy tissue and other materials	bleaches such as hydrogen peroxide; acids such as sulfuric acid, hydrochloric acid; bases such as ammonia, sodium hydroxide	Wear goggles, gloves, and an apron.	Immediately flush the affected area with water and notify your teacher.
TOXIC	Substance may be poisonous if touched, inhaled, or swallowed	mercury, many metal compounds, iodine, poinsettia plant parts	Follow your teacher's instructions.	Always wash hands thoroughly after use. Go to your teacher for first aid.
OPEN FLAME	Open flame may ignite flammable chemicals, loose clothing, or hair.	alcohol, kerosene, potassium permanganate, hair, clothing	Tie back hair. Avoid wearing loose clothing. Avoid open flames when using flammable chemicals. Be aware of locations of fire safety equipment.	Notify your teacher immediately. Use fire safety equipment if applicable.

Eye Safety
Proper eye protection should be worn at all times by anyone performing or observing science activities.

Clothing Protection
This symbol appears when substances could stain or burn clothing.

Animal Safety
This symbol appears when safety of animals and students must be ensured.

Radioactivity
This symbol appears when radioactive materials are used.

SI—Metric/English, English/Metric Conversions

	When you want to convert:	To:	Multiply by:
Length	inches	centimeters	2.54
	centimeters	inches	0.39
	yards	meters	0.91
	meters	yards	1.09
	miles	kilometers	1.61
	kilometers	miles	0.62
Mass and Weight*	ounces	grams	28.35
	grams	ounces	0.04
	pounds	kilograms	0.45
	kilograms	pounds	2.2
	tons (short)	tonnes (metric tons)	0.91
	tonnes (metric tons)	tons (short)	1.10
	pounds	newtons	4.45
	newtons	pounds	0.22
Volume	cubic inches	cubic centimeters	16.39
	cubic centimeters	cubic inches	0.06
	liters	quarts	1.06
	quarts	liters	0.95
	gallons	liters	3.78
Area	square inches	square centimeters	6.45
	square centimeters	square inches	0.16
	square yards	square meters	0.83
	square meters	square yards	1.19
	square miles	square kilometers	2.59
	square kilometers	square miles	0.39
	hectares	acres	2.47
	acres	hectares	0.40
Temperature	To convert °Celsius to °Fahrenheit		$°C \times 9/5 + 32$
	To convert °Fahrenheit to °Celsius		$5/9 \, (°F - 32)$

*Weight is measured in standard Earth gravity.

REFERENCE HANDBOOK D

PERIODIC TABLE OF THE ELEMENTS

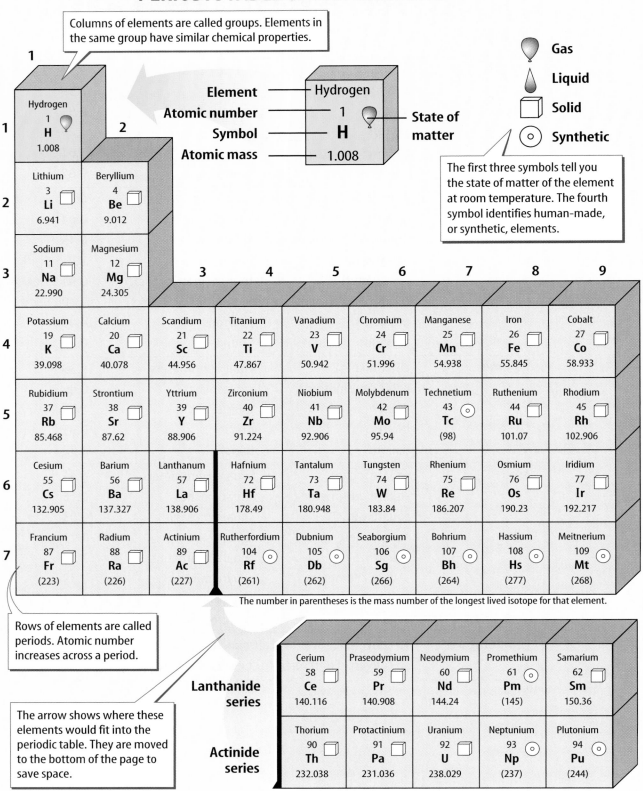

Columns of elements are called groups. Elements in the same group have similar chemical properties.

Gas

Liquid

Solid

Synthetic

Element — Hydrogen
Atomic number — 1
Symbol — **H**
Atomic mass — 1.008

State of matter

The first three symbols tell you the state of matter of the element at room temperature. The fourth symbol identifies human-made, or synthetic, elements.

Rows of elements are called periods. Atomic number increases across a period.

The arrow shows where these elements would fit into the periodic table. They are moved to the bottom of the page to save space.

1		2		3	4	5	6	7	8	9
1 Hydrogen 1 **H** 1.008										
2 Lithium 3 **Li** 6.941		Beryllium 4 **Be** 9.012								
3 Sodium 11 **Na** 22.990		Magnesium 12 **Mg** 24.305								
4 Potassium 19 **K** 39.098		Calcium 20 **Ca** 40.078		Scandium 21 **Sc** 44.956	Titanium 22 **Ti** 47.867	Vanadium 23 **V** 50.942	Chromium 24 **Cr** 51.996	Manganese 25 **Mn** 54.938	Iron 26 **Fe** 55.845	Cobalt 27 **Co** 58.933
5 Rubidium 37 **Rb** 85.468		Strontium 38 **Sr** 87.62		Yttrium 39 **Y** 88.906	Zirconium 40 **Zr** 91.224	Niobium 41 **Nb** 92.906	Molybdenum 42 **Mo** 95.94	Technetium 43 **Tc** (98)	Ruthenium 44 **Ru** 101.07	Rhodium 45 **Rh** 102.906
6 Cesium 55 **Cs** 132.905		Barium 56 **Ba** 137.327		Lanthanum 57 **La** 138.906	Hafnium 72 **Hf** 178.49	Tantalum 73 **Ta** 180.948	Tungsten 74 **W** 183.84	Rhenium 75 **Re** 186.207	Osmium 76 **Os** 190.23	Iridium 77 **Ir** 192.217
7 Francium 87 **Fr** (223)		Radium 88 **Ra** (226)		Actinium 89 **Ac** (227)	Rutherfordium 104 **Rf** (261)	Dubnium 105 **Db** (262)	Seaborgium 106 **Sg** (266)	Bohrium 107 **Bh** (264)	Hassium 108 **Hs** (277)	Meitnerium 109 **Mt** (268)

The number in parentheses is the mass number of the longest lived isotope for that element.

	Cerium 58 **Ce** 140.116	Praseodymium 59 **Pr** 140.908	Neodymium 60 **Nd** 144.24	Promethium 61 **Pm** (145)	Samarium 62 **Sm** 150.36
Lanthanide series					
Actinide series	Thorium 90 **Th** 232.038	Protactinium 91 **Pa** 231.036	Uranium 92 **U** 238.029	Neptunium 93 **Np** (237)	Plutonium 94 **Pu** (244)

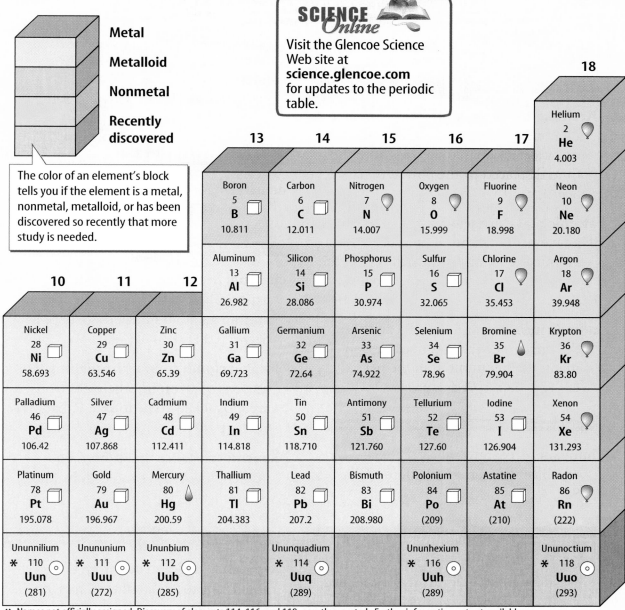

Metal

Metalloid

Nonmetal

Recently discovered

The color of an element's block tells you if the element is a metal, nonmetal, metalloid, or has been discovered so recently that more study is needed.

SCIENCE *Online*
Visit the Glencoe Science Web site at **science.glencoe.com** for updates to the periodic table.

					18
13	**14**	**15**	**16**	**17**	Helium 2 **He** 4.003
Boron 5 **B** 10.811	Carbon 6 **C** 12.011	Nitrogen 7 **N** 14.007	Oxygen 8 **O** 15.999	Fluorine 9 **F** 18.998	Neon 10 **Ne** 20.180
Aluminum 13 **Al** 26.982	Silicon 14 **Si** 28.086	Phosphorus 15 **P** 30.974	Sulfur 16 **S** 32.065	Chlorine 17 **Cl** 35.453	Argon 18 **Ar** 39.948

10	**11**	**12**						
Nickel 28 **Ni** 58.693	Copper 29 **Cu** 63.546	Zinc 30 **Zn** 65.39	Gallium 31 **Ga** 69.723	Germanium 32 **Ge** 72.64	Arsenic 33 **As** 74.922	Selenium 34 **Se** 78.96	Bromine 35 **Br** 79.904	Krypton 36 **Kr** 83.80
Palladium 46 **Pd** 106.42	Silver 47 **Ag** 107.868	Cadmium 48 **Cd** 112.411	Indium 49 **In** 114.818	Tin 50 **Sn** 118.710	Antimony 51 **Sb** 121.760	Tellurium 52 **Te** 127.60	Iodine 53 **I** 126.904	Xenon 54 **Xe** 131.293
Platinum 78 **Pt** 195.078	Gold 79 **Au** 196.967	Mercury 80 **Hg** 200.59	Thallium 81 **Tl** 204.383	Lead 82 **Pb** 207.2	Bismuth 83 **Bi** 208.980	Polonium 84 **Po** (209)	Astatine 85 **At** (210)	Radon 86 **Rn** (222)
Ununnilium * 110 **Uun** (281)	Unununium * 111 **Uuu** (272)	Ununbium * 112 **Uub** (285)		Ununquadium * 114 **Uuq** (289)		Ununhexium * 116 **Uuh** (289)		Ununoctium * 118 **Uuo** (293)

* Names not officially assigned. Discovery of elements 114, 116, and 118 recently reported. Further information not yet available.

Europium 63 **Eu** 151.964	Gadolinium 64 **Gd** 157.25	Terbium 65 **Tb** 158.925	Dysprosium 66 **Dy** 162.50	Holmium 67 **Ho** 164.930	Erbium 68 **Er** 167.259	Thulium 69 **Tm** 168.934	Ytterbium 70 **Yb** 173.04	Lutetium 71 **Lu** 174.967
Americium 95 **Am** (243)	Curium 96 **Cm** (247)	Berkelium 97 **Bk** (247)	Californium 98 **Cf** (251)	Einsteinium 99 **Es** (252)	Fermium 100 **Fm** (257)	Mendelevium 101 **Md** (258)	Nobelium 102 **No** (259)	Lawrencium 103 **Lr** (262)

English Glossary

This glossary defines each key term that appears in bold type in the text. It also shows the chapter, section, and page number where you can find the word used.

A

Archimedes' (ar kuh MEE deez) **principle:** states that the buoyant force on an object is equal to the weight of the fluid displaced by the object. (Chap. 2, Sec. 3, p. 59)

atomic mass: average mass of an atom of an element; its unit of measure is the atomic mass unit (u), which is 1/12 the mass of a carbon-12 atom. (Chap. 1, Sec. 2, p. 22)

atomic number: number of protons in the nucleus of each atom of a given element; the top number in the periodic table. (Chap. 1, Sec. 2, p. 21)

B

buoyant force: upward force exerted on an object immersed in a fluid. (Chap. 2, Sec. 3, p. 58)

C

catalyst: substance that can make something happen faster but is not changed itself. (Chap. 4, Sec. 3, p. 113)

chemical change: change in which the composition of a substance changes. (Chap. 3, Sec. 2, p. 80)

chemical property: characteristic that cannot be observed without altering the substance. (Chap. 3, Sec. 1, p. 76)

condensation: change of matter from a gas to a liquid state. (Chap. 2, Sec. 2, p. 51)

D

density: mass of an object divided by its volume. (Chap. 2, Sec. 3, p. 59)

E

electron: negatively charged particle that exists in an electron cloud formation around an atom's nucleus. (Chap. 1, Sec. 1, p. 11)

electron cloud: region surrounding the nucleus of an atom, where electrons are most likely to be found. (Chap. 1, Sec. 1, p. 17)

element: substance that cannot be broken down into simpler substances. (Chap. 1, Sec. 1, p. 9)

F

freezing: change of matter from a liquid state to a solid state. (Chap. 2, Sec. 2, p. 49)

G

gas: matter that does not have a definite shape or volume; has particles that move at high speeds in all directions. (Chap. 2, Sec. 1, p. 44)

group: family of elements in the periodic table that have similar physical or chemical properties. (Chap. 4, Sec. 1, p. 99)

H

heat: movement of thermal energy from a substance at a higher temperature to a substance at a lower temperature. (Chap. 2, Sec. 2, p. 46)

I

isotope (I suh tohp): two or more atoms of the same element that have different numbers of neutrons in their nuclei. (Chap. 1, Sec. 2, p. 21)

L

law of conservation of mass: states that mass is neither created nor destroyed—and as a result the mass of the substances before a physical or chemical change is equal to the mass of the substances present after the change. (Chap. 3, Sec. 2, p. 87)

liquid: matter with a definite volume but no definite shape that can flow from one place to another. (Chap. 2, Sec. 1, p. 42)

M

mass number: sum of the number of protons and neutrons in the nucleus of an atom. (Chap. 1, Sec. 2, p. 21)

matter: anything that has mass and takes up space. (Chap. 2, Sec. 1, p. 40)

melting: change of matter from a solid state to a liquid state. (Chap. 2, Sec. 2, p. 47)

metal: element that has luster, is malleable, ductile, and a good conductor of heat and electricity. (Chap. 3, Sec.2, p. 22) (Chap. 4, Sec. 1, p. 102)

metalloid: element that has characteristics of both metals and nonmetals and is a solid at room temperature. (Chap. 3, Sec. 2, p. 23) (Chap. 4, Sec. 1, p. 102)

N

neutron (NEW trahn): electrically neutral particle that has the same mass as a proton and is found in an atom's nucleus. (Chap. 1, Sec. 1, p. 15)

nonmetal: element that is usually a gas or brittle solid at room temperature and is a poor conductor of heat and electricity. (Chap. 1, Sec. 2, p. 23) (Chap. 4, Sec. 1, p. 102)

P

Pascal's principle: states that when a force is applied to a confined fluid, an increase in pressure is transmitted equally to all parts of the fluid. (Chap. 2, Sec. 3, p. 60)

period: horizontal row of elements in the periodic table whose properties change gradually and predictably. (Chap. 4, Sec. 1, p. 99)

English Glossary

physical change: change in which the form or appearance of matter changes, but not its composition. (Chap. 3, Sec. 2, p. 78)

physical property: characteristic that can be observed, using the five senses, without changing or trying to change the composition of a substance. (Chap. 3, Sec. 1, p. 72)

pressure: force exerted on a surface divided by the total area over which the force is exerted. (Chap. 2, Sec. 3, p. 54)

proton: positively charged particle in the nucleus of an atom. (Chap. 1, Sec. 1, p. 14)

S

semiconductor: element that does not conduct electricity as well as a metal but conducts it better than a nonmetal. (Chap. 4, Sec. 2, p. 107)

solid: matter with a definite shape and volume; has tightly packed particles that move mainly by vibrating. (Chap. 2, Sec. 1, p. 41)

T

temperature: measure of the average kinetic energy of the individual particles of a substance. (Chap. 2, Sec. 2, p. 46)

V

vaporization: change of matter from a liquid state to a gas. (Chap. 2, Sec. 2, p. 50)

Este glosario define cada término clave que aparece en negrillas en el texto. También muestra el capítulo, la sección y el número de página en donde se usa dicho término.

A

Archimedes' principle / principio de Arquímides: establece que la fuerza de flotación de un cuerpo equivale al peso del líquido que ese cuerpo desplaza. (Cap. 2, Sec. 3, pág. 59)

atomic mass / masa atómica: masa promedio de los átomos de un elemento; su unidad de medida es la unidad de masa atómica (u), la cual equivale a 1/12 de la masa de un átomo de carbono-12. (Cap. 1, Sec. 2, pág. 22)

atomic number / número atómico: número de protones en el núcleo de cada átomo de un elemento dado; en la tabla periódica, es el número superior. (Cap. 1, Sec. 2, pág. 21)

B

buoyant force / fuerza de flotabilidad: fuerza ascendente que se ejerce sobre un cuerpo sumergido en un líquido. (Cap. 2, Sec. 3, pág. 58)

C

catalyst / catalizador: sustancia que hace que algo ocurra más rápidamente pero que no se altera ella misma. (Cap. 4, Sec. 3, pág. 113)

chemical change / cambio químico: transformación que experimenta la composición de una sustancia. (Cap. 3, Sec. 2, pág. 80)

chemical property / propiedad química: característica que no se puede observar sin alterar la muestra. (Cap. 3, Sec. 1, pág. 76)

condensation / condensación: cambio de la materia del estado gaseoso al líquido. (Cap. 2, Sec. 2, pág. 51)

D

density / densidad: la masa de un objeto dividida entre su volumen. (Cap. 2, Sec. 3, pág. 59)

E

electron / electrón: partícula con carga negativa que existe en una nube electrónica, la cual se forma alrededor del núcleo de un átomo. (Cap. 1, Sec. 1, pág. 11)

electron cloud / nube electrónica: región que rodea el núcleo de un átomo, en donde es más probable encontrar los electrones. (Cap. 1, Sec. 1, pág. 17)

element / elemento: sustancia que no se puede separar en sustancias más simples. (Cap. 1, Sec. 1, pág. 9)

F

freezing / congelación: cambio de la materia del estado líquido al sólido. (Cap. 2, Sec. 2, pág. 49)

G

gas / gas: materia que no posee una forma o un volumen definido; posee partículas que se mueven a gran velocidad en todas direcciones. (Cap. 2, Sec. 1, pág. 44)

group / grupo: familia de elementos de la tabla periódica que posee propiedades físicas o químicas semejantes. (Cap. 4, Sec. 1, pág. 99)

H

heat / calor: movimiento de la energía térmica de una sustancia con mayor temperatura a una sustancia con menor temperatura. (Cap. 2, Sec. 2, pág. 46)

I

isotope / isótopo: dos o más átomos del mismo elemento que poseen distintos números de neutrones en su núcleo. (Cap. 1, Sec. 2, pág. 21)

L

law of conservation of mass / ley de conservación de la masa: establece que la masa no se puede crear ni destruir y como resultado la masa de una sustancia antes de pasar por un cambio químico o físico es igual a la sustancia presente después del cambio. (Cap. 3, Sec. 2, pág. 87)

liquid / líquido: materia que posee un volumen definido pero no una forma definida y que puede fluir de un lugar a otro. (Cap. 2, Sec. 1, pág. 42)

M

mass number / número de masa: suma del número de protones y neutrones en el núcleo de un átomo. (Cap. 1, Sec. 2, pág. 21)

matter / materia: todo lo que ocupa espacio y posee masa. (Cap. 2, Sec. 1, pág. 40)

melting / fusión: cambio de la materia del estado sólido al líquido. (Cap. 2, Sec. 2, pág. 47)

metal / metal: elemento que posee brillo, es maleable, dúctil y es buen conductor del calor y la electricidad. (Cap. 3, Sec. 2, pág. 22; Cap. 4, Sec. 1, pág. 102)

metalloid / metaloide: elemento que comparte algunas propiedades tanto con los metales como con los no metales. (Cap. 3, Sec. 2, pág. 23; Cap. 4, Sec. 1, pág. 102)

Spanish Glossary

N

neutron / neutrón: partícula eléctricamente neutra que posee la misma masa que un protón y que se encuentra en el núcleo del átomo. (Cap. 1, Sec. 1, pág. 15)

nonmetal / no metal: elemento que por lo general es un gas o un sólido quebradizo a temperatura ambiente y es mal conductor del calor y la electricidad. (Cap. 1, Sec. 2, pág. 23; Cap. 4, Sec. 1, pág. 102)

P

Pascal's principle / principio de Pascal: establece que cuando se le aplica una fuerza a un líquido confinado, un aumento en la presión se transmite de manera uniforme a todas las partes del líquido. (Cap. 2, Sec. 3, pág. 60)

period / período: hilera horizontal de elementos en la tabla periódica cuyas propiedades cambian paulatinamente y son predecibles. (Cap. 4, Sec. 1, pág. 99)

physical change / cambio físico: cambio que experimenta la forma o apariencia de una sustancia pero sin alterar su composición. (Cap. 3, Sec. 2, pág. 78)

physical property / propiedad física: característica que se puede observar usando los cinco sentidos, sin alterar o tratar de alterar la composición de una sustancia. (Cap. 3, Sec. 1, pág. 72)

pressure / presión: fuerza ejercida sobre una superficie dividida entre el área total sobre la cual se ejerce la fuerza. (Cap. 2, Sec. 3, pág. 54)

proton / protón: partícula con carga positiva en el núcleo del átomo. (Cap. 1, Sec. 1, pág. 14)

S

semiconductor / semiconductor: elemento que no conduce la electricidad tan bien como un metal, pero la conduce mejor que un no metal. (Cap. 4, Sec. 2, pág. 107)

solid / sólido: materia con forma y volumen definidos; tiene partículas muy apretadas que se mueven principalmente por vibración. (Cap. 2, Sec. 1, pág. 41)

T

temperature / temperatura: medida de la energía cinética promedio de las partículas individuales de una sustancia. (Cap. 2, Sec. 2, pág. 46)

V

vaporization / vaporización: cambio de la materia del estado líquido al gaseoso. (Cap. 2, Sec. 2, pág. 50)

Index

The index for *The Nature of Matter* will help you locate major topics in the book quickly and easily. Each entry in the index is followed by the number of the pages on which the entry is discussed. A page number given in boldfaced type indicates the page on which that entry is defined. A page number given in italic type indicates a page on which the entry is used in an illustration or photograph. The abbreviation *act.* indicates a page on which the entry is used in an activity.

Index

Index

Index

Credits

Art Credits

Glencoe would like to acknowledge the artists and agencies who participated in illustrating this program: Absolute Science Illustration; Andrew Evansen; Argosy; Articulate Graphics; Craig Attebery represented by Frank & Jeff Lavaty; CHK America; Gagliano Graphics; Pedro Julio Gonzalez represented by Melissa Turk & The Artist Network; Robert Hynes represented by Mendola Ltd.; Morgan Cain & Associates; JTH Illustration; Laurie O'Keefe; Matthew Pippin represented by Beranbaum Artist's Representative; Precision Graphics; Publisher's Art; Rolin Graphics, Inc.; Wendy Smith represented by Melissa Turk & The Artist Network; Kevin Torline represented by Berendsen and Associates, Inc.; WILDlife ART; Phil Wilson represented by Cliff Knecht Artist Representative; Zoo Botanica.

Photo Credits

Abbreviation Key: AA=Animals Animals; AH=Aaron Haupt; AMP=Amanita Pictures; BC=Bruce Coleman, Inc.; CB=CORBIS; DM=Doug Martin; DRK=DRK Photo; ES=Earth Scenes; FP=Fundamental Photographs; GH=Grant Heilman Photography; IC=Icon Images; KS=KS Studios; LA=Liaison Agency; MB=Mark Burnett; MM=Matt Meadows; PE=PhotoEdit; PD=PhotoDisc; PQ=PictureQuest; PR=Photo Researchers; SB=Stock Boston; TSA=Tom Stack & Associates; TSM=The Stock Market; VU=Visuals Unlimited.

Cover Roine Magnusson/Stone; **iv** Layne Kennedy/CB; **v** Bonnie Kamin/PE; **vi** SuperStock; **vii** (l)MM, (r)Stewart Cohen/Index Stock; **2** Charles O'Rear/CB; **3** (t)Philip Hayson/PR, (b)David A. Wagner/PhotoTake NYC; **4 5** Charlie Varley/Sipa; **6** H.R. Bramaz/Peter Arnold, Inc.; **6-7** Courtesy IBM; **7** MM; **8** Artville; **9** (tl)Culver Pictures/PQ, (tr)E.A. Heiniger/PR, (b)Andy Roberts/Stone; **10** Elena Rooraid/PE; **11** (t)L.S. Stepanowicz/Panographics, (b)Skip Comer; **12** AH; **16** Fraser Hall/Robert Harding Picture Library; **18** Fermi National Accelerator Laboratory/Science Photo Library/PR; **19** Tom Stewart/TSM; **20** (t cl cr)Bettmann/CB, (b)New York Public Library, General Research Division, Astor, Lenox, and Tilden Foundations; **22** Emmanuel Scorcelletti/LA; **24** DM; **25** NASA; **26** MB; **27** Klaus Guldbrandsen/Science Photo Library/PR; **28** (tl)Mark Thayer, (tr)CB, (bl)Kenneth Mengay/LA, (bc)Arthur Hill/VU, (br)RMIP/Richard Hayes; **28-29** KS; **30** IC; **31** Michael Newman/PE; **32** (tl)Stone, (tr)John Eastcott & Yva Momatiuk/DRK, (c)Robert Essel/TSM, (bl)Ame Hodalic/CB, (br)Norman Owen Tomalin/BC; **34** (t)DM, (c)Skip Comer, (b)AMP; **38** Jim Cummins/FPG; **38-39** Roger Ressmeyer/CB; **39** First Image; **40** Layne Kennedy/CB; **41** (t)Telegraph Colour Library/FPG, (b)Paul Silverman/FP; **42** Bill Aron/PE; **43** (l)John Serrao/PR, (r)H. Richard Johnston/FPG; **44** Tom Tracy/Photo Network/PQ; **45** Annie Griffiths Belt/CB; **46** AMP; **47** (t)David Weintraub/SB, (b)James L. Amos/Peter Arnold, Inc.; **48** Dave King/DK Images; **49** Joseph Sohm/ChromoSohm/CB; **50** Michael Dalton/FP; **51** Swarthout & Associates/TSM; **52** Tony Freeman/PE; **54** David Young-Wolff/PE; **55** (tl tr)Joshua Ets-Hokin/PD, (b)Richard Hutchings; **56** Robbie Jack/CB; **57** David Young-Wolff/PE; **58** A. Ramey/SB; **59** First Image; **60** (l)Tony Freeman/PE, (r)Stephen Simpson/FPG; **62** (l)Lester Lefkowitz/TSM, (r)Bob Daemmrich; **63** Bob Daemmrich; **64 64-65 65** Daniel Belknap; **66** (t bl)KS, (br)Jeff Smith/Fotosmith; **67** (l)Andrew Ward/Life File/PD, (r)NASA/TRACE; **70** Breck P. Kent/ES; **70-71** Brenda

Tharp/TSM; **71** Breck P. Kent/ES; **72** Fred Habegger from GH; **73** (t)David Nunuk/Science Photo Library/PR, (c)AMP, (bl)David Schultz/Stone, (bc)SuperStock, (br)Kent Knudson/PD; **74** KS; **75** Gary Retherford/PR; **76** (l)Peter Steiner/TSM, (c)Tom & DeeAnn McCarthy/TSM, (r)Super-Stock; **77** Timothy Fuller; **78** (l cl)A. Goldsmith/TSM, (cr r)Gay Bumgarner/Stone; **79** (t)MM, (bl bc br)Richard Megna/FP; **80** (t)Ed Pritchard/Stone, (cl bl)Kip Peticolas/FP, (cr br)Richard Megna/FP; **81** Rich Iwasaki/Stone; **82** (t)MM, (c)Layne Kennedy/CB, (bl br)Runk/Schoenberger from GH; **83** (tl tr)AMP, (bl br)Richard Megna/FP; **84** Anthony Cooper/Ecoscene/CB; **85** (t, l to r)Russell Illig/PD, John D. Cunningham/VU, Coco McCoy/Rainbow/PQ, SuperStock, (bl)Bonnie Kamin/PE, (br)Super-Stock; **86** (t)Grantpix/PR, (c)Mark Sherman/Photo Network/PQ, (bl)Sculpture by Maya Lin, courtesy Wexner Center for the Arts, Ohio State Univ., photo by Darnell Lautt, (br)Rainbow/PQ; **87** MB; **88 89** MM; **90** (t)Michael Newman/PE, (cl)C. Squared Studios/PD, (cr)Susan Kinast/Food Pix, (b)Timothy Fuller; **91** Darren McCollester/Newsmakers; **92** (l)Larry Hamill, (r)AH; **93** Kip Peticolas/FP; **96** Vaughan Fleming/Science Photo Library/PR; **96-97** Stewart Cohen/Index Stock; **97** DM; **98** Stamp from the collection of Prof. C.M. Lang, photo by Gary Shulfer, University of WI Stevens Point;

102 (tl)Tom Pantages, (tr)Elaine Shay, (b)Paul Silverman/FP; **105** AMP; **106** (l)Joail Hans Stern/LA, (r)Leonard Freed/Magnum/PQ; **107** (l)David Young-Wolff/PE/PQ, (c)Jane Sapinsky/TSM, (r)Dan McCoy/Rainbow/PQ; **108** (t)George Hall/CB, (b)AH; **109** SuperStock; **110** (t)Don Farrall/PD, (b)MM; **111** (t)file photo, (b)CB; **112** CB; **113** (t)Geoff Butler, (c)MM, (b)CB; **114** AMP; **115** (l)Achim Zschau, (r)Ted Streshinsky/CB; **117** AMP; **119** MB; **120** Tim Flach/Stone; **121** Nancy Reifsteck; **122** Jeff J. Daly/FP; **123** (l)Yoav Levy/PhotoTake NYC/PQ, (r)Louvre, Paris/Bridgeman Art Library, London/New York; **124** George Hall/CB; **128-129** PD; **130** MM; **131** (l)Eric Neurath/SB, (r)AH; **132** (t)Michael Newman/PE, (b)Felicia Martinez/PE; **133** (t)AH, (b)DM; **134** Timothy Fuller; **138** Roger Ball/TSM; **140** (l)Geoff Butler, (r)Coco McCoy/Rainbow/PQ; **141** Dominic Oldershaw; **142** StudiOhio; **143** First Image; **145** MM; **148** Paul Barton/TSM; **151** Davis Barber/PE.

Acknowledgments

"Anansi Tries to Steal All the Wisdom in the World," adapted by Matt Evans. Reprinted with the permission of the Afro-American Newspapers.

PERIODIC TABLE OF THE ELEMENTS

Columns of elements are called groups. Elements in the same group have similar chemical properties.

Gas

Liquid

Solid

Synthetic

Element	→	Hydrogen
Atomic number	→	1
Symbol	→	H
Atomic mass	→	1.008

State of matter

The first three symbols tell you the state of matter of the element at room temperature. The fourth symbol identifies human-made, or synthetic, elements.

1

	1	2	3	4	5	6	7	8	9
1	Hydrogen 1 H 1.008								
2	Lithium 3 Li 6.941	Beryllium 4 Be 9.012							
3	Sodium 11 Na 22.990	Magnesium 12 Mg 24.305							
4	Potassium 19 K 39.098	Calcium 20 Ca 40.078	Scandium 21 Sc 44.956	Titanium 22 Ti 47.867	Vanadium 23 V 50.942	Chromium 24 Cr 51.996	Manganese 25 Mn 54.938	Iron 26 Fe 55.845	Cobalt 27 Co 58.933
5	Rubidium 37 Rb 85.468	Strontium 38 Sr 87.62	Yttrium 39 Y 88.906	Zirconium 40 Zr 91.224	Niobium 41 Nb 92.906	Molybdenum 42 Mo 95.94	Technetium 43 Tc (98)	Ruthenium 44 Ru 101.07	Rhodium 45 Rh 102.906
6	Cesium 55 Cs 132.905	Barium 56 Ba 137.327	Lanthanum 57 La 138.906	Hafnium 72 Hf 178.49	Tantalum 73 Ta 180.948	Tungsten 74 W 183.84	Rhenium 75 Re 186.207	Osmium 76 Os 190.23	Iridium 77 Ir 192.217
7	Francium 87 Fr (223)	Radium 88 Ra (226)	Actinium 89 Ac (227)	Rutherfordium 104 Rf (261)	Dubnium 105 Db (262)	Seaborgium 106 Sg (266)	Bohrium 107 Bh (264)	Hassium 108 Hs (277)	Meitnerium 109 Mt (268)

The number in parentheses is the mass number of the longest lived isotope for that element.

Rows of elements are called periods. Atomic number increases across a period.

The arrow shows where these elements would fit into the periodic table. They are moved to the bottom of the page to save space.

	Cerium 58 Ce 140.116	Praseodymium 59 Pr 140.908	Neodymium 60 Nd 144.24	Promethium 61 Pm (145)	Samarium 62 Sm 150.36
Lanthanide series					
Actinide series	Thorium 90 Th 232.038	Protactinium 91 Pa 231.036	Uranium 92 U 238.029	Neptunium 93 Np (237)	Plutonium 94 Pu (244)